THE CLIMATE OF THE BRITISH ISLES

THE CLIMATE OF THE BRITISH ISLES

BEING AN INTRODUCTORY STUDY OF THE
OFFICIAL RECORDS, FOR STUDENTS
AND GENERAL READERS

BY

E. G. BILHAM

A.R.C.Sc., D.I.C., B.Sc.

FELLOW OF THE ROYAL METEOROLOGICAL SOCIETY; SUPERINTENDENT OF
BRITISH CLIMATOLOGY AND THE BRITISH RAINFALL ORGANIZATION,
METEOROLOGICAL OFFICE, AIR MINISTRY

MACMILLAN AND CO., LIMITED
ST. MARTIN'S STREET, LONDON
1938

COPYRIGHT

PREFACE

My purpose in writing this book has been to collect together the essential facts about the climate of the British Isles in a form suitable for the needs of students and others who require information of a fairly comprehensive character. In recent years a large amount of summarized data has been made available in the form of official publications such as the *Book of Normals*, *Averages of Temperature* and *Averages of Sunshine*, as well as in papers by individual authors published in the form of *Professional Notes* or *Geographical Memoirs* by the Meteorological Office or as contributions to various technical journals. To these sources of information, and to the vast store of data preserved in manuscript form in the Meteorological Office, the investigator in search of detailed climatic data for particular localities must necessarily resort. My aim here has been rather to survey the facts which have been established, to add a certain amount of data not hitherto available in digested form, and thus to compile a reasonably complete summary of the main climatic features of our area, within the compass of a volume of moderate size.

There are many purposes for which climatological information may be required, and it is perhaps too much to hope that the method of presentation adopted in this book will prove equally acceptable to the student of meteorology or of geography, the medical practitioner and the industrial technician. Having regard to the diversity of the needs of these and other possible readers it appeared desirable to include references to all important aspects of the subject, rather than to treat any one aspect in great detail. While the needs of specialist readers have been the main consideration, I venture nevertheless to hope that the book may be of interest to the general reader.

The principal sources of information have already been mentioned in a general way. The majority of the data have been published by the Stationery Office, and my thanks are due to the Controller for giving permission to reproduce a considerable amount of statistical material and a number of diagrams. To Sir George Simpson, Director of the Meteorological Office, I am indebted for permission to refer to unpublished data preserved in the Office ; this privilege was particularly valuable in dealing with the subject of atmospheric obscurity, which could otherwise have been treated only very inadequately. I am indebted also to the Council of the Royal Meteorological Society for permission to quote from the numerous papers on climatological subjects published in the Society's *Quarterly Journal*, and for the loan of the blocks from which Fig. 97 and Fig. 98 are reproduced ; to the Northamptonshire Natural History Society for the loan of the block for Fig. 86 ; to Mr. A. L. Kelley for supplying certain data for Birmingham (Edgbaston Observatory) ; and to Dr. H. Knox-Shaw for permission to quote from the summary of the observations made at the Radcliffe Observatory, Oxford, during the period 1815 to 1930, published as an Appendix to the *Radcliffe Observations*, 1926-1930. This summary by H. Knox-Shaw and J. G. Balk of a homogeneous series of observations covering the long period of 116 years is one of the most valuable climatological documents possessed by this or any other country. Acknowledgments to individual authors are made in the text but I should like to refer here to the valuable series of papers by Dr. J. Glasspoole, which have provided much of the material for the chapter on rainfall.

Finally, it is difficult to express in an adequate manner the indebtedness of all meteorologists to the great body of observers, many of whom receive no payment for their patient and conscientious work. To them we owe the solid foundation of fact upon which our superstructure of analysis and correlation must rest.

E. G. BILHAM

Teddington,
    Dec. 1937

CONTENTS

PAGE

PREFACE - - - - - - - - - - - - - v

LIST OF ILLUSTRATIONS - - - - - - - - - xiii

LIST OF TABLES - - - - - - - - - - xvii

CHAPTER

I. INTRODUCTORY - - - - - - - - - - 1
   1. The nature and scope of climatology - - - - - 1
   2. The nature of the data - - - - - - - - 2
   3. Wind - - - - - - - - - - - 3
   4. Temperature - - - - - - - - - - 3
   5. Humidity - - - - - - - - - - 8
   6. Rainfall - - - - - - - - - - - 8
   7. Evaporation - - - - - - - - - - 9
   8. Sunshine duration - - - - - - - - 9
   9. Visibility - - - - - - - - - - 10
   10. Averages and normals - - - - - - - 11
      Bibliography - - - - - - - - 14

II. GEOGRAPHICAL AND ENVIRONMENTAL FACTORS - - - - 15
   11. General considerations - - - - - - - 15
   12. Geographical features - - - - - - - 16
   13. Physical structure - - - - - - - - 17
   14. Temperature conditions over seas and land masses - - - 19
   15. Our meteorological environment - - - - - 20
   16. Variations from the mean conditions - - - - 25

III. CHARACTERISTIC TYPES OF WEATHER - - - - - 26
   17. Classification of weather types - - - - - - 26
   18. Frequency of occurrence of different types - - - - 27
   19. The normal south-westerly type - - - - - 30
   20. The cyclonic type - - - - - - - 32
   21. The north-westerly type - - - - - - 35
   22. The northerly type - - - - - - - 36
   23. The north-easterly type - - - - - - 37
   24. The south-easterly type - - - - - - 39
   25. Anticyclonic conditions - - - - - - 40
      Bibliography - - - - - - - 41

CONTENTS

CHAPTER   PAGE

IV. WIND - - - - - - - - - - - - -   42
26. Wind as a vector - - - - - - - - -   42
27. The frequency of winds from different directions - - -   48
28. Monthly percentage frequencies of wind direction - - -   49
29. Wind velocity - - - - - - - - - -   52
30. Mean monthly and yearly velocity - - - - -   55
31. Frequency-distribution of mean wind - - - - -   56
32. The gust-level - - - - - - - - -   60
33. Extreme winds recorded by anemometers - - - -   61
34. Gales on the coasts - - - - - - - -   65
35. Diurnal variation of wind direction—land- and sea-breezes -   68
36. Katabatic winds - - - - - - - - -   72
37. Diurnal variation of wind velocity - - - - -   72
    Bibliography - - - - - - - - -   74

V. RAINFALL - - - - - - - - - - - -   75
38. The annual average rainfall - - - - - -   75
39. The wettest places - - - - - - - -   78
40. The driest places - - - - - - - -   79
41. Areas of rainfall zones - - - - - - -   79
42. The fluctuations of annual rainfall - - - - -   80
43. Annual fluctuations at individual stations - - - -   82
44. Three driest consecutive years - - - - - -   85
45. Monthly rainfall - - - - - - - -   86
46. Fluctuations of monthly rainfall - - - - -   93
47. Very dry and very wet months - - - - -   95
48. Sequences of dry or wet months - - - - -   96
49. Conditions associated with abnormally wet or dry periods -   99
50. Days of rain - - - - - - - - - -   103
51. The frequency-distribution of daily rainfalls exceeding stated values - - - - - - - - - -   104
52. Some outstanding daily rainfalls - - - - -   105
53. Duration of rainfall - - - - - - - -   111
54. Heavy falls in short periods - - - - - -   116
    Bibliography - - - - - - - - -   119

VI. EVAPORATION AND PERCOLATION - - - - - -   121
55. Measurements of evaporation - - - - - -   121
56. Annual evaporation - - - - - - - -   121
57. Monthly averages for Camden Square and Southport - -   122
58. Percolation - - - - - - - - -   126
59. Evaporation in nature - - - - - - -   127
60. Underground water - - - - - - - -   130
61. The flow of rivers - - - - - - - -   131

PAGE

CHAPTER

62. Rainfall and run-off of the River Thames basin - - - 131
63. The Thames under normal and under drought conditions - - 135
64. " Dew ponds " - - - - - - - - - 137
    Bibliography - - - - - - - - - - 139

VII. TEMPERATURE OF THE AIR - - - - - - - - 140
65. Factors causing variations of temperature - - - 140
66. Mean annual temperature - - - - - - 142
67. Fluctuations of mean annual temperature - - - 145
68. The annual variation of temperature - - - - 147
69. Irregularities in the annual variation—" Buchan's periods " - 152
70. The distribution of mean temperature in winter and summer - 158
71. Fluctuations of monthly mean temperature - - - 159
72. Diurnal variation - - - - - - - - 163
73. Daily maximum and minimum temperatures - - - 165
74. Mean daily range - - - - - - - - 166
75. Mean maximum and mean minimum - - - - 168
76. The annual variation of mean maximum and mean minimum - 169
77. Monthly and yearly extremes - - - - - - 172
78. The highest and lowest temperatures on record - - 174
    Bibliography - - - - - - - - - 176

VIII. SUNSHINE AND CLOUD - - - - - - - - 177
79. Sunshine records - - - - - - - - 177
80. The sun's annual and diurnal movements - - - 177
81. The mean daily duration of sunshine - - - - 181
82. Percentage of possible sunshine - - - - - 184
83. Cloudiness and its relation to sunshine - - - - 184
84. Fluctuations of mean annual sunshine and cloudiness - - 186
85. The annual variation - - - - - - - 187
86. Distribution of sunshine in June - - - - - 189
87. Distribution of sunshine in December - - - - 189
88. Percentage of sunshine and cloudiness—annual variation - - 192
89. Fluctuations of monthly sunshine - - - - - 195
90. Fluctuations of sunshine and cloudiness in June at Oxford - 196
91. Frequency-distribution of sunshine duration - - - 197
92. Diurnal variation - - - - - - - - 200
93. Morning and afternoon sunshine - - - - - 201
    Bibliography - - - - - - - - - 204

IX. HUMIDITY OF THE AIR - - - - - - - - 205
94. Water-vapour in the atmosphere - - - - - 205
95. Modes of expression - - - - - - - 205
96. Vapour-pressure and moisture-content of saturated air - - 207

CHAPTER

IX. HUMIDITY OF THE AIR.—*Contd.* PAGE

97. Diurnal variation of relative humidity - - - - - 209
98. Diurnal and annual variations at six stations - - - - 211
99. Vapour-pressure and moisture-content at Kew - - - 215
100. Seasonal variation of vapour-pressure - - - - - 215
101. Seasonal variation of moisture-content - - - - - 216
102. Saturation-deficit - - - - - - - - - 217
103. The dew-point - - - - - - - - - 218
104. General remarks on the data - - - - - - - 220
105. Geographical distribution of relative humidity - - - - 221
106. Geographical distribution of vapour-pressure - - - - 225
107. Extremes of relative humidity - - - - - - - 226
108. Extremes of absolute humidity - - - - - - 228
     Bibliography - - - - - - - - - 230

X. GROUND FROST, SNOW, HAIL AND THUNDER - - - - 231
109. The " grass-minimum " temperature - - - - - 231
110. Results for Oxford and Glasgow - - - - - - 233
111. Frequency of ground frosts - - - - - - - 236
112. Days with snow - - - - - - - - - 238
113. Mornings with snow lying - - - - - - - 240
114. Depth of snow - - - - - - - - - 241
115. Permanent snow-beds - - - - - - - - 241
116. A great snowstorm, 25th-26th December, 1927 - - - 243
117. Kinds of hail - - - - - - - - - 246
118. Days with hail - - - - - - - - - 247
119. Seasonal variation of hail - - - - - - - 247
120. A remarkable hailstorm, 22nd September, 1935 - - - 248
121. Observations of thunder - - - - - - - 250
122. Annual frequency of thunder - - - - - - - 250
123. Seasonal variation - - - - - - - - 252
124. Conditions giving rise to thunderstorms - - - - 252
125. Rainfall in thunderstorms - - - - - - - 254
     Bibliography - - - - - - - - - 256

XI. ATMOSPHERIC OBSCURITY - - - - - - - 257
126. Observations of visibility - - - - - - - 257
127. Visibility at Croydon Aerodrome - - - - - - 259
128. Visibility at Holyhead - - - - - - - - 262
129. Visibilities above and below fixed limits - - - - 262
130. Frequency of very good visibility - - - - - - 264
131. Frequency of low visibility - - - - - - - 265
132. Days with fog - - - - - - - - - 270

CONTENTS

CHAPTER   PAGE

133. Annual frequency of fog - 272
134. Seasonal frequency of fog - 276
135. Persistent fog - 276
136. Factors in visibility - 277
137. Sea fogs - 278
138. Coastal fogs - 279
139. Inland water fogs - 280
140. The effects of smoke - 281
141. Suspended impurity in the atmosphere - 283
    Bibliography - 286

XII. SPECIAL TYPES OF CLIMATE - 287
142. Coastal climates - 287
143. Temperature inland and on the coast - 287
144. Comparison with sea-surface temperature - 292
145. The effect of the diurnal sea-breeze - 293
146. Rainfall on the coast - 294
147. General conclusions in regard to coastal climates - 296
148. Valley climates - 296
149. The sites of the Rickmansworth and Rothamsted stations - 297
150. Comparison of Rickmansworth and Rothamsted - 298
151. Conditions in a valley of the Cotswolds - 301
152. General conclusions in regard to valley climates - 302
153. Town climates - 303
154. London sunshine - 304
155. London temperatures - 307
156. London winds - 309
    Bibliography - 311

APPENDIX : CLIMATIC TABLES FOR REPRESENTATIVE STATIONS - 313

INDEX - 335

LIST OF ILLUSTRATIONS

(The word **chart** in heavy type indicates a chart showing the distribution of a climatological element over the British Isles.)

FIGURE   PAGE

1. North Atlantic Ocean and Western Europe ; mean isobars and winds, January - - - - - - - - - - - 21

2. North Atlantic Ocean and Western Europe ; mean isobars and winds, July - - - - - - - - - - - - 21

3. Currents in the North Atlantic Ocean - - - - - - - 22

4. North Atlantic Ocean and North Sea ; sea-surface isotherms, January - 23

5. North Atlantic Ocean and North Sea ; sea-surface isotherms, July - 24

6. Monthly and seasonal percentage frequencies of predominating weather types - - - - - - - - - - - - 29

7. South-westerly type, 5th July, 1936 - - - - - - - 30

8. Percentage frequency of south-westerly type, compared with rainfall at Seathwaite (Cumberland) - - - - - - - - 32

9. Cyclonic type, 20th January, 1936 - - - - - - - - 33

10. Northerly type, 3rd April, 1935 - - - - - - - - 36

11. North-easterly type, 14th May, 1935 - - - - - - - 38

12. South-easterly type, 21st June, 1936 - - - - - - - 39

13. Wind force and direction ; percentage frequencies for six stations - - 43

14. **Chart.** Average annual percentage frequencies of winds from each direction - - - - - - - - - - - 46

15a. Octagonal wind-rose for Stornoway - - - - - - - 50

15b. Octagonal wind-rose for Greenwich - - - - - - - 50

16. Dines anemometer record (Tiree, 28th-29th January, 1927) - - *facing* 53

17. Seasonal variation of mean wind velocity - - - - - - 55

18. **Chart.** Percentage frequencies of winds with velocity between stated limits - - - - - - - - - - - 57

19. **Chart.** Average annual number of gales on the coasts - - - - 67

20. **Chart.** Percentage frequency of gales from different directions - - 67

21. Seasonal variation of gale-frequency on the coasts - - - - - 68

22. Average hourly frequencies of winds from different directions at Southport (Lancs.) in January and July - - - - - - 70

23. Diurnal variation of wind velocity at Bell Rock and Kew - - - 73

24. **Chart.** Average annual rainfall - - - - - - - *facing* 75

25. England and Wales ; fluctuations of annual rainfall, 1863-1935 - - 82

xiii

FIGURE   PAGE

26. Annual rainfall at Oxford ; graduation curve - - - - - 83

27. **Chart.** Mean percentage deviation of annual rainfall - - - - 84

28. Diagrammatic table ; monthly percentages of rainfall - - - - 87

29. Average monthly and annual rainfall at representative stations - - 88

30. **Charts.** Monthly charts of average rainfall - - - - - - 90-91

31. Oxford (Radcliffe Observatory) ; means and extremes of monthly rainfall, 1815-1930 - - - - - - - - - - - 93

32. Oxford (Radcliffe Observatory) ; rainfall in March and October, graduation curves - - - - - - - - - - - 94

33. Extreme rainfalls in driest and wettest sequences of months from 1 to 12 98

34. **Chart.** Annual average number of days with rain - - - - 102

35. Monthly and annual averages of the number of days with rain at representative stations - - - - - - - - - - 104

36. Percentage frequency of days with rainfall exceeding stated amounts - 106

37. Counties in which a daily rainfall of four inches has never been exceeded 109

38. Curves showing the classification of heavy falls of rain in short periods - 115

39. Rainfall and evaporation at Camden Square (London) - - - - 123

40. Annual variation of mean daily evaporation at Camden Square (London) 125

41. Comparison of curves of Thames flow, water-level in a well at Chilgrove (Sussex), and variations of level in a tank - - - - - 126

42. Thames basin ; rainfall, run-off and loss - - - - - - 132

43. Thames basin ; correlation of rainfall and run-off - - - - - 133

44. Thames basin ; rainfall and run-off in 1933 and 1934 - - - - 136

45. **Chart.** Mean annual temperature reduced to sea level - - - - 143

46. Fluctuations of mean annual temperature at Oxford - - - - 145

47. Annual variation of mean temperature - - - - - - - 148

48. Annual variation of temperature of British coastal waters - - - 149

49. **Chart.** Annual range of mean temperature - - - - - - 151

50. Variations of daily average temperature in December - - - - 153

51. **Chart.** Mean temperature reduced to sea level, January - - - 156

52. **Chart.** Mean temperature reduced to sea level, July - - - - 157

53. Maximum positive and negative deviations of monthly mean temperatures (Glasgow and Oxford) - - - - - - - 160

54. Normal diurnal variation of temperature (Aberdeen and Kew) - - 163

55. **Chart.** Mean daily range of temperature - - - - - - 167

56. Variations of temperature at Kew Observatory - - - - - 171

57. Annual variation of mean duration of daylight in latitudes 50° N. and 60° N. - - - - - - - - - - - - 179

58. Diurnal variation of sun's altitude and azimuth in latitudes 50° N. and 60° N. - - - - - - - - - - - - 181

59. **Chart.** Mean daily duration of sunshine (whole year) - - - - 182

PAGE

FIGURE

60. Oxford (Radcliffe Observatory) ; fluctuations of mean daily duration of
sunshine and percentage of cloud (whole year) - - - - 186

61. Annual variation of mean daily duration of sunshine at typical stations - 188

62. **Chart.** Mean daily duration of sunshine in June - - - - - 190

63. **Chart.** Mean daily duration of sunshine in December - - - - 191

64. Annual variation of percentage of possible sunshine and percentage of
sky free from cloud - - - - - - - - - 193

65. Oxford (Radcliffe Observatory) ; monthly means and extremes of sunshine - - - - - - - - - - - - 196

66. Oxford (Radcliffe Observatory) ; fluctuations of mean daily duration of
sunshine and percentage of sky free from cloud in June - - - 197

67. Monthly percentage frequency of days with more than half the possible
sunshine - - - - - - - - - - - 199

68. Pressure of aqueous vapour and moisture-content of saturated air - - 208

69. Kew Observatory ; diurnal variation of relative humidity (seasons) - 210

70. Kew Observatory ; diurnal variation of relative humidity and temperature (whole year) - - - - - - - - - 210

71. Relative humidity; seasonal variation of early morning, mean and afternoon values - - - - - - - - - - 213

72. Vapour-pressure ; seasonal variation at Glasgow, Kew and Valentia - 215

73. Kew Observatory ; diurnal variation of saturation-deficit - - - 217

74. Kew Observatory ; diurnal variation of dew-point - - - - 218

75. **Chart.** Relative humidity, January 1935, 13 h. - - - - - 222

76. **Chart.** Relative humidity, April 1935, 13 h. - - - - - 222

77. **Chart.** Relative humidity, July 1935, 13 h. - - - - - 222

78. **Chart.** Relative humidity, October 1935, 13 h. - - - - 222

79. **Chart.** Vapour-pressure, January 1935, 13 h. - - - - - 223

80. **Chart.** Vapour-pressure, April 1935, 13 h. - - - - - 223

81. **Chart.** Vapour-pressure, July 1935, 13 h. - - - - - 223

82. **Chart.** Vapour-pressure, October 1935, 13 h. - - - - - 223

83. Kew Observatory ; variations of temperature, dew-point and relative
humidity, 10th July, 1934 - - - - - - - - 227

84. Glasgow Observatory ; percentage frequency of nights on which the
screened-minimum temperature exceeded the grass-minimum by more
than 10° F. - - - - - - - - - - - 235

85. The Christmas snowstorm, 1927 (synoptic chart) - - - - 244

86. Hailstones photographed near Northampton, 22nd September, 1935 *facing* 249

87. **Chart.** Annual average number of days with thunder - - - 251

88. Diurnal and seasonal variations of the percentage frequency of visibility
below and above fixed limits at Croydon and Holyhead - - - 263

89. Percentage frequencies of very good visibility - - - - 267

90. Percentage frequencies of low visibility - - - - - 269

FIGURE

PAGE

91. Monthly averages of the number of days with fog - - - - 271

92. **Chart.** Average annual number of days with fog - - - - 275

93. Diurnal variation of suspended impurity—weekdays, summer - - 284

94. Diurnal variation of suspended impurity—weekdays, winter - - - 284

95. Average differences of temperature between neighbouring coastal and inland stations - - - - - - - - - - 289

96. Comparison of sea temperature and inland temperature - - - 293

97. Topography of the vicinity of the Rickmansworth station - - - 298

98. Topography of a Cotswold valley near Leafield - - - - - 301

99. Percentage of country sunshine recorded by London stations - - 304

100. London sunshine, 1880-1935 (comparison with Kew) - - - - 306

101. Index chart showing the positions of stations - - - - - 312

LIST OF TABLES

TABLE   PAGE

I. The Beaufort scale of wind force - - - - - - 4-5

II. Scale for visibility observations - - - - - - - 11

III. Predominating weather types—percentage frequencies - - 28

IV. Seasonal percentages of weather types - - - - - 28

V. Wind force and direction ; frequency data for Lerwick - - 45

VI. Wind force and direction ; frequency data for Scilly - - - 45

VII. Percentage frequencies of winds from stated directions, and calms (whole year) - - - - - - - - - 47

VIII. Monthly percentage frequencies of winds from stated directions, and calms - - - - - - - - - - 51

IX. Mean wind velocity for each month and the whole year - - 56

X. Percentage frequencies of winds of stated velocities in January, July and the whole year - - - - - - - 59

XI. List of occasions since 1909 on which gusts of ninety miles per hour or more have been recorded - - - - - 63

XII. Gales and extreme winds at anemometer stations - - - 64

XIII. Average monthly and annual numbers of gales on various sections of the coasts - - - - - - - - - 66

XIV. General averages of rainfall, 1881-1915 - - - - - 76

XV. Areas of rainfall zones of the British Isles - - - - - 80

XVI. Range of fluctuations of general rainfall, 1863-1935 - - - 81

XVII. Driest and wettest sequences of months from 1 to 12 - - - 97

XVIII. Rainfall of the driest consecutive months of 1921 in the Isle of Thanet - - - - - - - - - 99

XIX. Percentage frequency of daily rainfall amounts - - - - 107

XX. Daily rainfalls of six inches or more, 1865-1935 - - - - 108

XXI. Average duration of rainfall in each month and the year - - 112

XXII. Rainfalls of very rare intensity lasting for one hour or less - - 114

XXIII. Total number of days on which specified amounts of rain fell in specified times, 1925-1934 - - - - - - 117

XXIV. Computed amounts of rain falling in stated times - - - 118

XXV. Annual averages of evaporation - - - - - 122

XXVIA. Monthly averages of evaporation and rainfall at Camden Square (London) - - - - - - - - - 124

XXVIB. Monthly averages of evaporation and rainfall at Southport (Lancs.) 124

xvii

LIST OF TABLES

TABLE   PAGE

XXVII. Observations of evaporation and percolation in 1935 - - - 128

XXVIII. Monthly averages of mean temperature for long periods - - 150

XXIX. Oxford (Radcliffe Observatory); highest and lowest monthly mean temperatures, 1815-1935 - - - - - - 161

XXX. Averages of hourly values of temperature - - - - - 162

XXXI. Variations of temperature at Kew Observatory - - - - 170

XXXII. Average annual extremes and absolute extreme temperatures - 174

XXXIII. Mean values of the duration of daylight in each month, and the year, with the values at the solstices - - - - - 178

XXXIV. Mean cloudiness (tenths of sky covered) - - - - - 185

XXXV. Sunshine at Oxford; highest and lowest monthly means, 1881-1935 - - - - - - - - - - 195

XXXVI. Percentage frequencies of days with bright sunshine between stated limits - - - - - - - - - 198

XXXVII. Hourly means of sunshine - - - - - - - - 202

XXXVIII. Percentage amounts of sunshine in the morning and afternoon - 203

XXXIX. Mean cloud amount at 9 h., 15 h. and 21 h. - - - - 203

XL. Humidity; diurnal variations at Kew Observatory - - - 211

XLI. Relative humidity; monthly means and diurnal ranges - - 212

XLII. Vapour-pressure and saturation-deficit; monthly means - - 214

XLIII. Moisture-content; monthly mean values - - - - - 216

XLIV. Dew-point; monthly mean values - - - - - - 219

XLV. Kew Observatory; occasions of high absolute humidity, 1900-1933 229

XLVI. Oxford (Radcliffe Observatory); screen-minimum and grass-minimum temperatures - - - - - - - 233

XLVII. Glasgow Observatory; screen-minimum and grass-minimum temperatures - - - - - - - - - 234

XLVIII. Glasgow; grass-minimum temperatures, percentage frequencies of readings below stated values - - - - - - 234

XLIX. Average annual frequency of ground frosts - - - - 237

L. Average number of days with snow - - - - - - 239

LI. Days with hail; monthly and annual averages for typical stations 247

LII. Seasonal frequency of thunderstorms - - - - - 253

LIII. Croydon Aerodrome; visibility frequencies - - - - 260

LIV. Holyhead; visibility frequencies - - - - - - 261

LV. Percentage frequency of very good visibility - - - - 266

LVI. Percentage frequency of low visibility - - - - - 268

LVII. Average number of days with fog at 7 h., 13 h. or 18 h. in each season, and the year - - - - - - - - 274

LVIII. Differences of temperature at neighbouring coastal and inland stations - - - - - - - - - - 288

TABLE   PAGE
LIX. Rainfall at coastal stations expressed as a percentage of the rainfall
      at neighbouring inland stations -   -   -   -   -   -   295

LX. Comparison of temperatures at Rickmansworth and Rothamsted
      in Hertfordshire -   -   -   -   -   -   -   -   -   299

LXI. Comparison of London and country sunshine   -   -   -   -   305

LXII. Comparison of temperatures in London and the country   -   -   308

LXIII. Number of hours of winds of stated mean velocities recorded at
      London stations in 1935   -   -   -   -   -   -   -   310

CLIMATIC TABLES FOR REPRESENTATIVE STATIONS   -   315-334
      (For list of stations see page 313)

CHAPTER I

INTRODUCTORY

1. The nature and scope of climatology. This book has for its object the presentation and discussion of the main features of the climate of the British Isles. It is hardly necessary to define the term " climate ", but it is desirable that we should draw a clear distinction between the study of climate and the study of weather. The two are certainly related very closely, but their aims and objects are different. In an official meteorological service, such as that of Great Britain, the immediate object of studying the weather is to ascertain its relationships with the existing barometric distribution with a view to forecasting what changes are likely to occur. For that purpose it is necessary to form a detailed picture of the meteorological conditions which exist over a wide area at a given moment, and for that reason the study is known as " synoptic " meteorology. The practitioner of synoptic meteorology must, of course, possess at least a general idea of the conditions normally to be expected in the area, and at the time of year, which he is studying at the moment. Consciously or unconsciously he is mainly concerned with deviations from the normal, with the fluctuations which disturb the regular seasonal progression of the elements.

Climatology, on the other hand, is mainly concerned with the ascertainment of the normal conditions for different times, places and seasons, and it is a study to be conducted at leisure from the accumulated records of the past. Everyone recognizes that however much they may be disturbed by the passing changes due to ephemeral causes, there are persistent underlying rhythms and patterns in our weather phenomena. The study of these rhythms and patterns is the concern of climatology, but they are not its only concern. The climate of an area cannot be regarded as completely ascertained when we know the normal seasonal values of temperature, rainfall and so forth, and have drawn maps of their geographical distribution. It is necessary also to study collectively the fluctuations which the synoptic meteorologist studies individually. The synoptic meteorologist is concerned about the probability of there

A   1 being an inch of rain in London to-morrow ; the climatologist is concerned about the general probability of there being an inch of rain in London on any day. That illustration may serve to convey a general idea of the aims of climatology, but a perusal of the headings and sub-headings in this book will serve even better.

The results of climatological study must obviously be of interest to the synoptic meteorologist, but they are also of interest to a much wider circle. The conditions in regard to rainfall, temperature, humidity and other climatic factors determine the suitability of a region as a place of residence, particularly for invalids, as well as for carrying on particular industries. The design of a water-supply system or of an air-conditioning plant must necessarily rest on data derived from past records, and the design will be successful in proportion to the precision and reliability of the fundamental data. Scientifically climatology has obvious relationships with physics and with geography. The physical aspects of climatology have perhaps been rather overshadowed by the geographical aspects ; at meetings of the British Association papers on climate are regarded as appropriate to Section E rather than to Section A. In this book we shall endeavour to approach the subject mainly from the physical standpoint, though we shall naturally find that geographical influences have to be considered and discussed at every stage of the work.

2. The nature of the data. The data we shall discuss have been furnished over a long period of years by numerous stations, many of them voluntarily maintained, in association with the Meteorological Office. At the present date climatological observations are available from about 350 stations in the British Isles. supplemented by rainfall observations at about 5,000 additional stations. The material for study is therefore very abundant ; much of it has been summarized and published in numerous papers, pamphlets and other publications. It is not proposed to deal here with the details of meteorological observing ; such information is to be found in the *Meteorological Observer's Handbook* (1).[1] It is necessary, however, that the reader should have clear ideas as to the meanings of the terms used. In many cases these are employed in meteorology in a rather specialized sense, due to the exigencies of observational methods, or to the need for giving precision to words which are used rather loosely in everyday speech. We proceed, therefore, to give brief details of the more important climatological terms as used officially in this country.

[1] Numbers in brackets refer to the bibliography at the end of the chapter.

3. Wind is specified by its direction and its speed or force. The direction refers to the point of the compass *from* which the air is moving; thus a north wind is a current of air moving from north to south. The speed of the wind is the velocity with which a very light object, such as a fragment of thistledown, would be carried along by it. The *force* of the wind is less easy to define ; it is an expression of the physical effect of the wind, on a scale ranging from " calm " (0) to " hurricane " (12). The scale in official use was drawn up early in the nineteenth century by Admiral Beaufort, originally for use on H.M. ships, and is known as the " Beaufort scale ". Details are given in Table I, along with the velocity-equivalents adopted by the Meteorological Office. It should be noted that these velocity-equivalents apply only to measurements of wind-speed made under specified conditions, viz., 10 metres (33 feet) above ground in a perfectly open situation, or at an equal " effective height ", allowance being made for the effect of local obstructions. The scale of equivalents was arrived at by comparing the estimates of wind force made by experienced observers at several stations with simultaneous records of velocity shown by anemometers (2) (3). Some further remarks on this subject will be found in Chapter IV.

4. Temperature. Although measurements of soil temperature and sea-surface temperature come within its scope, climatology is mainly concerned with the temperature of the air near ground level. In the British Isles such observations are usually made by means of thermo-meters placed in a louvred box or shelter known as the " Stevenson screen ", designed to exclude radiation while admitting free passage of the air. The screen is normally erected so that the thermometers are four feet above the surface of level grass-covered soil. The temperature thus indicated is sometimes referred to as the " shade temperature ". Formerly it was the custom to observe also the readings of a freely exposed thermometer with a blackened bulb enclosed in an outer glass jacket exhausted of air—the " black bulb *in vacuo* " or " solar radiation thermometer ". These readings are indeed still continued at a number of stations, but we shall not find it practicable to discuss them here. The temperature shown by such a thermometer is related, but not in a simple manner, to the intensity of the sun's radiation, and the readings do not give a reliable indication of the temperature reached by natural objects exposed to the sun's rays.

The Stevenson screen normally contains four thermometers—the dry-bulb and wet-bulb, maximum and minimum. The summarized temperature data for climatological stations are based mainly on the

TABLE

SPECIFICATION OF THE BEAUFORT SCALE OF WIND FORCE

Beaufort Number	Description of Wind	Specification of Beaufort Scale	
		For Coast use, based on Observations made at Scilly, Yarmouth and Holyhead	For use on Land, based on Observations made at Land Stations
(0)	(1)	(2)	(3)
0	Calm - -	Calm - - - -	Calm ; smoke rises vertically - -
1	Light air -	Fishing smack* just has steerage way.	Direction of wind shown by smoke drift, but not by wind vanes.
2	Light breeze -	Wind fills the sails of smacks, which then move at about 1–2 miles per hour.	Wind felt on face ; leaves rustle ; ordinary vane moved by wind.
3	Gentle breeze	Smacks begin to careen, and travel about 3–4 miles per hour.	Leaves and small twigs in constant motion ; wind extends light flag.
4	Moderate breeze	Good working breeze : smacks carry all canvas, with good list.	Raises dust and loose paper ; small branches are moved.
5	Fresh breeze	Smacks shorten sail -	Small trees in leaf begin to sway ; crested wavelets form on inland waters.
6	Strong breeze	Smacks have double reef in main sail. Care required when fishing.	Large branches in motion ; whistling heard in telegraph wires ; umbrellas used with difficulty.
7	Moderate gale§	Smacks remain in harbour, and those at sea lie to.	Whole trees in motion ; inconvenience felt when walking against wind.
8	Fresh gale -	All smacks make for harbour, if near.	Breaks twigs off trees ; generally impedes progress.
9	Strong gale -	- - - - -	Slight structural damage occurs (chimney pots and slates removed).
10	Whole gale -	- - - - -	Seldom experienced inland ; trees uprooted ; considerable structural damage occurs.
11	Storm - -	- - - - -	Very rarely experienced ; accompanied by widespread damage.
12	Hurricane -	- - - - -	- - - - - - -

* The fishing smack in this column may be taken as representing a trawler of average type and trim. For larger or smaller boats and for special circumstances allowance must be made.
† For converting estimates on the Beaufort scale into miles per hour (anemometer factor, 2·2).
‡ For finding the Beaufort number corresponding with a recorded velocity.
§ In statistics of gales prepared by the Meteorological Office only winds of force 8 and upwards are included.

I

WITH EQUIVALENTS OF THE NUMBERS OF THE SCALE

Equivalent Velocity in Miles per Hour †	Limits of Speed ‡				Mean Wind Force in lbs. per square ft. at standard density $(P = \cdot0105B^3)$	Corresponding Pressure in Millibars $(10^3$ dynes per cm.$^2)$	Beaufort Number
	Statute Miles per Hour	Nautical Miles per Hour	Metres per Second	Feet per Second			
(4)	(5)	(6)	(7)	(8)	(9)	(10)	(11)
0	Less than 1	Less than 1	Less than 0·3	Less than 2	0	0	0
2	1–3	1–3	0·3–1·5	2–5	0·01	0·01	1
5	4–7	4–6	1·6–3·3	6–11	0·08	0·04	2
10	8–12	7–10	3·4–5·4	12–18	0·28	0·13	3
15	13–18	11–16	5·5–7·9	19–27	0·67	0·32	4
21	19–24	17–21	8·0–10·7	28–36	1·31	0·62	5
27	25–31	22–27	10·8–13·8	37–46	2·3	1·1	6
35	32–38	28–33	13·9–17·1	47–56	3·6	1·7	7
42	39–46	34–40	17·2–20·7	57–68	5·4	2·6	8
50	47–54	41–47	20·8–24·4	69–80	7·7	3·7	9
59	55–63	48–55	24·5–28·4	81–93	10·5	5·0	10
68	64–75	56–65	28·5–33·5	94–110	14·0	6·7	11
Above 75	Above 75	Above 65	33·6 or above	Above 110	Above 17·0	Above 8·1	12

Note.—The speeds in columns (4) to (8) refer to a height of about 30 feet (10 m. approximately) above ground in an open situation. [For other heights approximate corrections are for 50 feet add 10 per cent., for 100 feet add 25 per cent. ; for 20 feet subtract 10 per cent., for 10 feet subtract 20 per cent., for 2 feet subtract 30 per cent.]

(*From Air Ministry Form* 3090, *by permission of the Controller of H.M. Stationery Office*) readings of the maximum and minimum thermometers ; the dry-bulb gives the air-temperature at the time of observation, but the tendency is rather to regard it as an adjunct to the wet-bulb for the purpose of determining the humidity. At the principal observatories both dry-bulb and wet-bulb temperatures are continuously recorded, and the dry-bulb readings have been very thoroughly summarized ; for the observatories we are thus able to make use of a very considerable amount of information in regard to the air-temperature at known times. The results derived from observations of daily maximum and minimum are in many ways less satisfactory than those derived from continuous records, but we have to face the fact that at most climatological stations the instruments are only read once daily at 9 h.[1] The readings of the maximum and minimum thermometers inform us of the limits between which temperature has varied since the thermometers were last set, and that information is decidedly more useful than the single observation of temperature at 9 h. In particular the arithmetic mean of the average daily maximum and the average daily minimum during a month is very nearly equal to the true mean temperature during that month, and it is in fact customary to describe the arithmetic mean of the two averages as the " mean temperature ". The disadvantages of maximum and minimum readings arise mainly from the fact that the result obtained depends quite appreciably upon the hour or hours at which the instruments are read and set. If all stations carried out the same procedure this would not matter much, but the actual position is that the procedure is different at the various type of stations. At " normal climatological stations " the thermometers are read and set at 21 h. ; at " auxiliary climatological stations ", which constitute the majority, they are read and set at 9 h. ; at official " synoptic " stations they are read and set both at 7 h. and 18 h. For the latter class of stations the readings on which averages are calculated are the " day maximum " covering the period 7 h. to 18 h. and the " night minimum " covering the period 18 h. to 7 h. Differences arise on occasions, mainly in winter months, when the daily variation of temperature is abnormal. Ordinarily the daily minimum occurs in the early hours of the morning, but changes in the source of the air supply often upset this regular régime. Thus a

---

[1] When referring to time of day in this book the hour will be stated with reference to the "24-hour clock"; thus 9 h. means 9 a.m., 15 h. 3 p.m. and 21 h. 9 p.m. The standard of time is Greenwich Mean Time (G.M.T.) except where otherwise stated. During the currency of British Summer Time clocks are one hour ahead of G.M.T. ; thus 15 h. in June is equivalent to 4 p.m. by public clocks.

mild night in winter with south-westerly winds may be followed by colder conditions during the day, causing the minimum temperature to occur during the daytime. On such an occasion the night minimum temperature read at 7 h. might be several degrees higher than the 24-hour minimum read at 21 h. It is obvious, on consideration, that the average value of the minimum for consecutive periods of 24 hours must be lower than the average minimum for any selected part of the 24 hours. Similarly the average value of the maximum for consecutive periods of 24 hours must be higher than the average maximum for a portion of the 24 hours. Thus the " mean daily range ", that is to say the mean difference between the maximum and minimum readings, is quite substantially greater at stations which observe 24-hour extremes than at stations where night-minimum and day-maximum readings are utilized. At Kew Observatory (4) the average difference between the 24-hour minimum to 9 h. and the night minimum approaches 2° F. in winter months, and the mean difference for the whole year is about 1° F. The effect on the mean maximum is less pronounced, but the combined effect results in a change of about 2·5° F. in the mean daily range for winter months. There can be no doubt that the mean daily range tends to be overestimated by the use of 24-hour extremes, having regard to the fact that the minimum read at the morning hour is always credited to the day of reading and the maximum to the day previous. Thus, let us suppose that a cold morning occurs on 5th March, giving a reading of 32° F. at 9 h. on that day, with milder conditions both before and afterwards ; then the minimum thermometer will obviously be reading 32° F. when it is set at 9 h. on 5th March and its index will show 32° F. when the thermometer is read again at 9 h. on 6th March. The result will be that 6th March is credited with a minimum temperature of 32° F. The reading on 5th will have been the same or lower ; a single cold morning thus gives rise to two low entries in the register of minimum temperatures.

The introduction of " day maximum " and " night minimum " as the standard values for climatological summaries for synoptic stations was thus a desirable reform, but it introduced an awkward discontinuity in the statistics for stations, many of which had records going back for many years. The change was made in 1921 and the latest available averages of day maximum and night minimum thus cover a period of only fifteen years. The comparison of the temperature data for these stations with those for climatological stations, where 24-hour extremes are observed, clearly presents some difficulties, especially when we attempt to study the details of geographical distribution.

5. Humidity. Our humidity data are derived almost exclusively from readings of the dry-bulb and wet-bulb thermometers exposed in Stevenson screens. From these readings the relative humidity,[1] vapour-pressure and dew-point are obtained by reference to tables. The official British tables (5) are based on a modification of Regnault's formula, viz. :

$$x = f - A(t - t'),$$

where x is the vapour-pressure in millibars at the time of observation, f is the saturation vapour-pressure at the temperature of the wet-bulb, also in millibars, t and t' are respectively the dry- and wet-bulb temperatures and A is a constant which has the value 0·444 when t' is above 32° F. or equal to 32° F., and 0·400 when t' is below 32° F. These constants are based on the assumption that the flow of air over the bulbs of the thermometers in the Stevenson screen is equivalent to a " light air ".

At some stations there is also a hair hygrograph which gives a direct record of relative humidity. The purpose of this instrument is partly to afford information in regard to the variation of relative humidity between the hours of observation, and partly to give a reading of relative humidity on occasions when the wet-bulb is thrown out of action by freezing of the water supply. At the principal observatories the humidity data are derived from hourly values of dry-bulb and wet-bulb temperature obtained from photographic records.

6. Rainfall. Our rainfall data are derived from the readings of rain-gauges five inches or eight inches in diameter placed with their rims twelve inches above ground level in an open, but not excessively exposed, situation. The reading is expressed in the form of the depth in inches or millimetres (usually the former) to which the rain would cover a flat area if none evaporated or ran off. One inch of rain is equivalent to 4·7 gallons per square yard or 101 tons of water per acre. In the case of snow or hail the solid precipitation is melted and included in the records as if it were rain ; thus the figure stating the " rainfall " of a place includes all forms of atmospheric precipitation as well as the small amounts of condensed moisture contributed by dew or hoar-frost. If the reading expressed to the nearest hundredth of an inch is ·01 inch or more the day is reckoned as a " day of rain " or " rain-day ". For the purposes of *British Rainfall* a day with ·04 inch or more is reckoned as a " wet day ". The " day " for purposes of rainfall measurement begins at the morning hour of observation, 7 h. or 9 h.

---

[1] For an explanation of the terms used here, see Chapter IX.

The *duration* of rainfall is derived from measurements of traces furnished by self-recording rain-gauges. In order to obtain the maximum degree of consistency in the measurements made by different observers using different types of rain-recorders, the convention is to tabulate only the duration of rain falling at a rate of not less than ·004 inch (0·1 mm.) per hour. Investigation has shown (6) that the duration tabulated according to this convention is substantially less than the true duration of perceptible rain. The actual amount of rain excluded by the adopted convention is, however, very small; it would take 500 hours of rain falling at half the standard minimum rate to produce as much as one inch of rain.

The *intensity* of rain may also be determined from autographic records by measuring the amount registered in a given time; intensity is usually expressed in inches per hour.

7. Evaporation is a measure of the amount of moisture returned to the atmosphere in the form of vapour, and is expressed in the same units as those used for rainfall. Measurements are made at a few stations by determining the daily change of water-level in a tank, usually six feet square and two feet deep, sunk into the ground so that its rim is about three inches above ground level. Allowance must, of course, be made for rainfall, and it is necessary to assume that the increment to the tank is equal to the depth of rain as measured in an adjacent rain-gauge. When rain is accompanied by a strong wind there may be appreciable losses by outsplashing from the tank (7), and in these circumstances the evaporation would thus tend to be overestimated.

Methods of determining the loss by evaporation from soil under natural conditions are referred to in the chapter on " Evaporation and Percolation ".

8. Sunshine duration is determined exclusively from the records of Campbell-Stokes sunshine recorders. In this instrument the record is in the form of a scorched or burnt line on a strip of standardized card on which a time-scale is printed, and the record is produced by a spherical lens acting as a burning-glass. The method of registration appears crude at first sight, but by careful standardization of the instrument, the cards and the methods of measurement, a high degree of precision and comparability has been attained. The sensitivity of the instrument is such that recording begins, in clear weather, when the sun is about three degrees above the horizon, that is to say about half an hour after sunrise, and ceases at a corresponding epoch before sunset. It is hardly ever possible to find a site for a sunshine recorder where the exposure is entirely unobstructed right down to the horizon ; consequently the loss of registration of very feeble sunshine in the early morning and late evening is not a matter of much practical importance. Some loss may, however, occur at other times of the day when the intensity of sunshine is reduced to a low value by mist, haze or thin cloud. On the other hand intermittent sunshine tends to be over-recorded, because the breadth of the burnt spot produced by only a few seconds' exposure to bright sunshine is considerable when reckoned in terms of the time-scale of the instrument. A period of intermittent sunshine may thus be recorded as a continuous burn.

On the whole, however, it may be assumed that the Campbell-Stokes instrument gives a satisfactory approximation to the true duration of sunshine strong enough to cast a perceptible shadow. It has the great merit of producing a permanent record which can be easily measured, and it is the only recording instrument known to meteorologists which works without the aid of clockwork.

9. Visibility is defined as the distance at which natural objects such as hills, trees and buildings can be seen clearly enough by an observer possessing normal vision to be recognized for what they are. For the purpose of determining the visibility, observations are made upon a series of objects at, or very near to, certain definite distances from the viewpoint. The standard distances range from twenty-five metres (twenty-seven yards) for object A, which may be a post, a bush, a rock or something of similar size, to fifty kilometres ($31\frac{1}{4}$ miles) for object M, which would usually be a hill or a mountain. A complete list is given in Table II. An observation consists in noting the furthest object in the series which is visible. At night the observer does his best with the aid of lights, etc., to estimate what the visibility would be if it were daylight.

A fog is defined as an occasion when object F at 1,000 metres (1,100 yards) cannot be seen, that is, when E at 500 metres (550 yards) is the furthest object visible. When F can be seen but not G, *i.e.* when visibility is between 1,000 and 2,000 metres (1,100-2,200 yards), " mist " or " haze " is said to exist. These precise definitions date only from the year 1921, when they were adopted by international agreement. It will be realized that the official definition of a fog differs from the meaning that would be given to it by, for example, a motorist, who is in the habit of applying the term only to conditions which seriously interfere with his driving. The motorist's " fog " would be classed as a " thick fog " or " dense fog " in meteorological summaries.

A few other terms will be defined as they arise in the course of our discussions.

TABLE II
SCALE FOR VISIBILITY OBSERVATIONS

Indication letter of Object	Standard distance of Object		Used when the Object given in column 1 is the furthest visible	
	Metres	Yards	Telegraphic Code Figure	Description
X*		}	0	Dense fog.
A	25	27		
B	50	55 }	1	Thick fog.
C	100	110		
D	200	220	2	Fog.
E	500	550	3	Moderate fog.
F	1,000	1,100	4	Mist, haze or very poor visibility.
G	2,000	Miles $1\frac{1}{4}$	5	Poor visibility.
H	4,000	$2\frac{1}{2}$ }	6	Moderate visibility.
I	7,000	$4\frac{1}{3}$		
J	10,000	$6\frac{1}{4}$	7	Good visibility.
K	20,000	$12\frac{1}{2}$ }	8	Very good visibility.
L	30,000	$18\frac{2}{3}$		
M	50,000	31	9	Excellent visibility.

* Object A not visible.   [From *Meteorological Observer's Handbook* (M.O. 191)][1]

10. Averages and normals. We have already pointed out that one of the principal aims of climatology is to determine the average or " normal " value appropriate to a given time and a given place. The use of the word " normal " used to be more common in meteorology

[1] All data taken from official publications are reproduced by permission of the Controller of H.M. Stationery Office.

than it is at the present day, when the tendency is to replace it by the word " average ". The term " normal " implies something ultimate, a final value from which the effects of chance fluctuations have been completely eliminated, but we have to realize that that is an unattainable ideal. In practice the best thing we can do is to take the average for a certain finite period and use that as the standard value with which to make comparisons. We can then apply the elementary theory of probability to estimate how much the adopted average is likely to differ from the true normal ; also we can calculate the number of years necessary to reduce the probable error to a given value. Calculations of this kind rest on the assumption that the deviations of individual values comply with the ordinary law of errors and that there is no " secular trend " or long-period oscillation. None of these assumptions are likely to be strictly true for meteorological variables, but the results of such calculations are of some interest. For a typical station in the British Isles the standard (or root mean square) deviation of the annual rainfall is of the order of fifteen per cent. of the annual average (8). The probable error of a 35-year average is therefore $\dfrac{2}{3} \times \dfrac{15}{\sqrt{35}}$, or about 1·7 per cent. For a station with an annual average rainfall of thirty inches the probable error is therefore about 0·5 inch. In other words if we adopt a 35-year average of annual rainfall as the normal we are as likely as not to be within half an inch of the truth. To reduce the probable error to 0·1 inch it would be necessary to average the results over a period of $5^2 \times 35$ or 875 years.

The averages which we shall quote in the following pages are based in a few cases on periods exceeding 100 years. In general we shall utilize rainfall averages referring to a 35-year period ; for temperature and sunshine much of the available material refers to a 30-year period. In other cases we are obliged by force of circumstances to use average values covering a period of only ten years or even less. It is necessary to remember, therefore, that some of our results may be appreciably in error. Our tables and charts must be regarded, in fact, merely as a summary of recent experience.

The fact that we cannot refer to records covering periods of hundreds of years is, however, not so serious a disadvantage as might be supposed, because it is not the main function of climatology to establish normal values to a very high order of precision. A long record such as the record of temperature and rainfall at the Radcliffe Observatory, Oxford, is mainly of interest because of the information it provides in regard to the slow upward or downward trends, or long-period oscillations, which underlie the fluctuations which we attribute, for want of a better explanation, to " casual " causes. We can never hope to possess many such long and uninterrupted records, and we should not, in fact, need many for investigations of long-term changes. The practical everyday needs of climatological study demand, rather, that we should possess comparable records from a large number of places within the area under consideration. It does not matter very much if these records cover comparatively short periods, and averages for recent years are in fact more appropriate for many purposes. Experience shows that the indefinite continuance of observations at the same place, under uniform conditions, cannot be assumed. If reference be made to a publication such as the *Monthly Weather Report* for the year 1900 and the list of stations is compared with the list of stations now in operation, it will be found that many stations which were working in 1900 have now ceased to exist, and that a large proportion of the stations in the current list did not exist in 1900. For the purpose of investigating the geographical distribution of climatological elements it is highly desirable that the data should be homogeneous in respect to the period covered by the observations. Such homogeneity can only be secured if a comparatively short period of years be adopted as standard. Considerations of this kind have recently led the Meteorological Office to fix thirty years as a standard number of years from which to compute averages of temperature and sunshine for climatological purposes. New averages are computed every five years : the first series published in accordance with this policy referred to the period 1901-1930 ; the second series, covering the period 1906-1935, has recently appeared, and we shall utilize these values in certain sections of this book. For rainfall, the standard period is the 35-years, 1881-1915.

The disadvantages of a short series of observations are felt most acutely when we wish to determine the form of the annual variation of a very variable element like rainfall or the duration of sunshine. The probable error of the mean value for say thirty Januaries or thirty Septembers is much greater than the probable error of the mean value for thirty whole years. A comparison of the mean values for Oxford and York (9) for two separate periods of thirty years has shown differences of the order of twenty-five to thirty per cent. in certain months. Such questions as which month of the year is in the long run the wettest, the driest or the sunniest cannot, therefore, be answered with complete certainty from the data at our disposal. In most cases the conclusions reached in regard to these matters are simply the expression of our experience in the last few decades.

Temperature is relatively a more stable element than either rainfall or sunshine. At British stations the standard deviation of mean annual temperature is of the order of 1° F. ; consequently the effect of casual fluctuations on a 30-year average may be regarded as negligible. In individual months the standard deviation at a typical inland station varies from about 2° F. in a summer month to 3·5° F. in a winter month, and the probable error of a 30-year average is about 0·3° F. to 0·5° F.

BIBLIOGRAPHY

(1) *The Meteorological Observer's Handbook* (M.O. 191). (H.M.S.O.)
(2) G. C. Simpson. *Meteorological Office Publication*, No. 180, 1906. (H.M.S.O.)
(3) G. C. Simpson, *Meteorological Office Professional Notes*, No. 44. (H.M.S.O.)
(4) *Averages of Temperature for periods ending* 1930 (M.O. 364). (Introduction.) (H.M.S.O.)
(5) *Hygrometric Tables* (M.O. 265). (H.M.S.O.)
(6) *Q.J.R. Meteor. Soc.*, **60**, 1934, pp. 310-312 (Discussion on "The statistical probability of rain in London," by D. Dewar).
(7) E. G. Bilham, "On measurements of evaporation at Valentia Observatory," *British Rainfall*, 1931, pp. 268-274. (H.M.S.O.)
(8) J. Glasspoole, "The relation between annual rainfall over Europe and that at Oxford and Glenquoich," *British Rainfall*, 1925. (H.M.S.O.)
(9) E. G. Bilham, "Variations in the climate of York during the sixty years 1871-1930 and comparison with Oxford," *Q.J.R. Meteor. Soc.*, **59**, 1933, pp. 138-150.

CHAPTER II

GEOGRAPHICAL AND ENVIRONMENTAL FACTORS

11. General considerations. The climate of any region is determined in broad outline by its latitude and by its geographical position in relation to continents and oceans. From the fact that the sun's altitude cannot exceed $23\frac{1}{2}$ degrees at either pole, while it varies at noon only through a range of $23\frac{1}{2}$ degrees on either side of the zenith at the equator, it follows that the equatorial regions must have a high mean temperature and the polar regions a low mean temperature. The continents, however, profoundly modify the course of the isotherms, or lines of equal mean temperature, particularly in middle latitudes, for reasons which we shall discuss later. In their turn the thermal anomalies created by the continents call into existence broad wind currents and pressure distributions, which are described in text-books under the heading of " the general circulation of the atmosphere ". The wind currents are the vehicles by which heat and moisture are transported in the atmosphere from one region to another ; also, by their action upon the sea surface, they set up persistent " drifts " in the oceans which result in the transport of warm water from equatorial regions towards the poles. Thus an explanation of the climatic features of any particular region necessitates a discussion of the meteorology of the whole Globe.

Our purpose here is to discuss the climate of a small group of islands in the northern hemisphere, and it is unnecessary for that particular purpose to go very deeply into questions of general atmospheric circulation. It is of interest, however, to glance briefly at our geographical position, and to examine the meteorological implications of that position, before proceeding to the detailed study of the facts before us. We shall also find it necessary to survey briefly the physical structure of the British Isles, because the local topography exerts an important influence, causing substantial variations of climate within a relatively small area. It is, in fact, incorrect to employ such a phrase as " the climate of the British Isles " except in a very broad sense. The reader will not need to be told that the climates of the Scilly Isles, London and the summit of Ben Nevis are very substantially different.

15

12. Geographical features. The British Isles form a group of islands on the western seaboard of the continent of Europe. Europe itself is joined to the larger continent of Asia to the east. To the south we have the continent of Africa, with the shallow and relatively narrow Mediterranean Sea intervening. The British Isles are thus an outlier of the greatest land mass of the Globe. To the south England is separated from this land mass only by the narrow and shallow waters of the English Channel. A wider sea, the North Sea, intervenes between our east coast and the European continent; north of latitude 54° N. this sea is 350 to 400 miles in width. To the west and south-west of the British Isles the North Atlantic Ocean presents an unbroken sea area, nowhere less than about 1,800 miles in breadth. To the north also we look out over many hundreds of miles of almost unbroken sea.

The mainland of Great Britain extends from latitude 50° N. at the Lizard to about 58½° N. at the Pentland Firth. This range of 8½ degrees in latitude is extended to nearly 12 degrees by outlying groups of islands—the Channel Islands in the south, the Orkneys and Shetlands in the north. In the south, between Land's End and the North Foreland, Great Britain has its maximum breadth of 330 miles. The length from the most southerly point, the Lizard, to the most northerly, Dunnet Head, is about 600 miles, and the area is approximately 88,000 square miles. The other large island of the group, Ireland, lies to westward of Great Britain and has an area of 32,600 square miles. Ireland is about 290 miles long from Mizen Head in the south to Malin Head in the north, and the maximum width from east to west is about 200 miles. The small islands off the south-west coast of Ireland are the most westerly portions of the continent of Europe.

On the north-east, Ireland is separated from Great Britain by the North Channel, which has a minimum width of thirteen miles between the Antrim coast and the Mull of Cantire. On the south-east, the St. George's Channel has a minimum width of forty-five miles between Carnsore Point and St. David's Head on the Welsh coast. Between these two channels lies the Irish Sea, which has a maximum breadth of about 140 miles.

In addition to Great Britain and Ireland the British Isles include a very large number of smaller islands, numbering more than 5,000 in all. The Orkneys, Shetlands and Channel Islands have already been mentioned; other important islands are the Isle of Wight off the south coast of England, Anglesey off the north coast of Wales, the Isle of Man in the Irish Sea, and the large groups, the Inner and Outer Hebrides, off the west coast of Scotland.

On all sides the coasts of Great Britain and Ireland are deeply indented with bays, channels and estuaries. As a result no point of the mainland is more than about seventy miles, and only a small proportion of the total area is more than fifty miles, from the sea.

13. Physical structure. The mountain systems of Great Britain are of no great height and lie almost entirely to westward of a line drawn northward from the Isle of Wight. *Scotland* is by far the most mountainous part of the area, and it is the only portion of the British Isles in which altitudes exceeding 4,000 feet are to be found. These Scottish mountains form three main groups: (*a*) the Northern Highlands merging westward into the Western Highlands, of which the rugged islands of the Inner Hebrides may be regarded as outliers; (*b*) the Grampians; and (*c*) the Southern Uplands. The Northern Highlands form a series of ridges oriented roughly from east to west, and include many peaks exceeding 3,000 feet. They occupy the whole of the area north-west of Glenmore (the Great Glen), which extends almost in a straight line from Loch Linnhe in the west to the Moray Firth in the north-east. This cleft is occupied by a series of narrow lochs, Loch Linnhe, Loch Lochy, Loch Oich and Loch Ness, which have been united by means of the Caledonian Canal to form a continuous navigable waterway across Scotland. The Grampians occupy the region between the Great Glen and a narrow plain which extends from the Firth of Forth to the Firth of Tay. The ridges of the Grampians have a general south-west to north-east direction. In Ben Nevis (4,406 feet), near Fort William, they attain the highest level found in the British Isles. In the Cairngorm Hills, north-west of Braemar, there is another group of peaks exceeding 4,000 feet. On these mountains the total area above the 4,000 feet level considerably exceeds the area above 4,000 feet on Ben Nevis. The Cairngorm region may be said to form an extensive plateau, a considerable area of which is above 2,000 feet. The Southern Uplands form a range running from W.S.W. to E.N.E. across southern Scotland, reaching a maximum altitude of 2,764 feet at Merrick, Kirkcudbright. Further south a parallel range, the Cheviots, marks the border between England and Scotland. The highest peak, The Cheviot, reaches 2,676 feet.

In *England* the most prominent orographic feature is the Pennine Range or Chain, the " backbone of England ", running almost due south from the Scottish border to the Peak of Derbyshire, with transverse ridges running eastward into Durham and Yorkshire. Numerous peaks exceed 2,000 feet. In the northern part of the range Cross Fell

B

reaches 2,932 feet ; further south Great Whernside rises to 2,310 feet. The Pennines are separated by the valley of the River Eden from the mountainous area of the Lake District in Cumberland and Westmorland, the valleys of which radiate from a common centre near Keswick. Among the highest summits are Scafell Pike, 3,210 feet, and Helvellyn, 3,118 feet. The only other important mountain group in England, excluding Wales, occurs in the south-west, where in Devon and Cornwall there is a considerable area of high land, mainly in the form of tablelands such as Dartmoor and Exmoor. The summits are for the most part below 1,600 feet, though 2,000 feet is exceeded by Yes Tor (2,077 feet) and High Willhays (2,039 feet). In the south of England we find a series of hill ranges such as the Cotswolds, the Chilterns, the Mendips and the North and South Downs, running either from south-west to north-east or from west to east. The summits are round about 800 feet, though 1,000 feet is reached here and there. The only important upland region near the east coast of England is the Yorkshire Moors, which reach an elevation of 1,489 feet at Botton Head. The Yorkshire Wolds, further south, are of much lower height and are continued south-ward of the Humber by the Lincolnshire Wolds.

In *Wales* we have an extensive mountainous region comparable with Scotland. The highest peaks are found in the north, where Snowdon rises to 3,570 feet. A number of summits in the immediate vicinity of Snowdon exceed 3,000 feet, but that height is not attained elsewhere in the Principality, though it is closely approached by Cader Iris in Merionethshire and by the Beacons of Brecknockshire. On the whole the ranges have a south-west to north-east trend like those of Scotland.

Ireland differs from England and Wales in that important mountain groups are found near the east coast as well as near the west coast. The eastern groups, starting in the north, include the Mountains of Antrim (Trostan, 1,817 feet), the Mourne Mountains in County Down (Slieve Donard, 2,796 feet), Slieve Gullion (1,893 feet) in Armagh, and the Mountains of Wicklow, which reach 3,039 feet, in Lugnaquilla. In the south-west we have a series of ranges divided by long sea inlets—Dingle Bay, Kenmare Bay and Bantry Bay. In county Kerry the Macgilli-cuddy's Reeks rise to 3,422 feet. An altitude of over 3,000 feet is also found in the Galty Mountains on the borders of counties Cork and Limerick. Many other ranges or groups of mountains, including the Knockmealdown Range in the south, the Slieve Bloom Range running north-eastward across Tipperary and Offaly, and the mountains of Donegal, Londonderry, Tyrone, Mayo and Galway, have peaks exceeding 2,000 feet.   These high lands are distributed very generally over Ireland and the only flat area of large extent is the Central Plain, which extends from west to east across the middle of the country.

14. Temperature conditions over seas and land masses. We have seen that the British Isles are contiguous to a large ocean on the west and to a large continental land mass on the east and south. The general climatic conditions over our area must therefore be related to the general climatic conditions of these two systems, and the nature of the relationship must depend upon the relative frequencies of winds which reach us from different directions at different seasons. Reference has already been made to the fact that the distribution of temperature over the Globe is profoundly modified by the continents, and it is worth while now to consider briefly how these modifications arise.

The sun is the prime source of the energy whose transformations constitute what we know as " weather ". The sun sends out a continuous stream of radiant energy in all directions, some of which falls upon that portion of the earth's atmosphere which is directed towards the sun at a given moment. About half of the incident energy is reflected back into space by clouds and there is some further loss mainly by scattering within the atmosphere. The balance which is transmitted to the surface of the earth suffers some loss by reflection and the remainder is absorbed. The result of the absorption of radiant energy is to raise the temperature of the material upon which the radiation falls, and the temperature of that material will continue to rise so long as the rate of gain of heat by the surface exceeds the rate at which heat is conveyed away by convection, conduction or re-radiation. For a given increment of heat per unit mass the rise of temperature is proportional to the specific heat of the material.

Of all known bodies water has the highest specific heat, consequently it shows the smallest rise of temperature for a given increment of heat. Moreover, water is transparent to most of the range of wave-lengths in the solar spectrum ; radiation incident obliquely upon its surface is partially reflected and the transmitted portion transfers its energy to a considerable depth of liquid during the process of absorption. The result is that the temperature of the sea surface is raised only very slowly by the sun's radiation, so slowly indeed that hardly any diurnal variation of temperature can be detected. Like every other body the sea continuously emits long-wave radiation into space at a rate determined by its temperature. Broadly speaking, we may say that the sea-surface temperature will rise progressively so long as the amount of solar radiation absorbed during the daytime exceeds the total amount of heat lost by radiation or by other means during the whole period of twenty-four hours. These conditions prevail during the late spring, summer and early autumn ; the reverse conditions hold during the remainder of the year. The ocean therefore plays the part of a reservoir in which heat is slowly stored for six months, and slowly given up during the remaining six months.

The physical properties of a land surface differ very materially from those of a sea surface. The materials of which the land area is composed have a smaller specific heat ; they are in general poor conductors of heat and as they are also solid materials, opaque to the short-wave solar radiation, the incoming energy is absorbed in a very shallow surface layer. A relatively large rise of temperature therefore occurs in response to a given intensity of incident radiation. At night the effect of the outgoing radiation is to produce a rapid chilling of the surface. The air in contact with the surface is also chilled and an " inversion " of temperature is thus created. In middle and high latitudes the small amount of solar radiation received during the short winter days, is inadequate to compensate for the loss of heat by outgoing radiation and a progressive cooling thus ensues, as the result of which very low temperatures may be attained in mid-winter in the central areas of large land masses. Thus a large land area produces large diurnal and seasonal variations of temperature. We shall see when we come to study the temperature statistics of the British Isles that even a land area as small as Great Britain or Ireland is large enough to show these characteristics quite conspicuously. Over the Eurasian continent we find them developed in a most striking manner, and this land mass is actually within sight of the south-east corner of England. We know, however, that our winters are not marked by the intense cold of the central continental areas which lie due east of us, and that our summers are not remarkable for intense heat. To understand these facts we must examine the details of our meteorological environment a little more closely. This may be done by means of the charts reproduced in Figs. 1 to 5.

15. Our meteorological environment. Fig. 1 shows the mean distribution of pressure at sea level and prevailing wind, during the month of January, over part of the North Atlantic Ocean and the continent of Europe. The dominating feature is a large depression centred near Iceland (the " Icelandic low "). A belt of high pressure covers the ocean in about the latitude of the Azores and extends over the southern portion of the European continent. (Further to east and north it links

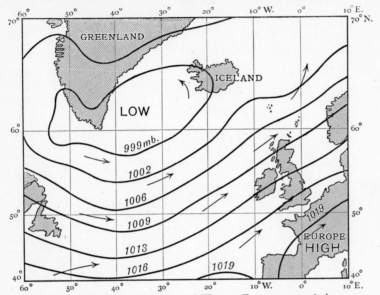

Fig. 1.—North Atlantic Ocean and Western Europe ; mean isobars
and winds, January.

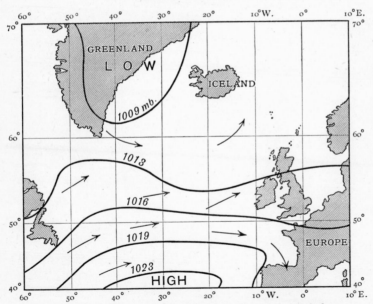

Fig. 2.—North Atlantic Ocean and Western Europe ; mean isobars
and winds, July.

up with a large anticyclone over Siberia.) From about longitude 40° W. the isobars run parallel in a direction from west-south-west to east-north-east right across the British Isles to north-west Europe and the associated wind is from west-south-west to south-west.

Fig. 2 is the corresponding chart for July. The Azores anticyclone has assumed the dominating rôle and the general barometric gradient over the North Atlantic is much more feeble. The isobars run from

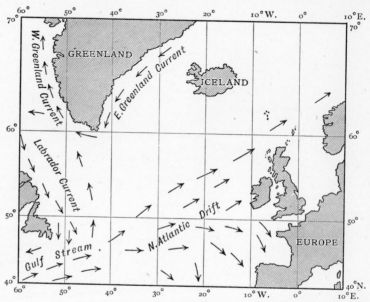

FIG. 3.—Currents in the North Atlantic Ocean.

west to east and the resultant surface flow of air over our islands is from west-south-west.

The conditions illustrated in Fig. 1 and Fig. 2 may be regarded as typical of the mean conditions in winter and summer. The charts for the intermediate months show the successive stages of the transition from winter to summer conditions and back again ; it is unnecessary to reproduce them here. There are some irregularities in the seasonal variation ; in May, June and September the average barometric gradient over the British Isles is very feeble indeed, and in October the resultant flow of air over our area is southerly rather than westerly. Broadly speaking, however, we may say that the general direction of air-flow is from south-west or west in all seasons, and it is particularly important to note that these conditions are most strongly developed during the months of November, December, January, February and March.

We may now turn to Fig. 3, on which the prevailing ocean currents in the North Atlantic are represented in diagrammatic form. The chart is just large enough to show the Gulf Stream in the bottom left-hand corner. This stream current is fed from equatorial sources and emerges

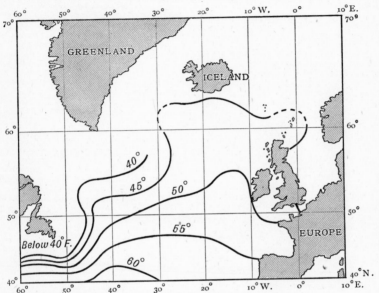

FIG. 4.—North Atlantic Ocean and North Sea; sea-surface isotherms, January.

from the Gulf of Mexico (where the surface temperature approximates to 80° F. even in winter) to flow northward and then eastward into the North Atlantic. In about longitude 45° W. the Gulf Stream has ceased to exist as a stream current. The warm water furnished by the Gulf Stream is, however, in such a position that it can be caused to move north-eastward towards the western seaboard of Europe by the prevailing winds. This action gives rise to the North Atlantic Drift, which may be regarded for practical purposes as a great extension north-eastward of the Gulf Stream. The resultant effect on the temperature of the Atlantic waters off our western shores is immediately obvious when we turn to Fig. 4, on which are marked the mean positions of the sea-surface isotherms, or lines of equal temperature, in January. Practically the whole of the sea surface south of Iceland over an area extending westward as far as longitude 30° W. has a temperature above 45° F. West of Ireland the 50° F. isotherm bulges northward and the 55° F. isotherm is encountered in the latitude of the Bay of Biscay.

Fig. 5 is the corresponding chart for July. In that month the isotherms, like the isobars, have a more westerly trend. The mean temperature of our coastal waters varies from slightly below 55° F. in the

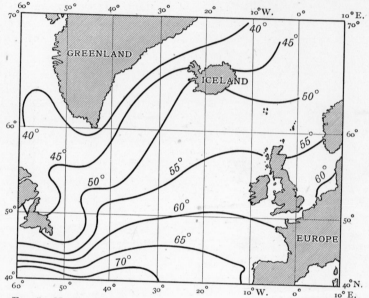

FIG. 5.—North Atlantic Ocean and North Sea; sea-surface isotherms, July.

north of Scotland to 60° F. at the mouth of the English Channel. Graphs of the annual variation of sea-surface temperature off various sections of our coasts will be found in Fig. 48, page 149.

The great area of warm sea lying westward of the British Isles in winter is the most important feature of our meteorological environment. We have seen that the general direction of air-flow over the British Isles is from between south-west and west, and that this flow is particularly marked during the winter season. These prevailing winds drive warm water towards our shores, and in order to reach our area they have to blow over the warm water so accumulated. The prevalent air-stream over the British Isles in winter is therefore both mild and moist, and it is this fact which imparts those features to our winter climate.

16. Variations from the mean conditions. The charts of average pressure distribution reproduced in Fig. 1 and Fig. 2 may be regarded as representations of the pattern which the isobars tend to assume when the fluctuations have been eliminated by taking averages for a long period of years. The low pressure near Iceland and the high pressure in the Azores region are features which recur in a large percentage of the daily weather charts. The latter feature is particularly persistent but the Icelandic low is decidedly less constant. If the reader has the opportunity of looking through a collection of charts such as those published in the *Daily Weather Report* he will find that an anticyclone appears not infrequently over Iceland and Greenland. At the same time the southern anticyclone may be displaced far to the southward, with the result that the general wind current over the British Isles is easterly instead of westerly. Also he will find that it is rather unusual for the north-eastern Atlantic to be covered by a series of parallel isobars. More often this area is occupied by one or more low-pressure systems which tend to move north-eastward skirting the British Isles, or on some occasions to pass directly over them. Our area lies, in fact, in a zone of highly variable weather conditions, due to the frequent passage of depressions and anticyclones. Almost every possible kind of pressure distribution is to be found on our weather charts, and each type of distribution is associated with a characteristic type of weather or sequence of weather. The average charts which we have examined have served the purpose of explaining certain broad features of our climate. In the next chapter we shall carry the enquiry a stage further by considering the variations associated with some of the more important types of pressure distribution which affect our area.

CHAPTER III

CHARACTERISTIC TYPES OF WEATHER

17. Classification of weather types. In the concluding paragraph of Chapter II reference was made to the fact that various types of pressure distribution over the British Isles are associated with different types of weather. The importance of the pressure distribution in this connection lies in the fact that it determines, or is closely correlated with, the general direction of air-flow. It would be possible, from an analysis of the records of individual stations, to draw up tables showing how the temperature, rainfall, humidity and cloudiness vary with the wind direction at different seasons. That has been done, in fact, in a few cases but it is more informative to deal with the problem on broader lines, by reference to weather charts. We shall not attempt to give a detailed statistical analysis of the weather conditions associated with each type of pressure distribution; our main object is to determine the frequency of occurrence of the various types, for the purpose of seeing the proportions in which the " ingredients " of our climate are mixed in different seasons.

The classification we shall adopt is based on one proposed by E. Gold (10). In Gold's classification pressure distributions are sorted into fifteen main types and a number of sub-types; it was not devised primarily for climatological purposes and it may be considerably simplified to meet our present needs. By grouping certain of Gold's types together we thus arrive at the following simplified classification :

Type A.—Low pressure to north or north-west of the British Isles, high pressure to south or south-east, resulting in a general flow of air off the Atlantic Ocean with a southerly component. This type represents, broadly speaking, the normal conditions indicated by Fig. 1 and Fig. 2.

Type B.—Low pressure to north-east, high pressure to south or south-west, resulting in a general flow of air from a point north of west.

Type C.—Low pressure to the east, high pressure to the west, giving northerly winds.

26

Type D.—Low pressure to south-east, high pressure to north-west, giving a general east or north-east wind current : this represents the complete reversal of the normal distribution (Type A).

Type E.—Low pressure to the west, high pressure to the east or north-east, giving south or south-east winds.

Type F.—An anticyclone or a belt or irregular area of high pressure covering the British Isles.

Type G.—A depression either centred over the British Isles or with its centre in the near vicinity of the south-west coasts.

18. Frequency of occurrence of different types. E. Gold's paper includes a table showing the number of occurrences of each of his types and sub-types during a period of fourteen years. From these data we have arrived at the percentages given in Table III.

We observe that Type A is by far the most frequent type, as might be expected. Over the whole year about one day in three complies more or less closely with the normal pattern of Figs. 1 and 2. In the winter months the frequency exceeds forty per cent., but it drops below twenty-five per cent. in April, May and June.

Type B shows a conspicuous maximum in July, when the frequency nearly equals that of Type A, but otherwise there is little seasonal variation. The average frequency throughout the year is about one day in seven.

Type C (north winds) shows a remarkable uniformity of incidence ; the mean frequency is about one day in fourteen.

Type D, associated with north-east or east winds, shows a very definite maximum in the spring and early summer months ; in April and May the frequency is about one day in eight. From August to February inclusive the frequency is only about one day in twenty. The tendency for spells of north-east or east winds in the spring months is a very conspicuous feature of our climate, and we may regard it as very fortunate that this is the rarest of types in the winter months.

Type E shows a considerable seasonal fluctuation, with low frequency in the summer months June to August. The spring and autumn show a relatively high frequency of this type (about one day in nine and seven respectively). January also gives a high frequency, but not December or February. When type E occurs in the summer, warm dry air flows over our area from the Continent and the day temperature may reach a sub-tropical level. The fact that this type occurs infrequently in the summer months is thus of definite significance in regard to our summer climate.

The anticyclonic type, F, occurs on the average on one day in seven. The frequency is a maximum in April, May and September.

TABLE III

PREDOMINATING WEATHER TYPES—PERCENTAGE FREQUENCIES

Month	General direction of air movement from					Anti-cyclone	Cyclone
	S.W.-W.	W.N.W. or N.W.	N.N.W. or N.	N.E. or E.	S.E. or S.		
	Type A	Type B	Type C	Type D	Type E	Type F	Type G
	%	%	%	%	%	%	%
January - -	41	13	5	3	17	11	10
February - -	45	14	5	5	7	13	11
March - - -	28	12	7	9	11	10	24
April - - -	23	14	8	13	10	19	14
May - - -	20	10	7	12	13	20	18
June - - -	24	16	8	11	8	17	16
July - - -	28	25	8	10	6	13	10
August - - -	33	15	7	5	5	15	21
September - -	26	15	8	6	15	19	11
October - -	29	11	8	4	18	9	21
November - -	35	14	7	5	10	13	16
December - -	45	11	6	3	9	7	20
Year - -	31	14	7	7	11	14	16

TABLE IV

SEASONAL PERCENTAGES OF WEATHER TYPES

Season	Type A	Type B	Type C	Type D	Type E	Type F	Type G
	%	%	%	%	%	%	%
Winter (Dec.-Feb.)	43	12	5	4	11	10	14
Spring (Mar.-May)	24	12	7	11	11	16	19
Summer (June-Aug.)	28	18	8	9	6	15	16
Autumn (Sept.-Nov.)	30	13	7	5	14	13	16

The cyclonic type, G, ranks next to Type A in order of mean frequency. In March it occurs on nearly one day in four, almost as frequently as Type A, and its frequency is one day in five in August, October and December. The intervening months, September and November, show a lower frequency of cyclones and a relatively higher frequency of anticyclones ; we shall see later that rainfall shows corresponding alternations

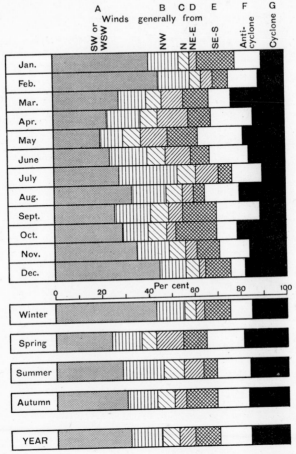

Fig. 6.—Monthly and seasonal percentage frequencies of predominating weather types.
(Each type is represented by a shaded band, the breadth of which is proportional to the percentage frequency.)

in many areas. It is rather surprising to find that Type G has a low frequency (one day in ten) in January.

To complete this brief survey of the facts presented in Table III we may group the months into the four seasons, and we then obtain the values given in Table IV. A diagrammatic representation of the data is given in Fig. 6. We may proceed now to describe the weather conditions associated with the various types of pressure distribution, with the aid of some examples.

19. The normal south-westerly type (Type A). This type is distinguished by the fact that the pressure distribution conforms, in general,

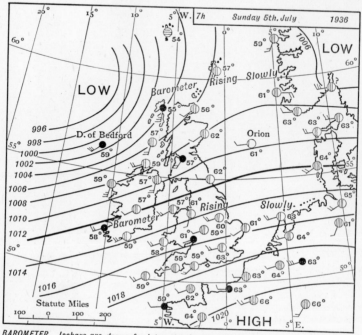

BAROMETER. *Isobars are drawn for intervals of two millibars*
WIND *Arrows fly with wind. A full length feather indicates two steps on the Beaufort Scale, and a short feather one step. Calm is indicated by circle outside weather symbol:-* ◎
TEMPERATURE *is given in degrees F.*

WEATHER SYMBOLS   ◯ *Clear sky*   ◔ *Sky less than 3/10 clouded*   ◑ *Sky 4/10 to 5/10 clouded*
◍ *Sky 7/10 to 9/10 clouded*   ⦿ *Overcast sky*   ● *Rain falling*   ✳ *Snow*   ✶ *Sleet*   ▲ *Hail*
≡ *Fog*   ≋ *Mist*   T *Thunder*   ℞ *Thunderstorm*   ∞ *Slight haze*

FIG. 7.—South-westerly type, 5th July, 1936.

to the pattern indicated as " normal " by the long-period averages. Pressure is low to the north or north-west and the general wind direction over the British Isles is from south-west, west-south-west or west. It occurs with considerable frequency at all times of the year. The example illustrated in Fig. 7 (5th July, 1936) may be regarded as fairly typical. The complete chart for the morning in question shows that the main depression was centred south of Iceland and was relatively shallow, the lowest identifiable isobar being marked 996 mb. The main area of high pressure (above 1,024 mb.) lay across the Atlantic a little south of the Azores and there was another anticyclone over France and Germany. The pressure gradient was not very steep over the British Isles and winds were, for the most part, light or moderate in strength. The chart shows that at stations on the western coasts the air temperature varied from 55° F. in the Hebrides to 59° F. at the mouth of the English Channel, agreeing closely with the normal temperature of the sea surface in July (Fig. 5). The black dots on the map show that rain was falling at many of the western stations. In the following twenty-four hours rainfall amounted to 1·3 inch at Scilly and 0·7 inch at the Lizard, smaller amounts being measured elsewhere. There were, nevertheless, good records of sunshine at many stations.

In winter examples of this type of distribution it is usual to find that the air temperature of the wind blowing off the Atlantic on to our western coasts has a temperature approximating to the sea-surface temperature, so that 45° F. would be a fairly representative value, rising sometimes to the neighbourhood of 50° F. An inspection of Fig. 4 shows that south-westerly winds having a long " fetch " pass over water which is decreasing in temperature towards the British Isles ; consequently such winds have a high relative humidity and often produce copious rainfall on the high ground in Ireland, Scotland and the western half of England and Wales. When moist air is caused to ascend by a range of hills or mountains in its path, it is cooled dynamically by the expansion due to the decrease of pressure accompanying the ascent. When the dew-point is reached cloud is formed and finally rain (or snow). Rain produced in this manner, which is quite distinct from the ascending motion involved in cyclonic action, is known as " orographic " rain. It is prominently associated with the Type A distribution at all times of year, and it is not surprising to find a fairly close parallelism between the frequency of occurrence of this type, as shown in Table III, and the amount of rain recorded in the different months at stations in the west and north. In Fig. 8 a comparison is given between the curve of monthly percentages of Type A, from Table III, and the average monthly rainfall at Seathwaite, in Cumberland, one of the wettest stations in the British Isles, where a considerable proportion of the rain is of the orographic type. It will be seen that the parallelism is almost perfect. It is not, of course, intended to imply that the rainfall under the conditions represented by Type A is *entirely* orographic; but we do find that if Type

A is more than usually frequent in an individual month, then the elevated districts in the west and north receive more than their normal amount of rainfall, while the low-lying districts in the east and south-east usually show a deficiency.

20. The cyclonic type (Type G). There are some advantages, at this stage, in proceeding to the consideration of Type G, in which there is a depression or a low-pressure area directly over the British Isles. We have included in this type also distributions in which a depression is

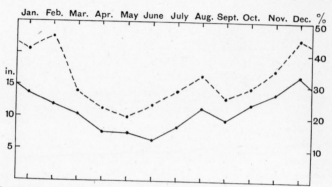

Fig. 8.—Upper curve (broken line)—percentage frequency of Type A pressure distribution.
Lower curve (full line)—average rainfall at Seathwaite (*Cumberland*).

centred near the mouth of the English Channel, because depressions in that position at the morning hour of observation frequently cross southern England or move up the English Channel during the ensuing twenty-four hours, causing gales, heavy precipitation and generally " cyclonic " weather.

Fig. 9 shows part of the weather map for 7 h. on 20th January, 1936, when a deep and fairly intense depression was centred over the Isle of Anglesey. Students of synoptic meteorology will recognize this as a very clear illustration of cyclonic structure as pictured by Bjerknes and his colleagues of the Bergen school. From the centre over Anglesey two radial lines are drawn, one south-eastward passing near London, the other south-westward. Each of these lines marks a discontinuity of wind direction and temperature ; the former is the " warm front " and the latter is the " cold front " (11). Between them is the " warm sector " in which the temperature is over 40° F. (48° F. at Portland Bill) and wind is blowing from west-south-west, force 5 to 6 on the Beaufort

scale. North of the warm front there is a south-east to east wind reaching
gale force on the east coast and the temperature is about 5° F lower.
West and north of the cold front we observe a cold north-east wind
causing snow in several places, with temperatures round about the
freezing point in Ireland and substantially below freezing point in parts
of Scotland. Rain is falling at stations near the warm front and also in

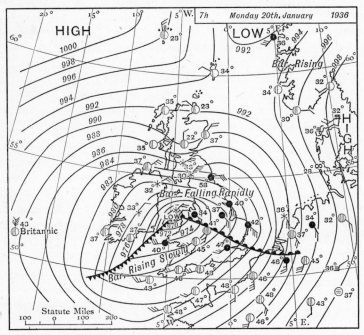

FIG. 9.—Cyclonic type; 20th January 1936.
(For explanation of symbols, see Fig. 7, p. 30.)

South Wales, which is within the warm sector. During the ensuing
twenty-four hours this depression moved north-eastward and was
centred in the North Sea off the east coast of Scotland at 7 h. on 21st
January. Its passage was accompanied by rain or snow in all parts of
the kingdom.

Many of the depressions which cross our area fail to show a warm
sector, because the wedge-shaped intrusion of warm air which was present during the earlier history of the depression has become " occluded "
by the advance of cold air in its rear. Depressions vary greatly in regard
to intensity, but it is exceptional for winter examples to fail to produce

c

a gale on some part of our coasts. Heavy rainfall is also an almost invariable concomitant. The characteristic feature of " cyclonic " rain is the generality of its distribution, without regard to configuration, though the orographic effect usually comes into operation as well, increasing the amounts of rain measured on high ground. Most of the rain is associated with the onset of the warm air, occurring in advance of the warm front or along the " line of occlusion ". This portion of the rain is usually steady and prolonged, resulting from the slow over-running of the cold air by the advancing warm air. The phenomena accompanying the passage of a well-developed cold front are much more violent and usually of brief duration. The advancing cold air undercuts the warm air, causing violent and turbulent ascending motion. This gives rise to an intense shower of rain, hail or snow, often acccompanied by thunder and lightning ; as the cold air arrives the temperature drops abruptly, perhaps 10° F. or more, the wind veers suddenly and a squall of gale force may occur. For that reason the cold front was originally known as the " squall-line " ; in pre-Bjerknes days the characteristic cold-front squall was known as a " line-squall ", and the name still persists.

In the example illustrated in Fig. 9 pressure is high over Iceland, and the depression shown was one of a series extending from the north-west coast of Norway to the Azores. It is rather uncommon to find a north-easterly wind in the rear of a depression crossing the British Isles. More frequently the polar air behind the cold front is from the north-west. Following a large depression, north-west winds may become general over the kingdom, accompanying the Type B distribution which we shall discuss presently. We may notice in Fig. 9 that the north-easterly current is not part of a general stream of air from that direction, such as would have occurred if pressure had been high instead of low off the north-west coast of Norway. By the following day the wind had, in fact, become generally north-westerly. It sometimes happens that a depression crosses southern England in circumstances such that the polar winds are part of a definite northerly or north-easterly stream of long fetch. When this occurs in winter a " blizzard " is the result, heavy falls of snow being experienced over a wide area (see Chapter X).

In summer depressions are usually less deep and less intense than in winter, though occasionally, as in August 1917, an example possessing all the characteristics of a well-developed winter depression may cross the British Isles during the summer period. It is not uncommon in summer for our area to be under the influence of a shallow and irregular low-pressure system with several minima, a situation which is very likely to give rise to local thunderstorms.

21. The north-westerly type (Type B). The essential difference between this type and Type A is that it represents an air-stream flowing towards our western shores from polar regions instead of from equatorial regions. This difference in the trajectory of the air gives it distinctive properties, notwithstanding the fact that the air-stream would often be observed, particularly at stations in the southern and south-eastern districts, as a due west wind.

Very commonly a north-westerly wind flows over the British Isles in the rear of a depression and will often attain gale force, subsiding gradually as the depression moves away eastward or north-eastward. The polar air of which the north-west current is composed normally has a steep lapse-rate of temperature, and its instability is increased by its south-eastward journey over a sea whose temperature tends to become higher as the journey proceeds. Such currents are therefore often squally in character, the squalls being accompanied by cold showers, taking the form of snow-flurries in winter, especially in the immediate rear of the depression. Thunderstorms of brief duration—" cold-front " storms—are also observed, and these are frequent enough in winter months to give some parts of our western coasts a winter maximum of thunderstorm frequency (see Chapter X). During the clear intervals the weather is brilliantly fine, with intensely blue skies and very good visibility, due to the cleanness and clearness of the polar air. Type B, indeed, produces some of the most exhilarating of our winter and early spring weather.

Polar winds reaching us from the west and north-west usually show a very large diurnal variation of velocity at inland stations. After sunset they die away almost to calm and in winter the nights are clear and frosty.

Very frequently Type B represents the eastern half of a wedge of high pressure between two depressions. It is often therefore of a transitory character, and its comparatively high frequency is to be attributed rather to the frequency of depressions than to persistence. Except for the outstanding maximum in July, to which attention has already been drawn, there is no marked seasonal variation in the frequency of Type B.

At all times of the year Type B produces precipitation which may be heavy for short periods but is hardly ever prolonged. The fair periods during the prevalence of this type contribute very materially to the duration of winter sunshine, particularly at inland town stations. In summer the weather associated with the type is at first cool and showery, but may merge gradually into fine anticyclonic conditions if high pressure continues to develop off our south-west coasts.

22. The northerly type (Type C). In this type of distribution the British Isles are overrun by a stream of air from due north or north-north-west. A spring example is illustrated in Fig. 10 (3rd April, 1935).

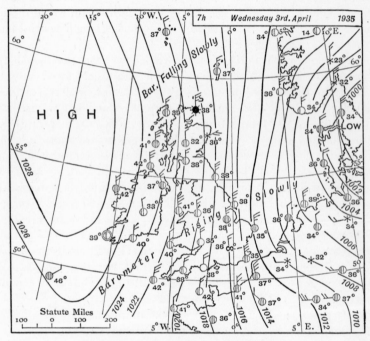

FIG. 10.—Northerly type, 3rd April 1935.
(For explanation of symbols, see Fig. 7, p. 30.)

The complete weather map shows a large depression over Sweden, with other depressions north and south of the main centre, the whole forming an elongated low-pressure system covering the whole of Scandinavia, Central Europe and Italy. An anticyclone extends from south of Iceland to the west of Ireland and another large anticyclone lies over eastern Greenland. There is thus a corridor for the flow of a northerly wind current from near the North Pole to France. Over the British Isles the temperature is below 40° F. at most stations and snow or sleet is falling at two of the Scottish stations (Wick and Aberdeen). During the following twenty-four hours hail and sleet occurred over the north and east of Great Britain generally and the night minimum temperature fell below freezing point at several stations in the south.

Occurrences of this type in winter produce our most bitter weather. The nursery rhyme

> " The north wind doth blow
> And we shall have snow "

is very true, but it requires the passage of a cyclonic centre with a strong polar current of low temperature to produce really heavy falls of snow on the low ground of eastern and southern England. The northerly wind associated with Type C often dies down as the result of the spreading of a cold anticyclone over our area ; and as a snow covering stops upward conduction of heat from the ground, very low night temperature may be observed. On other occasions a north-eastward movement of the anti-cyclone may cause the distribution to change to Type D. One or other of these lines of development has usually occurred in association with severe spells of wintry weather. It will be observed from Table III that Type C is infrequent at all seasons and is least frequent in the winter months, when Type D is also uncommon. We may attribute the relative immunity of the British Isles from spells of really severe winter weather to these facts.

23. The north-easterly type (Type D). This type is of special importance owing to its relatively high frequency in spring. It is very definitely a cold-weather type, and its liability to occur during the blossoming season is a serious source of anxiety to fruit growers. The type is also a persistent one, giving spells of cold unpleasant weather which form a prolongation of or reversion to winter conditions. The example illustrated in Fig 11 represents one phase of the famous May frost of 1935, when a spell of severe wintry weather did immense damage to fruit crops. The distribution was not of Type D during the whole of the eight days, 12th to 19th May, during which the spell persisted ; it started and finished, indeed, as Type C with northerly winds. During this period extraordinarily low temperatures for the time of year occurred all over the British Isles, and a heavy fall of snow was experienced on the 17th even in the Scilly Isles. This example can hardly be regarded, therefore, as typical of the conditions associated with north-east winds in the middle of May, but it shows what may happen in spring when high pressure becomes established to the north or north-west of the British Isles. A full account of this frost will be found in the *Meteorological Magazine* for June 1935.

Apart from the low temperatures associated with Type D, there are

certain other characteristics of easterly and north-easterly winds that
may be mentioned. The incidence of these winds produces effects on the
east coast of England rather similar to south-westerly winds on the west
coast. When, as sometimes happens, south-westerly winds are deficient
and easterly winds are in excess for a considerable period the eastern
districts may receive a normal amount of rain or an excess above normal,

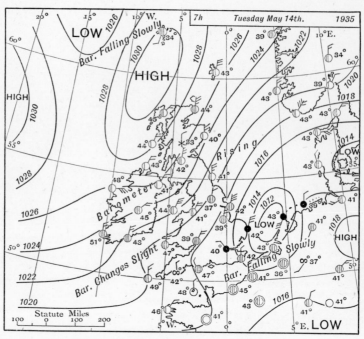

FIG. 11.—North-easterly type, 14th May, 1935.
(For explanation of symbols, see Fig. 7, p. 30.)

while the western districts show a decided deficiency. Easterly winds
also very commonly produce persistently overcast skies over our eastern
and south-eastern districts, the cloud height being in the neighbourhood
of 4,000 feet. A peculiarity of these winds is the fact that they show
only a small diurnal range of velocity, continuing to blow during the
night with a speed little below their daytime velocity. In a general
north-east or east wind these conditions prevent a large diurnal variation
of temperature, and very low temperatures are not often recorded.
During the prevalence of these winds in winter temperature usually

remains round about freezing point, but the dryness of the air causes
them to produce a cooling effect on the skin appropriate to much lower
temperatures. They thus have a peculiarly " biting " quality, which
is too well known to need emphasis.

24. **The south-easterly type (Type E).**   Under this general heading
are grouped distributions in which the direction of the general air-
current over the British Isles is from south-east or due south.   In the

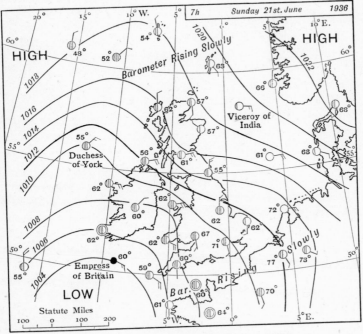

Fig. 12.—South-easterly type, 21st June, 1936.
(For explanation of symbols, see Fig. 7, p. 30.)

example illustrated in Fig. 12 (21st June, 1936) a shallow depression is
centred west of the Bay of Biscay and pressure is high over northern
Europe.   Over the British Isles winds are light, mainly from between
south and east, and the air supply is clearly derived from southern
Europe.   In these circumstances the temperature at Kew Observatory
is as high as 71° F. at 7 h.   During the day the temperature rose to
83° F. at Kew Observatory and Croydon, and exceeded 85° F. at some
other inland stations.   We include under Type E also cases in which the

isobars run from south to north with low pressure to the west, giving south winds over the British Isles. In either case, when the type occurs in summer the surface air supply is derived from a warm source and high temperatures are to be expected. In winter a southerly air-stream is also productive of temperature above the normal, but the addition of an easterly component may produce a different result.

The distribution illustrated in Fig. 12 is associated very frequently with hot-weather thunderstorms. The surface wind from south-east is often overrun by a cool, moist south-westerly wind giving a rapid fall of temperature with height, that is to say a steep lapse-rate, over inland areas during the warmest hours of the day, and circumstances favourable to the development of thunderstorms thus arise. On the day in question, 21st June, 1936, these conditions existed and violent thunderstorms occurred over a wide area accompanied by heavy rain ; at Rothamsted, in Hertfordshire, the unusual amount of 3·15 inches was measured, occurring mainly in two showers each lasting about half an hour. In Scotland the day was fine and more than seventeen hours of sunshine were recorded at Lerwick, in the Shetlands.

We have already noted that Type E is infrequent in the summer months, June, July and August, a circumstance which contributes in some measure to the relative coolness of our summers as compared with those of, say, Paris. We may also note that Type E is more frequent in autumn than in spring, while the reverse is true of Type D. These variations in the frequency of warm and cold air-currents largely account for the fact that in the British Isles autumn is a distinctly warmer season that spring, even when allowance is made for the lag of the annual maximum and minimum of temperature behind the summer and winter solstices.

25. **Anticyclonic conditions (Type F)** occur over the British Isles with considerable frequency at all times of the year. As in other parts of the world, they produce quiet wind conditions and an absence of precipitation ; in other respects the weather associated with an anti-cyclone may vary over a wide range.

In summer anticyclonic conditions are synonymous with fine settled weather, and high day temperatures are experienced both inland and on the coast. In anticyclones the lapse-rate of temperature is usually slight, and this circumstance is not favourable either for the development of cloud or of a diurnal sea-breeze (see Chapter IV, para. 35). Once established, anticyclonic conditions may persist long enough at any time of year to give rise to drought.

At other times of year, but more particularly in late autumn and winter, the absence of air movement favours the development of fog, which may last for days and may, in towns, be accompanied by gloom or day-darkness, a phenomenon which will be dealt with more particularly in Chapter XI. Our anticyclones may develop either as off-shoots from the Azores anticyclone, in which case they are " warm ", or as off-shoots from the winter continental anticyclone, or again from the spreading southward of a high-pressure system from the region of Iceland ; in the two latter cases they are " cold ". In cold anticyclones temperature may be low both night and day, but tends to rise as time goes on, as a result of the subsidence, and consequent dynamic warming, of the polar air of which they are composed. When the centre of the anticyclone is over the northern half of the British Isles, our southeastern districts may experience a light or moderate north-east wind giving rise to conditions similar to those of Type D. It will be realized that anticyclonic conditions in winter may not be altogether pleasant. Much depends on the origin of the anticyclone and on the position of the locality in respect to the centre, but to the town-dweller a winter anticyclone is apt to be an unwelcome visitant owing to its accompaniments of fog, frost and gloom. In these circumstances the contrast between London and the south coast is often very pronounced, the latter area enjoying fine sunny weather while the metropolis is darkened by a murky canopy of its own smoke.

BIBLIOGRAPHY

(10) E. Gold, " Aids to Forecasting," *Geographical Memoir*, No. 16. (H.M.S.O.)
(11) The Weather Map (M.O. 225 *i*). (H.M.S.O.)

CHAPTER IV

WIND

26. Wind as a vector. In the preceding chapter we discussed the results obtained from a consideration of the general flow of air over the British Isles, in association with certain predominant patterns of pressure distribution. We proceed now to consider the winds observed at individual stations. There can be no doubt that, as wind is a vector involving both direction and speed, or force, the most satisfactory method of treatment is to discuss the two aspects of wind simultaneously. For a given place, our knowledge of wind as a climatological element cannot be described as complete unless we know the average duration of winds of given speed from a given direction and the maximum speeds observed from each direction. Unfortunately, however, the summarization of wind statistics in this complete form is very laborious and the expression of the monthly and yearly results for a single station occupies a considerable amount of space. For these reasons the published statistics refer in the main to velocity or force, and direction, considered separately, and we have comparatively little summarized information in which the two are combined.

By way of example we give in Tables V and VI data showing the number of observations in five years (1911-1915) of winds of each force on the Beaufort scale, from each of sixteen compass points, at Lerwick (Shetland) in the extreme north and Scilly in the south of the British Isles. The tables were compiled from observations made twice daily, at 7 h. and 18 h. (G.M.T.), and are taken from *The Weather of the British Coasts* (12). To assist the eye the maximum entry in each column is printed in heavy type, thus identifying the Beaufort number occurring most frequently with each direction. We also give in Fig 13 a diagrammatic representation of the data for Lerwick and Scilly and for four other stations, Blacksod Point in north-west Ireland, Leith, near Edinburgh, Liverpool, and Clacton on the East Anglian coast. In these diagrams the classification in respect to force has been simplified by grouping together forces 1 to 3 (light winds), 4 to 7 (moderate and strong winds) and 8 and above (gales). A further simplification has been

42

introduced by expressing the data as percentages of the total number of observations. These diagrams are also taken from *The Weather of the British Coasts.*

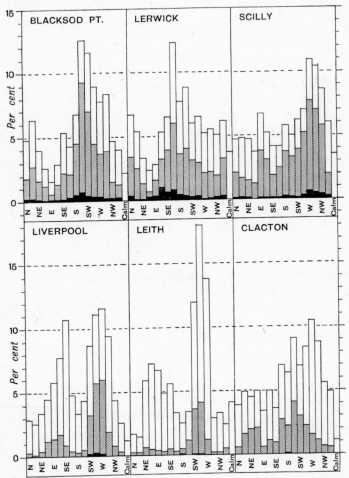

FIG. 13.—Wind force and direction; percentage frequencies for six stations; light winds (unshaded), moderate to strong winds (shaded), gales (black).

(From *The Weather of the British Coasts*)

Referring first to Table V, we observe that at Lerwick force 3 is the most frequently observed of the Beaufort numbers, taking all the observations in bulk. This is also true for most directions considered individually; for north winds force 5 is slightly more frequent than force 3, but for other directions the maximum frequency occurs either with forces 2, 3 or 4. As the force increases, the number of observations tends to fall off rather rapidly but not very regularly; we observe, for example, that for east-south-east winds force 9 is distinctly more frequent than force 7, and that for several other directions force 8 is more frequent than force 7. We may mention, however, that the observations we are considering are estimates made by a coastguardsman without instrumental aid and he may have had a slight bias in favour of force 8. The number of occurrences of a wind force exceeding 8 is relatively small even at this stormy station in the Shetlands, and it is of interest to note that the majority of them occurred with winds in the south-east quadrant. Of the eighty-three observations of forces 9 and 10, fifty-one occurred with directions east-south-east, south-east or south-south-east.

The Scilly table shows several important differences from the Lerwick table. Here force 4 occurs with the greatest frequency in all directions except north, north-north-east, north-east, east-north-east and south-east, which are observed most frequently as light winds of force 2 or 3. Entries above force 6 are uncommon except for directions west-south-west to north-west, inclusive, and gales (force 8 or more) from any but these directions are decidedly rare.

It is surprising to find that gales from the south-west occurred at Scilly only twice in the period to which Table VI refers. This apparent immunity from gales having that direction is not, however, confirmed by observations for a longer period which we shall consider later in this chapter.

In the diagram, Fig. 13, the total height of each column represents the percentage frequency of all winds from the corresponding directions, and the lengths of the shaded and black portions of the columns represent respectively the percentages of winds of forces 4-7, and 8 or above. By comparing the lengths of the different sections of a given column we can therefore form an idea of the relative frequencies of winds of forces 1-3, 4-7 and 8 or more, having a given direction. The percentage frequency of calms is also indicated for each station. The diagrams for Lerwick and Scilly call for no additional remarks. At Blacksod Point there is a great preponderance of strong winds and gales from south, south-south-west and south-west; east winds are least frequent and gales from directions between north-east and south-east are rare. At Leith, south-west and west-south-west are the only directions which give a substantial frequency of winds exceeding force 3, but even for

TABLE V

Number of Observations of Stated Direction and Force at 7 h. and 18 h. at Lerwick (Shetlands) in the Five Years 1911–1915

Force. Beaufort Scale	N.	N.N.E.	N.E.	E.N.E.	E.	E.S.E.	S.E.	S.S.E.	S.	S.S.W.	S.W.	W.S.W.	W.	W.N.W.	N.W.	N.N.W.	Calm	Total
0	—	—	—	—	—	—	—	—	—	—	—	—	—	—	—	—	140	140
1	28	13	7	10	9	11	16	29	28	24	23	16	19	14	16	19	—	282
2	44	39	30	**26**	16	26	29	93	58	64	40	47	**51**	43	34	35	—	675
3	48	**50**	**35**	25	18	**36**	**46**	**115**	**59**	**76**	42	**71**	39	**56**	**64**	54	—	**834**
4	46	49	23	15	**21**	23	40	75	56	61	**54**	36	42	37	29	**55**	—	662
5	**49**	23	17	4	15	28	34	71	35	45	25	34	21	33	28	34	—	496
6	15	19	8	3	7	21	33	26	25	30	18	22	8	9	12	20	—	276
7	6	2	2	1	5	8	12	11	7	7	12	3	8	5	2	1	—	92
8	5	2	3	2	8	13	17	21	14	5	3	6	2	2	3	6	—	112
9	4	—	—	5	4	20	9	8	1	3	2	2	—	1	1	3	—	63
10	2	—	—	—	1	7	3	4	—	1	1	1	—	—	—	—	—	20
11	—	—	—	—	—	—	—	—	—	—	—	—	—	—	—	—	—	—
12	—	—	—	—	—	—	—	—	—	—	—	—	—	—	—	—	—	—
Total	247	197	125	91	104	193	239	453	283	316	220	238	190	200	189	227	140	3652

[From *The Weather of the British Coasts* (M.O. 230)]

TABLE VI

Number of Observations, as Table V, at Scilly

Force. Beaufort Scale	N.	N.N.E.	N.E.	E.N.E.	E.	E.S.E.	S.E.	S.S.E.	S.	S.S.W.	S.W.	W.S.W.	W.	W.N.W.	N.W.	N.N.W.	Calm	Total
0	—	—	—	—	—	—	—	—	—	—	—	—	—	—	—	—	129	129
1	13	19	21	17	19	17	24	10	18	6	12	9	22	27	22	20	—	276
2	30	**55**	**52**	**39**	37	31	**35**	16	23	18	30	25	46	38	43	25	—	543
3	**45**	36	45	32	44	30	27	37	36	33	43	37	49	59	44	26	—	623
4	40	35	23	25	**79**	**51**	28	**42**	**56**	**52**	**70**	**68**	**94**	**75**	**65**	**27**	—	**830**
5	26	22	14	12	36	37	23	33	48	40	41	62	78	60	63	19	—	614
6	12	3	15	8	18	21	14	15	23	25	24	38	57	65	46	17	—	401
7	4	2	—	—	7	4	5	3	4	4	5	16	32	38	24	6	—	154
8	1	2	1	—	1	2	1	1	5	2	1	—	20	16	12	3	—	68
9	—	—	—	—	—	—	—	—	—	—	1	4	2	2	2	1	—	12
10	1	—	—	—	—	—	—	—	—	—	—	—	—	1	—	—	—	2
11	—	—	—	—	—	—	—	—	—	—	—	—	—	—	—	—	—	—
12	—	—	—	—	—	—	—	—	—	—	—	—	—	—	—	—	—	—
Total	172	174	171	133	241	193	157	157	213	180	227	259	400	381	321	144	129	3652

[From *The Weather of the British Coasts* (M.O. 230)]

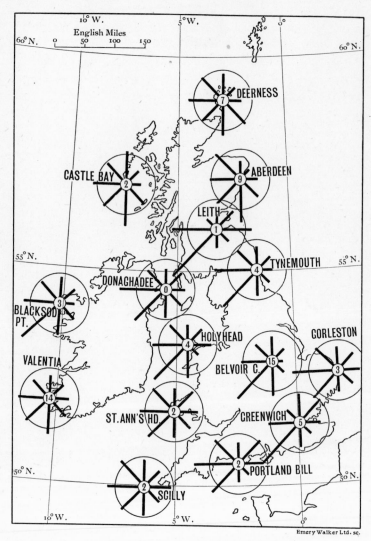

FIG. 14.—Average annual percentage frequencies of winds from each direction. The difference between the radii of the large and small circles represents 12½ per cent. The figures in the small circles show the percentage frequencies of calms.

these directions light winds are in the majority at this sheltered station. Easterly winds occur with considerable frequency, but few of them reach the force of a moderate or strong breeze. At Liverpool, conditions are rather similar to those at Leith ; the proportion of winds of force 4

TABLE VII

Percentage Frequencies of Winds from Stated Directions, and Calms (Whole Year)

Station	N.	N.E.	E.	S.E.	S.	S.W.	W.	N.W.	Calm
Scotland									
Lerwick (*Shetlands*) - -	14	10	6	13	14	11	**16**	10	6
Deerness (*Orkneys*) - -	11	6	7	14	**15**	12	**15**	13	7
Stornoway (*Hebrides*) -	10	9	7	8	13	**20**	16	11	6
Aberdeen (*Aberdeen*) -	7	4	6	10	**20**	15	13	16	9
Inchkeith (*Fife*)* - -	4	11	16	6	6	**31**	21	4	1
Tiree (*Hebrides*) - -	13	6	5	12	**19**	13	15	12	2
England and Wales									
Tynemouth (*North'd*) -	9	8	6	7	11	**24**	20	11	4
Spurn Head (*Yorks.*) -	10	8	8	9	14	17	**18**	13	1
Gorleston (*Norfolk*) - -	9	10	9	8	10	17	**21**	13	3
Greenwich Observatory (*London*) - - -	12	12	9	6	10	**27**	13	6	5
Belvoir Castle (*Leics.*) -	10	6	2	5	15	**24**	13	10	15
Dover (*Kent*) - - -	10	10	10	4	10	**29**	15	10	2
Portland Bill (*Dorset*) -	8	13	11	6	7	18	**21**	14	2
Holyhead (*Anglesey*) -	8	9	10	5	14	**23**	16	11	4
St. Ann's Head (*Pembroke*)	9	12	11	10	11	**16**	**16**	13	2
Scilly (St. Mary's) - -	11	9	12	8	12	14	**17**	15	2
Ireland									
Blacksod Pt. (*Mayo*) -	10	8	5	9	14	**23**	16	12	3
Donaghadee (*Down*) -	8	10	8	9	12	20	**22**	11	0
Dublin (*Dublin*) - -	4	6	7	12	17	16	**21**	7	10
Valentia Observatory (*Kerry*) - - -	9	7	7	10	**16**	14	13	10	14

* Earlier observations from Leith.   (Mainly from Admiralty Pilots)

or more is greatest for south-westerly and westerly winds, but there is an appreciable percentage of such winds from easterly directions. At Clacton, it is of interest to note that although due west winds were most frequent in the period under notice, the stronger winds show a maximum frequency from direction south-south-west.

These brief remarks may be regarded as applying, more or less, to considerable stretches of the coast in the areas represented by the selected stations. A detailed discussion would hardly be profitable in view of the short period covered by the averages, which may not, for that reason, be entirely representative. We are in a position to make deductions having a better basis of certainty when we consider direction without regard to velocity or velocity without regard to direction, or when we consider gales as a separate subject for study. We pass on now to the consideration of wind direction as a separate entity.

27. The frequency of winds from different directions. Surface observations of wind are normally made with reference to the sixteen-point scale employed in Tables V and VI and Fig. 13. In official summaries, however, it is usual to reduce the observations to the eight-point scale of the cardinal and semi-cardinal points. This is done by sharing the observations from intermediate directions such as north-north-east equally between the adjacent directions north and north-east and so on. We shall employ the eight-point scale in the following discussion.

Table VII gives the percentage frequencies of winds from each direction, and calms, at twenty representative stations. In most cases the results, which refer to the whole year, are based on observations made at 7 h., 13 h. and 18 h. (G.M.T.) over a period of the order of forty years. Fig. 14 is a chart on which the values for certain stations are represented graphically in the form of "wind roses". The position of the station is at the centre of the small circle wherein is written a figure giving the percentage of calms. Radiating from the centre are eight arms, whose lengths are proportional to the percentage frequencies of winds from the corresponding directions. To indicate the scale, a circle is drawn whose radius exceeds that of the small circle by an amount representing 12·5 per cent. (=100/8) ; if winds were equally frequent from all directions and there were no calms at a given station, the ends of the eight arms would all lie on the circumference of this circle.

From this chart and table we see very clearly that south, south-west and west are the dominant wind directions ; one or other of these directions gives the maximum frequency at all stations. There is considerable variation, however, from station to station, in regard to the actual percentage frequency of the predominant direction. At the two most northerly stations, Lerwick and Deerness, there is not much difference in the frequencies of winds from the four directions south-east, south, south-west and west, and it will be noticed that south-west is the *least* frequent of these four directions. There is also a relatively high frequency of winds from north at Lerwick and from north-west at Deerness.

At most other stations south-west is the most frequent direction, and in some cases, *e.g.* Inchkeith, Greenwich, Belvoir Castle, Holyhead and Blacksod Point, the frequency of south-west winds greatly exceeds that of winds from any other direction. A secondary maximum of frequency is also observable in most of the records, from a direction near north-east. At Lerwick, the secondary maximum (for north winds) nearly equals the major maximum for west winds. At Inchkeith there is a very conspicuous secondary maximum frequency for east winds. This station, on a small island in the Firth of Forth, shows the greatest variability of frequency of all the stations in Table VII. Eighty per cent. of the winds observed there are from north-east, east, south-west or west, a result which suggests that some " canalization " of the wind currents is produced by the local configuration. The Firth of Forth runs roughly east and west, and there are ranges of hill running nearly parallel with both banks. Thus the wind tends to blow either up or down the firth, and this tendency may also be accentuated by the tides. The results for Portland Bill indicate, though in a less marked degree, a tendency for the wind currents to be canalized in the English Channel. We may remark here that all the stations whose results we have been discussing are well exposed in open situations. The wind direction observed at an inland station may often differ materially from the direction of the general air-stream owing to such canalization effects, due to the local topography.

28. Monthly percentage frequencies of wind direction. In Table VIII the monthly percentage frequencies of winds from different directions, and of calms, are given for six stations on different parts of the coast. The graphical representation of data of this kind is not easy ; it might take the form of a separate wind rose for each month of the year, and one could in this way produce a set of twelve charts similar to Fig. 14, but it is difficult on such a sequence of diagrams to follow the changes from month to month in the percentage frequency of winds from a given direction, say west or north-east. These difficulties are overcome to some extent in the " octagonal " wind rose designed by Sir Napier Shaw and Capt. L. G. Garbett, R.N. We give two examples in Figs. 15*a* and 15*b* which refer respectively to Stornoway, on the eastern side of the island of Lewis and Harris, and Greenwich Observatory.

The sides of the octagon face towards the directions on the eight-point scale. Projecting from each side are twelve columns representing

D

the twelve months of the year, and the lengths of the columns are proportional to the percentage frequencies of the winds from the given direction in the successive months, working round clockwise from January to December. To indicate the scale, an outer octagon has been drawn, separated from the inner octagon by a distance representing 12½ per cent. The tops of the columns would all be on this outer octagon if winds from the eight directions were equally frequent, and there were

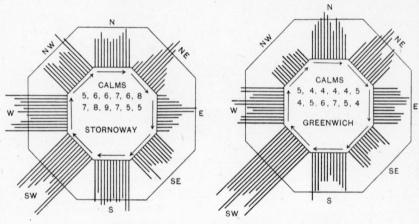

FIG. 15a.—Octagonal wind-rose for Stornoway (Hebrides).

FIG. 15b.—Octagonal wind-rose for Greenwich.

no calms. The percentage frequency of calms in the twelve months is shown by figures within the octagon. We may thus regard the octagonal wind-rose as equivalent to a set of eight diagrams, each showing the annual variation of winds from the direction towards which the ordinates point.

Looking first at the diagram for Stornoway we observe that south-west winds show a fairly regular form of annual variation with a maximum of twenty-five per cent. in January and February and a minimum of thirteen per cent. in June. West winds show a rather similar variation, but with the minimum in May. North-west winds and north winds do not vary much in frequency from month to month, apart from a rather prominent maximum for north-west winds in November; the maximum for north winds also occurs in the same month. For north-east winds there is a beautifully regular seasonal variation with a minimum in January and a maximum (seventeen per cent.) in June. The curve for east winds is almost as regular, with a maximum in May. South-east winds have their minimum frequency in September and their maximum

TABLE VIII

Monthly Percentage Frequencies of Winds from Stated Directions, and Calms

Month	LERWICK (*Shetland*)									INCHKEITH (*Fife*)								
Direction	N	NE	E	SE	S	SW	W	NW	Calm	N	NE	E	SE	S	SW	W	NW	Calm
	%	%	%	%	%	%	%	%	%	%	%	%	%	%	%	%	%	%
January	12	4	3	14	17	14	28	8	6	3	3	6	5	10	45	24	3	1
February	14	7	3	13	19	13	17	8	6	5	8	15	9	6	29	21	6	1
March	18	9	5	13	14	11	15	9	6	5	14	22	9	4	22	19	4	1
April	14	10	7	17	14	10	13	10	5	5	15	22	6	5	23	18	5	1
May	13	18	9	11	12	9	13	11	4	5	18	28	4	5	20	15	4	1
June	13	19	8	12	9	7	16	12	4	4	15	24	4	4	24	20	3	2
July	15	15	6	11	10	9	17	12	5	3	12	17	3	5	34	22	2	2
August	12	13	9	10	11	9	17	13	6	4	11	14	4	4	34	24	3	2
September	13	10	5	11	14	12	19	10	6	5	11	11	3	4	37	23	4	2
October	17	8	6	16	17	9	14	6	7	4	6	8	6	8	38	22	7	1
November	15	8	4	12	14	12	18	10	7	7	5	11	8	8	34	19	6	2
December	13	7	4	15	18	13	17	7	6	3	8	9	10	9	34	23	3	1

Month	VALENTIA (*Kerry*)									HOLYHEAD (*Anglesey*)								
Direction	N	NE	E	SE	S	SW	W	NW	Calm	N	NE	E	SE	S	SW	W	NW	Calm
January	6	6	10	13	21	16	12	7	9	4	7	11	7	18	24	18	9	2
February	6	9	9	13	19	14	11	7	12	5	9	10	6	19	23	15	9	4
March	9	10	8	8	15	15	11	10	14	7	10	12	5	13	22	16	10	5
April	11	10	8	9	15	13	12	9	13	10	11	13	6	13	19	13	11	4
May	13	7	7	10	15	12	10	11	15	11	13	12	3	12	22	10	12	5
June	12	5	5	10	15	13	13	12	15	10	9	10	2	13	24	12	15	5
July	11	3	2	6	15	16	16	17	14	12	6	5	2	12	27	17	15	4
August	8	4	3	8	17	16	15	13	16	9	7	7	3	14	26	18	12	4
September	9	6	8	11	15	11	12	10	18	9	8	10	5	11	22	16	12	7
October	9	11	9	10	14	11	12	9	15	7	10	14	6	13	18	16	11	5
November	8	9	10	10	15	14	13	9	12	7	9	13	5	14	21	17	11	3
December	6	5	9	11	19	17	13	9	11	5	7	9	7	16	24	19	10	2

Month	SCILLY (*St. Mary's*)									GORLESTON (*Norfolk*)								
Direction	N	NE	E	SE	S	SW	W	NW	Calm	N	NE	E	SE	S	SW	W	NW	Calm
January	9	7	11	10	14	17	18	13	1	4	7	9	8	11	21	25	12	3
February	8	10	12	10	14	15	17	13	1	6	8	10	7	12	19	23	12	3
March	13	12	13	6	10	14	17	14	1	8	11	10	6	10	16	22	14	3
April	13	13	15	6	10	11	15	16	1	12	17	12	8	9	12	15	12	3
May	13	11	15	8	12	12	13	14	2	16	18	9	8	11	11	13	10	4
June	14	10	12	7	10	13	15	17	2	16	16	8	8	9	11	16	13	3
July	13	7	7	4	9	16	21	20	3	11	10	5	7	9	16	22	17	3
August	10	6	8	6	11	17	22	17	3	9	8	5	7	10	17	25	15	4
September	11	10	14	10	11	12	14	15	3	8	10	9	7	7	16	24	16	3
October	12	10	12	11	12	12	15	14	2	7	8	10	8	11	19	22	12	3
November	10	9	11	8	13	15	18	15	1	5	8	9	8	11	21	23	13	2
December	8	7	11	8	14	17	20	14	1	4	4	8	7	13	24	25	13	2

(From Admiralty Pilots)

frequency in the following month, October; south winds resemble south-west winds in giving a maximum in January and February, but there is little variation in other months.

The Greenwich wind rose shows some points of resemblance to that of Stornoway, but there are also some conspicuous differences. We may note in particular that south-west winds reach their maximum frequency (thirty-four per cent.) in *summer*, the season when winds from due south or south-east are least frequent. Among other interesting points in Fig. 15b we may note the low and uniform frequency of north-west winds (five, six or seven per cent. in all months) and the spring maximum for north, north-east and east winds.

It is hardly necessary to discuss the values in Table VIII in detail. There is general agreement among the stations in regard to the spring or early summer maximum for north-east winds, but we may note that in May east winds are the most frequent of all winds at Scilly and at Inchkeith, where they reach the high frequency of twenty-eight per cent. North-east winds have that distinction at Lerwick and Stornoway in June and at Gorleston in April and May. At Valentia there is no month in which south-west is definitely the most frequent wind direction, and the same is true for Lerwick and Scilly. The maximum for south-west winds is, however, very conspicuous in all months at Holyhead and at Inchkeith except in spring and early summer.

The results from these few representative stations serve to give a general idea of the direction of air-flow over the British Isles. Additional information of a similar character is to be found in the meteorological tables attached to Admiralty Pilots for British coastal waters, from which much of the foregoing data has been taken.

29. Wind velocity. In Tables V and VI and in Fig. 13 we presented some information in regard to the frequency of occurrence of different wind forces, measured on the Beaufort scale, the specification of which is given in Table I (pp. 4, 5). The force of the wind, as judged by its physical effects, such as the movements of trees or the raising of waves, is obviously related to its velocity, a property capable of measurement by a suitably designed instrument. An experienced observer, especially a sailor, a lighthouse-keeper or a coastguardsman, is able to make reliable estimates of wind force by making use of criteria such as those set out in Table I. A large proportion of our published wind statistics have been obtained in this rather rough-and-ready fashion; since the beginning of the present century, however, a number of stations have been equipped with recording anemometers of the pressure-tube type,

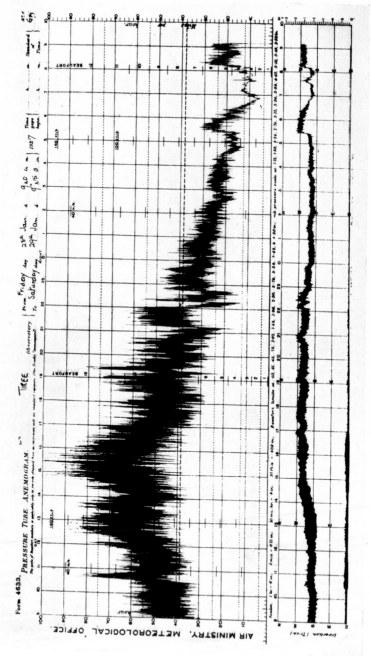

FIG. 16.—Dines anemometer record ; Tiree, January 28-29, 1927.

designed by the late W. H. Dines, a description of which will be found
in the *Meteorological Observer's Handbook* (1).   An example of the
records produced by the Dines anemometer is shown in Fig. 16.   They
are of a peculiar character, having the appearance of a band or ribbon
of varying width with irregular edges.   The breadth of the band is
found to vary very considerably from station to station, and from time
to time at the same station.   At a station surrounded by sea—of which
Bell Rock Lighthouse, on a semi-submerged rock twelve miles out to sea
off the Firth of Tay, is almost an ideal example—the ribbon is relatively
narrow at all times, though there may be a perceptible broadening in
winds which reach the station by the shortest sea route.   At a station
such as Spurn Head, on a narrow promontory projecting out to sea from
flat country, the breadth of the ribbon is almost as small, but increased
broadening is evident in winds blowing directly off the land.   At an
ordinary coast station the record is narrow with on-shore winds, broad
with off-shore winds.   At inland stations the record is relatively broad
with winds from all directions.   Broader records are obtained at stations
where the surface is much broken by trees or buildings.   Finally, at a
station in the middle of a large town, the ribbon becomes so broad that
its lower edge approximates to the base line, representing zero velocity.

At many stations an arrangement is fitted so that the wind direction
is recorded continuously, below the record of velocity as in Fig. 16.   The
direction record shows similar features to the velocity record, a broad
direction trace being obtained when the velocity trace is broad.

These peculiarities of wind records arise from the fact that the air
movement which we call wind is not a purely translational movement.
The surface irregularities, humps, hollows, trees and buildings, set up
eddies in the same sort of way that stones in the bed of a stream set up
eddies in the flowing water.   Over the open sea the surface irregularities
take the form of waves, which increase in amplitude as the wind force
increases ;   consequently at a station like Bell Rock there is a definite
increase in the " gustiness " shown by the wind-record, with increase
of wind speed.   The upper edge of the velocity record represents the
gusts and the lower edge the lulls, due to these eddies.   Running through
the middle of the record we may imagine the existence of a mean line
about which the oscillations occur.   The mean line may be regarded as
a representation of the translational movement of the air, upon which
the eddies are superimposed, and this is often referred to as the " mean
wind ".   The velocity equivalents of the Beaufort numbers given in
Table I relate to the mean wind and take no account of the velocities

reached in the gusts. The wind velocities which we shall discuss in the next two paragraphs also refer to the mean wind.

The ratio of the range of the oscillations to the mean wind velocity is a measure of the turbulence in the air-stream and is known as the gustiness ratio or gustiness factor. The value of this factor may approach 2·0 for an anemometer in the middle of a town. The average value of the factor at the open coastal sites of the Holyhead and Scilly anemometers is no more than 0·5 ; at the Bell Rock it is as low as 0·2 for winds up to about thirty miles per hour.

It will be realized that a very large amount of information is derivable from the records of a Dines anemometer. Its predecessor, the Robinson cup anemometer, some specimens of which are still in use after many years of good service, furnished information in regard to the mean wind, but it was not designed to record the velocities reached in gusts. It was, indeed, the urgent need for information about extreme winds and the pressures produced by such winds on structures, following the Tay Bridge storm of 1879, that led W. H. Dines to undertake the research work that resulted in the design of his very efficient anemometer. Some of the values quoted for mean wind in the following paragraphs are derived from Robinson records, but we must, of course, utilize only the Dines records in obtaining information relating to gusts.

The exposure of an anemometer is naturally a matter of very great importance. To obtain an accurate idea of the natural flow of air over a locality it is necessary to select the most open and unobstructed site that can be found, and then to erect the instrument with its vane at a standard height. The standard height adopted by the Meteorological Office is ten metres (thirty-three feet) but the anemometer vanes are usually placed higher than this in order to make allowance for the disturbance caused by the office buildings or other structures ; in short, the anemometer is given an " effective " height of thirty-three feet whenever possible. Local circumstances have sometimes made it necessary to depart from this standard ; for example, at Croydon Aerodrome the effective height of the anemometer is seventy feet. For the purpose of conversion of mean wind velocities to Beaufort forces, a logarithmic formula due to Hellmann is used in such cases. The following table gives the ratio of the mean wind at a given height to the mean wind at the standard height derived from this formula :

Height in metres	2	3	4	5	10	15	20	25	30	35	40
Height in feet	-	7	10	13	16	33	49	65	82	98	115	131
Velocity ratio	-	0·78	0·82	0·85	0·89	1·00	1·08	1·15	1·20	1·24	1·28	1·32

At some of the older stations the site of the anemometer is by no means so open as could be desired. This applies in particular to the observatories at Kew (Richmond), Aberdeen and Valentia, which were not sited with special regard to their suitability for the measurement of wind. In particular we may feel reasonably certain that the Valentia records give an underestimate of the frequency of strong winds and gales on the south-west coast of Ireland.

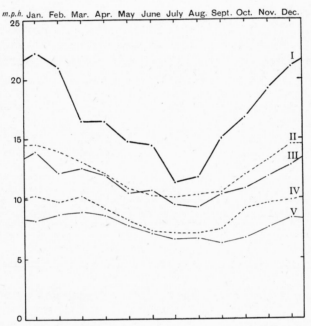

Fig. 17.—Seasonal variation of mean wind velocity. I—Lerwick (Shetlands), II—Valentia, III—Eskdalemuir, IV—Aberdeen, V—Kew.

30. Mean monthly and yearly velocity. In Table IX we give the mean velocities for each month and the year for the five observatories. These are derived from hourly values covering thirty-five years at Valentia, Aberdeen and Kew, twenty years at Eskdalemuir and nine years at Lerwick. The values are shown graphically in Fig. 17. The curves show some points of interest. The mean values are highest at Lerwick in all months of the year, by a large margin; the maximum occurs in January and the minimum in July. Valentia shows the most regular form of annual variation, from a winter maximum of nearly fifteen miles per hour to a summer minimum of about ten miles per hour. At Eskdalemuir, the maximum of fourteen miles per hour occurs in January but there is a secondary maximum in March. This feature is also seen in the Aberdeen curve, where the January and March values are the same, and we observe that at Kew the maximum for the year occurs in March, a month proverbially associated with high winds. Another interesting point is the shifting of the month of minimum velocity from July at Lerwick and Valentia through August at Eskdalemuir to September at Kew. At Lerwick and Valentia we have solsticial maxima and minima ; at Kew we have equinoctial maxima and minima. In view of the sheltered positions of the observatories, except Lerwick, we must suppose that the actual values of velocity given in Table IX are of purely local significance, but we may presume that the form of annual variation disclosed by the curves of Fig. 17 is a definite climatic characteristic.

TABLE IX

MEAN WIND VELOCITY FOR EACH MONTH AND THE WHOLE YEAR

(IN MILES PER HOUR)

	Jan.	Feb.	Mar.	Apr.	May	June	July	Aug.	Sep.	Oct.	Nov.	Dec.	Year
Lerwick Observatory (*Shetlands*)	22·2	21·0	16·5	16·5	14·8	14·5	11·4	11·8	15·0	16·8	19·2	21·0	16·6
King's College, Aberdeen - -	10·2	9·8	10·2	9·1	8·2	7·4	7·1	7·1	7·5	9·1	9·6	9·9	8·8
Eskdalemuir Observatory (*Dumfries*) - -	14·0	12·1	12·6	12·0	10·5	10·7	9·5	9·2	10·3	10·8	11·9	12·9	11·4
Kew Observatory, Richmond (*Surrey*) - - -	8·2	8·7	8·9	8·6	7·8	7·1	6·6	6·7	6·2	6·7	7·6	8·4	7·6
Valentia Observatory, Cahirciveen (*Kerry*) - -	14·6	14·0	13·1	12·1	10·9	10·2	10·1	10·3	10·5	12·0	13·2	14·5	12·1

31. Frequency-distribution of mean wind. The monthly mean velocity of the wind is a matter of relatively minor interest, and it is the modern practice to summarize the data on a frequency basis. In Table X we give for eighteen representative stations the percentage frequency of occurrence of winds whose velocities fall within stated limits. For an anemometer with a standard effective height these limits correspond with Beaufort forces 8 or more (gales), 6-7 (strong winds), 4-5 (moderate or fresh winds), 2-3 (light winds) and 0-1 (calms and light airs). The data are derived from hourly values and results are given for January,

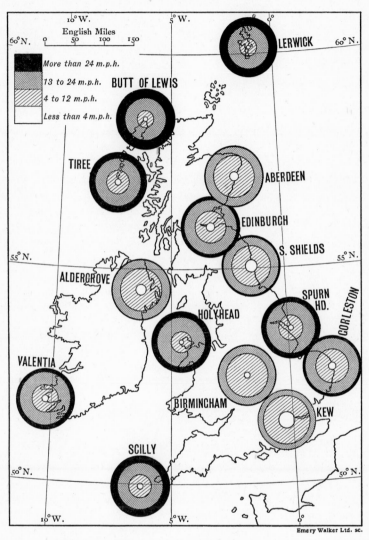

Fig. 18.—Percentage frequency of winds with velocity between stated limits (whole year, all directions).

The radius of the outer circles represents 100 per cent.; the radii of the small inner circles represent the percentage frequencies of winds of less than four miles per hour.

the windiest month in most areas, July, the calmest month, or nearly the calmest month, in most areas, and the whole year. The values for the whole year are represented on a chart (Fig. 18) in which the radius of the central circle over each station represents the percentage frequency of winds under four miles per hour, and the percentages for the other categories are shown by the breadths of successive zones. The percentage frequency of winds above thirty-eight miles per hour is too small at most stations to be represented separately ; we have accordingly shown in the outer, black, zone the frequency of all winds exceeding twenty-four miles per hour.

In regard to strong winds and gales, the most remarkable results are those from the Butt of Lewis, a coastguard station at the northern extremity of the Outer Hebrides. For the whole year this station shows the high percentage of twenty-nine for winds exceeding twenty-four miles per hour, and in the month of January the percentage is as high as forty-eight, which means that the duration of strong winds or gales averages practically twelve hours per day in that month. At the other extreme we have Kew Observatory, on the western outskirts of London, where for twenty-seven per cent. of all hours the wind speed is under four miles per hour, while a velocity exceeding twenty-four miles per hour is only reached in four hours out of every 1,000.

Lerwick, in the Shetlands, ranks next to Butt of Lewis as the windiest station in the list, the records from the two stations for the whole year being very similar. Bell Rock is not included in the list, but it may be mentioned that its records in respect to high winds approximate to those of Lerwick. At Bell Rock, however, the anemometer is on top of the lighthouse and has the exceptional effective height of 126 feet.

Tiree (Hebrides), Holyhead and Scilly show very similar results, the annual frequency of strong winds and gales averaging seventeen to nineteen per cent., increasing to about thirty per cent. in January. One would have expected Valentia to fall into this group, but actually it shows a strong-wind frequency not much exceeding that of Edinburgh (Blackford Hill Observatory), a result which we may attribute to the sheltered position of Valentia Observatory. Spurn Head, the best exposed station on the east coast of England, shows a markedly lower frequency of strong winds than Holyhead. Kew Observatory has already been mentioned ; the other two inland stations, Aldergrove, in northern Ireland, and Birmingham (Edgbaston), show similar results, but the greater effective height of the Birmingham anemometer must not be overlooked. One of the most puzzling sets of results is that for

TABLE X

PERCENTAGE FREQUENCIES OF WINDS OF STATED VELOCITIES IN JANUARY, JULY AND THE WHOLE YEAR (FROM HOURLY VALUES AT ANEMOMETER STATIONS)

Station	Height above sea level	Effective height above ground	Period	More than 38 m.p.h.	25 to 38 m.p.h.	13 to 24 m.p.h.	4 to 12 m.p.h.	Under 4 m.p.h.
	ft.	ft.		%	%	%	%	%
SCOTLAND								
Lerwick (*Shetlands*)	310	39	Jan.	8	31	40	17	4
6 years			July	1	10	46	39	5
			Year	3	22	44	27	4
Kirkwall (*Orkney*) -	170	35	Jan.	2	18	49	25	6
7 years			July	0	3	42	45	10
			Year	0·6	12	44	36	7
Butt of Lewis	170	35	Jan.	12	36	38	13	1
(*Hebrides*)			July	0·2	14	42	34	10
6 years			Year	4	25	43	23	5
Aberdeen (*Aberdeen*)	120	32	Jan.	0·2	5	35	50	10
			July	0	0·2	13	63	24
12 years			Year	0·1	3	25	57	15
Edinburgh	485	23	Jan.	1·1	16	43	31	9
11 years			July	0	0·7	29	50	20
			Year	0·3	6	36	42	16
Tiree (*Hebrides*)	75	42	Jan.	3	25	40	26	6
10 years			July	0·1	4	40	44	11
			Year	1·3	16	42	32	8
ENGLAND AND WALES								
South Shields	73	44	Jan.	0·2	10	37	42	11
(*Durham*)			July	0	0·7	23	50	27
12 years			Year	0·1	4	29	48	19
Spurn Head	64	34	Jan.	1·5	17	51	25	6
(*Yorks.*)			July	0·2	7	40	44	9
15 years			Year	0·6	12	47	35	6
Gorleston (*Norfolk*)	52	34	Jan.	0·2	10	43	42	5
9 years			July	0	2	30	53	14
			Year	0·1	6	36	46	11
Kew Observatory	92	50	Jan.	0	1	26	54	19
(*Surrey*)			July	0	< 0·1	10	62	28
12 years			Year	< 0·1	0·4	17	55	27
Birmingham	643	73	Jan.	< 0·1	2	33	57	8
(*Warwick*)			July	0	0·1	21	69	10
13 years			Year	< 0·1	0·8	27	63	9
Dover (*Kent*)	66	60	Jan.	0·3	10	40	43	6
13 years			July	0	2	38	48	11
			Year	0·2	7	38	46	9

TABLE X—*Continued*

Station	Height above sea level	Effective height above ground	Period	More than 38 m.p.h.	25 to 38 m.p.h.	13 to 24 m.p.h.	4 to 12 m.p.h.	Under 4 m.p.h.
	ft.	ft.		%	%	%	%	%
Holyhead	64	38	Jan.	3	29	50	17	1
(*Anglesey*)			July	0	5	49	38	8
12 years			Year	1	16	48	29	6
Scilly (St. Mary's)	230	57*	Jan.	4	29	43	20	4
21 years			July	0·3	5	43	39	12
			Year	2	17	42	31	9
IRELAND								
Aldergrove (*Antrim*)	282	20	Jan.	< 0·1	4	34	43	19
9 years			July	0	0·2	20	63	17
			Year	< 0·1	1	28	55	16
Kingstown (*Dublin*)	49	27	Jan.	2	22	43	28	5
7 years			July	0·1	6	38	46	10
			Year	0·6	12	41	38	8
Dunfanaghy Road	180	47	Jan.	2	13	30	32	23
(*Donegal*)			July	0·1	3	21	46	30
10 years			Year	0·7	6	24	42	27
Valentia Observatory	98	33	Jan.	0·6	18	44	29	8
(*Kerry*)			July	< 0·1	2	41	44	13
19 years			Year	0·2	8	43	37	11

* 30 ft. prior to 1928.

Dunfanaghy Road, a station in a very exposed position close to the coast in county Donegal, northern Ireland. Some noteworthy gusts have been recorded there but the frequency of strong winds and gales is less than one would expect in such a situation. The curious feature of the results is the remarkably high percentage of winds under four miles per hour in all months. Light winds and calms are apparently as frequent at Dunfanaghy Road as at Kew Observatory, a most unexpected result. Incidentally this station illustrates an interesting practical application of anemometry; the instrument was installed by the Londonderry, Lough Swilly and Letterkenny Railway Company in order to give automatic warnings of winds strong enough to constitute a danger to trains running over a very exposed section of the line. Another anemometer fulfilling a similar purpose was installed at Quilty, in county Clare, as long ago as 1910.

32. **The gust-level.** The data discussed in the preceding paragraphs refer to the " mean wind ". We now have to consider the velocity in gusts. This is a matter of some importance, because it is the gusts which remove slates and chimney-pots or blow down hoardings and

trees during stormy weather. A scrutiny of the criteria for the estimation of Beaufort force given in Table I rather suggests that an observer without instrumental aid is likely to be considerably influenced by the effects due to gusts. This would not matter if the " gustiness factor " were the same for all localities, but we have already had occasion to notice that that is not the case. At Scilly, the gustiness factor (usually denoted by G) is about 0·5 ; consequently a mean wind of thirty miles per hour would be accompanied by gusts averaging about thirty-seven miles per hour. At Kew, the gustiness factor is about 1·0, so that a mean wind of thirty miles per hour would produce a gust-level of forty-five miles per hour. From this illustration we see that a wind averaging thirty miles per hour at an inland station is a different thing, so far as physical effects are concerned, from a wind averaging thirty miles per hour at a coastal or island station. This fact must be kept in mind when wind data for inland stations are scrutinized. To emphasize this point still further, we may note that a wind classified as force 8 at a well exposed coastal station, on the basis of mean velocity, would be accompanied by gusts of about fifty-four miles per hour. At inland anemometer stations it is very unusual for the mean wind to reach the force 8 limit, but gusts exceeding fifty-four miles per hour are by no means uncommon. During 1935 there were seventy-four hours of such winds at Catterick (Yorkshire), sixty-three hours at Cranwell (Lincs.), eighty-eight hours at Renfrew, 146 hours at Eskdalemuir (Dumfries), 120 hours at Cardington (Beds.), twenty-three hours at Kew, thirty-four hours at Croydon, eighty-five hours at Lympne (Kent), fifty-two hours at Lark-hill (Salisbury Plain) and 145 hours at Barton Airport (Manchester). In most cases these records for inland stations are of the same order of magnitude as those for well exposed coastal stations, e.g. Shoeburyness (fifty-six hours), Calshot (Hants.) (sixty-two hours), Southport (Lancs.) (114 hours), Holyhead (165 hours). In regard to the general level of wind velocity reached in gusts, there is therefore much less difference between coastal and inland stations than might be supposed from the data given in the preceding tables and diagrams. Even at South Kensington, London, where the anemometer is installed on the roof of the Science Museum in a region where the mean velocity of the wind is generally reduced to a low value by the frictional resistance of the neighbouring buildings, as many as twenty hours with gusts exceeding fifty-four miles per hour were registered in 1935.

33. Extreme winds recorded by anemometers. In Table XI we give a list of occasions since 1909 when a gust of ninety miles per hour or more has been registered by at least one anemometer. The highest velocity shown in this list is " >112 (?) " at Quilty, on the west coast of Ireland, in 1920. The sign > implies that the recording pen passed beyond the upper edge of the chart and the ? sign means that the authenticity of the record is doubtful. We may safely accept 111 miles per hour on 6th December, 1929, at Scilly as the highest recorded wind velocity in the British Isles. There are several other entries of 100 miles per hour or more ; one of these, 104 miles per hour at the Coats Observatory, Paisley, on 28th January, 1927, is particularly noteworthy because it was recorded at an inland station. It will be noticed that the entries are much more frequent for recent years than for earlier years. This does not mean that stormy weather is becoming more frequent. The Lerwick anemometer has been in operation since 1923 and Tiree since 1926, but the instruments at Bell Rock and Butt of Lewis were erected only in the autumn of 1929. This group of instruments in stormy localities round the Scottish coasts has contributed many of the entries for recent years. It should also be mentioned that in recent years anemometers have been fitted with wide connecting pipes, which produce much less damping effect on the transmitted wind pressures than the narrower pipes formerly used.

Lt.-Col. E. Gold's Presidential Address to the Royal Meteorological Society in 1935 on " Wind in Britain " (13) contains a very large amount of information in regard to extreme winds. Col. Gold makes the following remarks in regard to the highest gusts :

" Three things emerge from an examination of these records. The first is that the extreme gusts came with south-west or west winds. That is not quite universal. At Valentia, the highest gust came with a south-south-east wind ; and at Kew with a north wind.

" The second thing is that the highest gust came nearly always after, though not immediately after, a veer of the wind of two or three points.

" The third thing is that the highest gusts all came in the afternoon or in the night ; none of them in the forenoon."

Table XII shows, for each of the anemometer stations operating in 1935, the average annual number of hours with mean wind exceeding thirty-eight miles per hour (i.e. " hours of gale " at stations with a standard effective height), the highest gust on record, to 1935, and the highest mean hourly wind recorded during the period 1909 to 1935.

TABLE XI

LIST OF OCCASIONS SINCE 1909 ON WHICH GUSTS OF NINETY MILES
PER HOUR OR MORE HAVE BEEN RECORDED

Date		Station	Miles per hour
1909	23rd October	Scilly	90
1911	5th November	Eskdalemuir	90
1912	4th March	Pendennis Castle	98
	26th December	Pendennis Castle	98
1914	14th September	Southport	90
	4th December	Quilty	92
1916	27th October	Pendennis Castle	91
1917	25th October	Eskdalemuir	90
	16th December	Scilly	96
1920	27th January	Quilty	>112 (?)
1922	8th March	Pendennis Castle	103
	8th March	Plymouth	96
1923	7th February	Valentia	95
1924	25th December	Lerwick	90
1927	28th January	Tiree	108
	28th January	Paisley	104
	28th January	Lerwick	92
	28th January	Dunfanaghy Road	109
	29th January	Pendennis Castle	92
	29th October	Southport	96
1929	6th December	Scilly	111
	6th December	Pendennis Castle	103
1930	2nd January	Liverpool (Bidston)	91
	12th January	Pendennis Castle	102
	12th January	Scilly	97
1932	13th January	Bell Rock	95
	17th December	Lerwick	94
	31st December	Valentia	96
1934	17th January	Dunfanaghy Road	94
	17th January	Butt of Lewis	92
	7th February	Butt of Lewis	92
1935	25th January	Butt of Lewis	100
	16th September	Pendennis Castle	98
	16th September	Lizard	92
	16th September	Scilly	96
	18th October	Tiree	90
	19th October	Bell Rock	101
	19th October	Abbotsinch	92
	19th October	Dunfanaghy Road	90
1936	9th January	Liverpool (Bidston)	92
	9th January	Lizard	91
	10th February	Valentia	92
	10th February	Pendennis Castle	90

TABLE XII

Gales and Extreme Winds at Anemometer Stations
(Italics indicate fewer than five years' observations)

Station	Lat. N.	Long.	Height above M.S.L.	Effective height	Average number of hours of gale	Highest gust on record	Highest hourly mean, 1909-35
	° ′	° ′	ft.	ft.		m.p.h.	m.p.h.
SCOTLAND, N.							
Lerwick - - -	60 8	1 11W	310	39	236	95	66
Kirkwall - - -	50 59	2 57W	170	35	52	89	54
Butt of Lewis - -	58 31	6 16W	170	35	378	100	64
SCOTLAND, E.							
Aberdeen - - -	57 10	2 6W	120	32	3	82	54
Balmakewan - -	56 48	2 33W	140	20	0·6	84	47
Bell Rock Lighthouse -	56 26	2 24W	130	126	255	101	68
Edinburgh - - -	55 55	3 11W	485	23	20	85	56
SCOTLAND, W.							
Tiree - - - -	56 32	6 55W	75	43	110	108	66
Paisley - - -	55 51	4 26W	188	31	0·6	104	42
Abbotsinch - - -	*55 52*	*4 26W*	*65*	*33*	*5*	*92*	*55*
Eskdalemuir - -	55 19	3 12W	825	35	40	90	62
ENGLAND, N.E.							
South Shields - -	55 0	1 26W	73	44	14	87	54
Catterick - - -	*54 22*	*1 37W*	*220*	*33*	*3*	*77*	*41*
Spurn Head - - -	53 35	0 7E	64	34	50	84	59
Cranwell - - -	53 2	0 31W	284	33	3	80	50
ENGLAND, E.							
Gorleston - - -	52 35	1 43E	52	34	12	77	54
Felixstowe Aerodrome -	51 57	1 20E	65	40	4	72	45
Cardington - - -	*52 7*	*0 25W*	*185*	*135*	*33*	*88*	*53*
Shoeburyness - -	51 33	0 50E	115	89	20	83	55
MIDLAND COUNTIES							
Birmingham - -	52 29	1 56W	643	73	0·5	78	34
ENGLAND, S.E.							
South Kensington - -	*51 30*	*0 10W*	*137*	*30*	*0*	*70*	*27*
Kew Observatory -	51 28	0 19W	92	50	0·1	72	41
Croydon - - -	51 21	0 7W	313	70	4	81	49
Dover - - - -	51 7	1 19E	66	60	18	85	56
Lympne - - -	51 5	1 1E	418	48	17	79	54
Calshot - - -	50 49	1 18W	58	42	22	81	51
Boscombe Down - -	*51 10*	*1 45W*	*462*	*33*	*3*	*70*	*42*
Larkhill - - -	51 11	1 48W	491	36	10	80	50
ENGLAND, N.W.							
Fleetwood - - -	53 56	3 1W	112	31	78	84	66
Manchester (Barton) -	*53 28*	*2 23W*	*153*	*80*	*45*	*75*	*50*
Southport - - -	53 39	2 59W	60	33	105	96	70
Liverpool (Bidston) -	53 24	3 4W	262	39	25	91	50

TABLE XII—*continued*

Station	Lat. N.	Long.	Height above M.S.L.	Effective height	Average number of hours of gale	Highest gust on record	Highest hourly mean, 1909-35
	° ′	° ′	ft.	ft.		m.p.h.	m.p.h.
WALES							
Holyhead - - -	53 19	4 37W	64	38	91	94	60
Sealand - - -	53 13	3 0W	81	42	7	88	50
St. Ann's Head - -	*51 41*	*5 11W*	*212*	*—*	*—*	*—*	*68*
ENGLAND, S.W.							
Plymouth - - -	50 22	4 8W	185	65	48	96	65
Lizard - - - -	*49 57*	*5 12W*	*315*	*60*	*227*	*92*	*63*
Pendennis Castle - -	50 9	5 3W	256	42	271	103	70
Scilly Isles - - -	49 56	6 18W	230	57	139	111	70
IRELAND, N.							
Dunfanaghy Rd. - -	55 11	7 58W	180	30	63	109	57
Aldergrove - - -	54 39	6 13W	282	20	1	84	44
Armagh - - -	54 21	6 39W	246	—	—	—	47
IRELAND, S.							
Kingstown - - -	53 17	6 8W	49	27	60	—	68
Quilty - - - -	52 50	9 28W	100	32	44	>112?	63
Valentia Observatory -	51 56	10 15W	98	33	16	96	57
Cork - - - -	*51 54*	*8 29W*	*132*	*40*	*—*	*69*	*33*

34. Gales on the coasts. In Table XIII we have averages of the number of days on which gales were logged by lightships, lighthouses and coastguard stations on various sections of the British coasts. The boundaries of each section are indicated on Fig. 19, where the averages for the whole year are plotted in large figures. The small figures show the number of gales classed as " generally severe " ; no gale was placed in this category unless at least half the stations logged force 10 or more on the Beaufort scale.

We see from this chart that the north-west coast of Ireland is the stormiest region in the British Isles with forty gales per annum, of which about thirteen are generally severe. Then follow the Bristol Channel, south-west Ireland, the Irish Sea, north-east Scotland and south-west England. Gales are least frequent on the east coast of England, south-east England and east Scotland. Speaking generally, we may say that gales on the western and northern seaboard occur on from thirty to forty days per annum ; on the North Sea coast and in the central and eastern parts of the English Channel they occur on from eighteen to twenty-five days per annum.

E

TABLE XIII

AVERAGE NUMBER OF GALES RECORDED IN EACH MONTH AND THE
WHOLE YEAR ON VARIOUS SECTIONS OF THE BRITISH AND IRISH
COASTS DURING THE FORTY YEARS 1876–1915

Coasts	Jan.	Feb.	Mar.	Apr.	May	June	July	Aug.	Sep.	Oct.	Nov.	Dec.	Year
SCOTLAND													
North-east　-	**5·4**	3·9	3·7	1·9	1·1	0·4	0·3	0·7	1·7	3·4	4·7	5·3	32·4
East　-　-	**3·5**	2·5	2·9	1·1	0·7	0·4	0·4	0·5	1·4	2·6	3·4	2·9	22·3
North-west　-	**5·0**	3·9	3·0	1·5	1·0	0·4	0·5	0·7	2·0	2·8	4·6	**5·0**	30·3
West　-　-	4·1	3·4	2·5	1·3	0·7	0·4	0·3	0·9	1·7	2·9	4·0	**4·2**	26·3
IRELAND													
North-west　-	**6·5**	4·6	4·1	2·3	1·2	0·8	1·0	1·3	2·7	4·2	5·6	6·4	40·5
South-west　-	5·7	4·9	3·9	2·0	1·2	0·5	0·5	1·4	1·9	3·4	4·8	**5·9**	36·1
Irish Sea -　-	5·0	4·2	4·3	1·9	1·0	0·7	0·7	1·3	2·0	3·6	5·0	**5·6**	35·3
St. Geo. Chan. -	4·6	3·6	3·4	1·4	0·8	0·4	0·4	1·0	1·5	3·4	4·5	**5·3**	30·1
Bristol Channel	5·2	4·7	3·6	·2·0	0·9	0·7	0·7	1·7	2·1	4·4	5·2	**6·3**	37·6
ENGLAND													
South-west　-	4·4	4·2	3·5	1·6	1·1	0·4	0·5	1·3	1·3	3·5	4·7	**5·6**	32·0
South　-　-	3·5	3·1	2·4	1·1	0·6	0·3	0·6	1·4	1·2	3·1	4·0	**4·4**	25·5
South-east　-	3·0	2·4	2·1	0·9	0·5	0·2	0·4	1·0	1·0	2·8	3·7	**4·1**	21·9
East　-　-	2·4	2·2	1·8	1·0	0·5	0·2	0·2	0·6	0·7	2·3	**3·0**	3·0	17·9
North-east　-	3·7	3·0	3·1	1·2	0·7	0·4	0·4	0·5	1·3	2·7	3·1	**4·0**	24·0
Mean for British Isles　-　-	4·4	3·6	3·2	1·5	0·9	0·4	0·5	1·0	1·6	3·2	4·3	**4·9**	29·4

The month with the highest frequency of gales on each section of the coast is indicated by printing the figures in heavy type.

[From *The Weather of the British Coasts* (M.O. 230)]

The percentage frequency with which gales blow from different directions is indicated by wind roses in Fig. 20. The small circle at the centre of each wind rose contains a figure giving the percentage of occasions when the gale blew from different directions at different stations in the area, so that no single direction could be assigned to it. From this chart we see that gales blow most frequently from south-west or west at most stations. A fair proportion of gales also come from north-west on the western and northern seaboard, and on the east coast of England. On the north-east coast of Scotland gales from south-east are numerous, but with this exception there are few gales from an easterly point. The north-east coast of England is peculiar in showing a considerable number of gales from north. Charts similar to Fig. 20 for individual months show that gales from north, north-east or east tend to occur in the spring and summer months. In June nearly all the gales on the north-east coast of Scotland come from north-west, north or north-east. Summer gales very rarely reach the " severe " level.

DIRECTIONS FROM WHICH GALES BLOW.

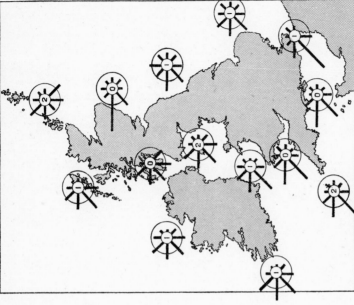

Fig. 20.—Percentage frequency of gales from different directions.

The figures in small circles show percentage frequencies of gales to which a single direction could not be assigned. The difference between the radii of the large and small circles represents a frequency of 12½ per cent.

(From The Weather of the British Coasts)

AVERAGE NUMBER OF GALES.

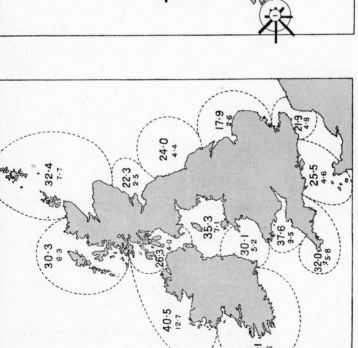

Fig. 19.—Average annual number of gales on the coasts (large figures), and of generally severe gales (small figures).

The monthly frequencies of gales on the coasts of north-west Ireland, south-west England and eastern England are shown graphically in Fig. 21. Each of the three curves shows a minimum round about the summer solstice, when gales are very infrequent on all coasts. The maximum frequency occurs round about the winter solstice—a little earlier on the East Anglian coast. In December and January the frequency exceeds six days per month on the north-west coast of Ireland; and the frequency is practically as high in the Bristol Channel in December. On the northern and western coasts the gale frequency increases quite regularly

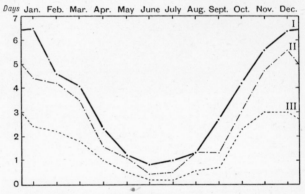

FIG. 21.—Seasonal variation of gale-frequency on the coasts.   I—North-west Ireland, II—South-west England, III—Eastern England.

from the summer minimum to the winter maximum, but we notice in the values for southern England that after increasing from June to August the gale frequency drops slightly in September before resuming its upward trend. A similar tendency is to be seen in the data for other coasts of England, except the north-east coast, where September is a decidedly more stormy month than August.

35. Diurnal variation of wind direction—land- and sea-breezes. If data in regard to the frequency of winds from different directions at the various hours of the day are analysed over a period of years, effects due to the local topography can usually be detected. Such effects are usually small at an inland station. At coastal stations, however, very considerable changes are often found, due to the incidence of " sea-breezes " during the day and land-breezes at night. In the case of a coast following the same direction for several miles, uncomplicated by estuaries or islands, the diurnal sea-breeze is often a more important

factor than the pressure gradient in determining the direction of the wind during the warmer portion of the day during quiet weather in spring, summer and early autumn.

The diurnal sea-breeze is generally explained as being due to the heating of air over the land, as a result of which the air tends to ascend and to be replaced by an inflow of cold air from the sea. This explanation can only be regarded as true in broad outline. In so far as it implies a mass movement upwards of air over the heated land surface it is definitely incorrect. A very simple calculation will serve to show that if an upward velocity of no more than one or two miles per hour is to be maintained over any considerable area, say the area of Ireland, the velocity of the surface inflow, confined to a layer say half a mile deep, would be of an altogether fantastic order. During quiet summer weather it is certainly true that upward convectional currents are to be found, but these are largely balanced by downward currents. The upward currents are found under cumulus clouds and the downward currents in the clear interspaces—a fact well known to devotees of the art of gliding. There is on balance a slight, but only very slight, upward displacement, and it is this small loss from the surface that is replaced by inflow across the boundaries—that is to say, from the sea.

Another point to notice is that the development of the sea-breeze is facilitated by the existence of conditions favouring a strong convectional circulation. These conditions exist when there is a steep lapse-rate of temperature. If the air is cold aloft, as usually happens in " polar " air from between west and north, the necessary steep lapse-rate may become established at quite an early hour of the morning, when the temperature is actually below the normal for the season. The sea-breeze is not necessarily associated in an absolute sense with the surface temperature, and if the upper-air temperature is high it may fail to appear when the surface temperature is many degrees above the sea temperature. Every summer visitor to the south coast can recall stifling summer afternoons when the sea breeze has been conspicuously absent, and, on the other hand, coolish days of the showery type when a vigorous sea-breeze has rendered conditions unpleasantly chilly.

The " land-breeze " is a gravitational flow of cold air outwards from a cold land area. We have spoken of the land-breeze as occurring at night, but that remark needs a little amplification. In the summer, the land-breeze must occur at night if it occurs at all, because the night is the only part of the twenty-four hours during which the temperature inland is below the sea temperature. During the winter, the temperature inland often remains below the sea temperature throughout the day, and this happens quite frequently during anticyclonic weather, when there is little or no gradient of pressure. On such occasions there is no reason why the land-breeze should not continue all day and all night.

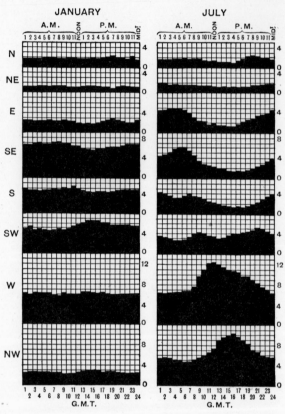

FIG. 22.—Average hourly frequencies of winds from different directions at Southport (Lancs.) in January and July (1899-1933).
(After J. Baxendell.)

As an example of the part played by land- and sea-breezes in the determination of wind direction we will take the case of Southport, on the Lancashire coast, where a large amount of attention has been given to the subject by Mr. J. Baxendell, late Meteorologist to the Corporation. At Southport the coast runs roughly from south-west to north-east, the sea being to the west and north-west. In Fig. 22 we give diagrams, taken from Mr. Baxendell's report (14) for the year 1935, showing the average duration of winds from different directions for each hour of the day, based on hourly tabulations over the thirty-five years 1899 to 1933. Diagrams were prepared for each of the twelve months, but those for January and July will suffice for purposes of illustration. For January the curves for all wind directions are very flat ; a slight diurnal variation is observable in some of the curves—for example, south-east winds are slightly more frequent in the early morning hours than in the middle of the day. Speaking generally, however, there is no very marked tendency for a change during the day in the relative frequencies. The July curves are very different. The landward directions east, south-east, and south show a very pronounced maximum frequency in the early morning hours and a very low frequency in the afternoon. The " sea-breeze " directions west and north-west show exactly the reverse effects ; they have a very high frequency in the middle of the day and a much lower frequency at night. If one follows the column headed 2 p.m. down the diagram it will be seen that nearly all the winds at that hour blow from a westerly point—that is to say, off the sea.

The diagrams for the remaining months, not reproduced here, show that similar effects are discernible in all months from March to October, and are most conspicuous from May to August. Mr. Baxendell makes the following comments on the results :

Of the diurnal, fine-weather, littoral sea-breeze, there are two varieties ; an extreme, or practically complete-turnover kind, generated only on nearly calm, hot days, when the general air current is from some easterly point ; and a more frequent type, occurring also with stronger winds, when general currents from northerly or southerly directions are *twisted* until at least somewhat, and generally, by afternoon, completely, off the sea, along our coastline. The former variety attain their maximum frequency, upon the average, in May ; the latter in August (when they—unlike the former, or complete " turnover ", type—have the interesting effect of very slightly increasing the local air pressure, with the result that the phases of the 24-hour term of the diurnal variation of that element are then reversed).

The so-called local land-breeze is a very different phenomenon, manifesting itself chiefly in autumn and winter, and more often than not prevailing both by day and night. So far from being " local ", it frequently draws from many miles inland, and nearly all weak south-westerly winds seem to be diverted by it ; with the result that, owing to Southport's north-westerly sea aspect, south-east is the most prevalent of all wind directions here from October to February.

The due easterly winds of spring do not attain their maximum until May, but they are then sufficiently in evidence to occasion a distinct, temporary, set-back in the considerable spring to summer increase of frequency of due westerly winds.

Few data exist for other stations, but they tend to confirm the view that Southport is not exceptional in regard to the importance of land- and sea-breezes. An analysis of ten years' observations from Aberdeen shows a similar predominance of on-shore winds during the middle of the day, and of off-shore winds during the night and early morning, from spring to autumn (15). At Yarmouth, on the east coast facing the North Sea, the majority of winds at 15 h. during these seasons were found to have an easterly component (16). In general one may conclude that convectional and gravitational effects are of considerable importance in determining the shape of the wind direction-frequency curves during the summer half-year. The climatic effects produced by these winds will be considered in a later chapter.

36. Katabatic winds. Winds due to a gravitational flow of cold air are known as " katabatic " winds, a term introduced by Sir Napier Shaw. They are observable in many localities on calm, clear nights and their direction is determined by the local topography. In valleys they take the form of streams, often of quite shallow depth, draining down the hill-sides and flowing almost like water along the valley bottom. In such cases they rarely attain an appreciable velocity. In the case of a long ridge or range of hills the katabatic run-off may, however, appear as a very noticeable " night breeze ". At Benson, Oxfordshire, E. V. Newnham (17) observed the frequent occurrence of a katabatic south-east wind from the Chilterns, reaching force 4 on the Beaufort scale. Climatically, katabatic winds are of some importance because they are an agency affecting the transport of cold air at night. In a locality where the topography is such that "ponding " of the cold air occurs, very low night minimum temperatures may be experienced. Thus katabatic air-flow plays an important part in the distribution of damage to fruit trees and other plants in spring frosts. For that reason katabatic winds are receiving much attention at the present time from horticulturists. (See also the section on " Valley Climates ", p. 296.)

37. The diurnal variation of wind velocity. At inland stations in the British Isles there is, in general, a well-marked diurnal variation of wind speed, the maximum occurring in the middle of the day and the minimum shortly before sunrise. In Fig. 23 we give the Kew average curves for January and July, based on thirty-five years' observations. It will be seen that the amplitude of the daily oscillation is much greater in summer than in winter, and it is of interest to note that there is not much difference between the velocities represented by the midday maximum in the two curves.

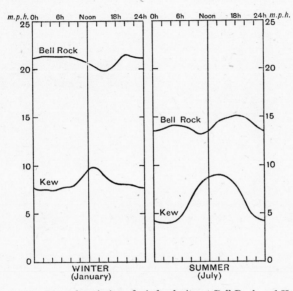

Fig. 23.—Diurnal variation of wind velocity at Bell Rock and Kew in winter and summer.

This diurnal variation is a direct result of the eddy-motion set up by heating of the land surface by the sun's radiation. The eddies cause a vertical transport not only of heat but of momentum ; slow-moving air is carried upward and more rapidly-moving air is brought downwards to replace it. This process of eddy-diffusion reaches its maximum development shortly after noon ; consequently the average wind-speed measured at the surface reaches its maximum value at that time. It is clear from this argument that a diurnal variation of wind velocity of the kind observed at Kew is a surface phenomenon, closely linked up with the diurnal variation of temperature. We saw in Chapter II that no appreciable diurnal variation of temperature occurs over the open sea, and we should not expect, therefore, to find a diurnal variation of

wind velocity.   A. H. R. Goldie (18) has recently analysed three years'
hourly values from the Bell Rock Lighthouse and has obtained the
results shown by the upper curves in Fig. 23.   It is hardly correct to say
that these curves show no diurnal variation, but the inequalities shown
are very small in relation to the mean for the whole twenty-four hours.
The shapes of the curves are, moreover, entirely different from those
for Kew.   In place of a single minimum in the early morning and a single
maximum near midday we have double-humped curves with two
minima and two maxima.   The discussion of these curves is rather
beyond the scope of this work and the reader who wishes to pursue the
subject is accordingly referred to Dr. Goldie's paper.

BIBLIOGRAPHY

(12) *The Weather of the British Coasts* (M.O. 230).   (H.M.S.O.)
(13) E. Gold, " Wind in Britain," *Q.J.R. Meteor. Soc.*, **62**, 1936, p. 167.
(14) Annual Report of the Fernley Observatory, Southport, 1935.
(15) Meteorological Office MS. data.
(16) E. G. Bilham, " The sea-breeze as a climatic factor," *Journal of State Medicine*,
     42, 1934, p. 40.
(17) E. V. Newnham, " Notes on examples of katabatic winds in the valley of the
     Upper Thames," *Professional Notes*, No. 2.   (H.M.S.O.)
(18) A. H. R. Goldie, " Wind records from the Bell Rock Lighthouse," *Geophysical
     Memoirs*, No. 63.   (H.M.S.O.)

See also :

" Anemometers and the Beaufort scale of wind force," *Meteorological Magazine*,
     67, 1932, p. 278.

Fig. 24

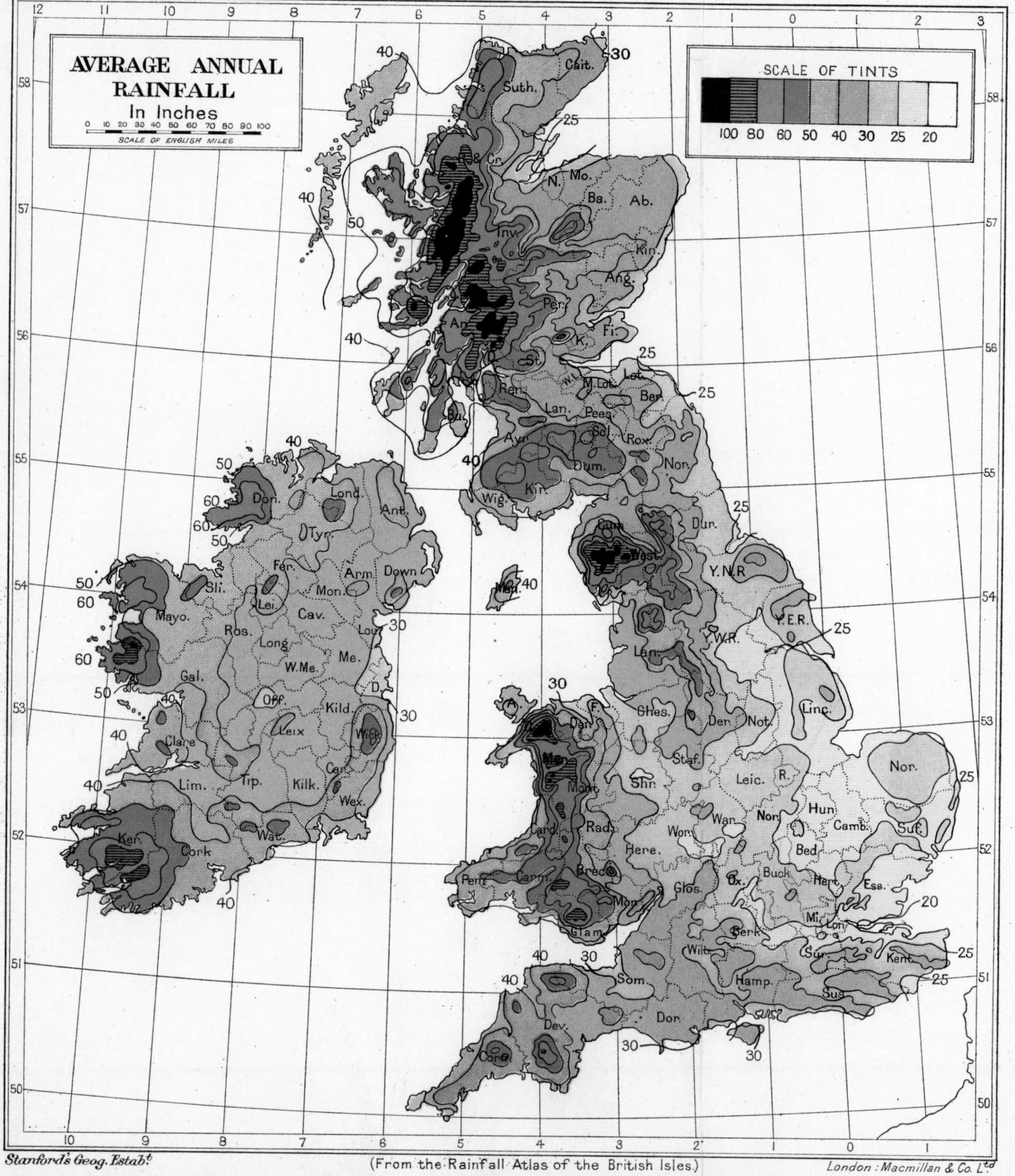
AVERAGE ANNUAL RAINFALL
In Inches
SCALE OF ENGLISH MILES
SCALE OF TINTS
100 80 60 50 40 30 25 20

Stanford's Geog. Estab.t

(From the Rainfall Atlas of the British Isles.)

London: Macmillan & Co. L.td

CHAPTER V

RAINFALL

38. The annual average rainfall. Of all climatic elements, rainfall may claim the first place in practical importance. A water supply is the first requirement for human, animal and vegetable life; a region without rainfall cannot maintain a population unless water is conveyed to that region by rivers or canals. There are no deserts in the British Isles but there is a very large population which must be supplied with water; a large percentage of this population is engaged in industries which depend directly or indirectly on the rainfall. The most obvious of these is agriculture, but there are many other industries which can only be maintained so long as an adequate supply of water is available. The amount of water required for some of these industrial purposes is very great—for example, probably few Londoners realize that the quantity of water passing in and out of the Battersea Electric Power Station in the course of a day exceeds by a large margin the daily consumption of water by the whole population of the metropolis. That is the main reason why large central power stations are sited beside large river estuaries instead of on the coalfields.

Besides being the most important of the climatic elements, rainfall is also the most variable, both in place and time. Of two places five miles apart, one may have double the average rainfall of the other; in the drier areas, the normal rainfall of a month may fall in an hour. The study of rainfall, in sufficient detail to meet all the needs of those who require the information, therefore demands an organization of a different order from that which suffices for the general needs of climatology. In Britain the official climatological records are compiled from returns received from about 350 stations; but *British Rainfall*, the annual publication devoted exclusively to rainfall matters, contains data furnished by more than 5,500 stations, an average of one to every twenty square miles of the British Isles. These very voluminous data have to be discussed from numerous aspects, and we shall accordingly find it necessary to devote more space to the subject of rainfall than to any other subject. The literature of British rainfall study is very extensive, and we can do no more than indicate in broad outline the main results of the various researches and of the routine work of the British Rainfall Organization, a body founded privately by G. J. Symons in 1861 but now a part of the official meteorological service.

We shall deal first with the average annual rainfall and its geographical distribution, that being the most important piece of information, in regard to rainfall, to be ascertained for any region. Following

TABLE XIV

General Averages of Rainfall, 1881–1915

Month	England	Wales	Scotland	Ireland	Isle of Man	England and Wales	British Isles
	in.	in.	in.	in.	in.	in.	in.
January - -	2·69	4·72	4·90	4·07	3·40	2·99	3·78
February - -	2·34	3·94	4·18	3·53	3·25	2·57	3·26
March - - -	2·47	3·82	4·05	3·36	3·03	2·67	3·22
April - - -	1·98	2·96	2·99	2·75	2·47	2·12	2·52
May - - -	2·19	2·95	3·01	2·75	2·82	2·30	2·61
June - - -	2·33	3·05	2·83	2·82	2·54	2·44	2·64
July - - -	2·75	3·60	3·78	3·37	3·22	2·87	3·25
August - - -	3·11	4·71	4·51	4·20	4·01	3·35	3·88
September - -	2·37	3·51	4·00	3·13	3·22	2·54	3·09
October - -	3·69	5·63	4·90	4·08	4·64	3·97	4·25
November - -	3·19	5·25	5·29	4·28	4·73	3·49	4·19
December - -	3·56	6·00	5·88	4·96	4·97	3·92	4·72
Year - -	32·67	50·14	50·32	43·30	42·30	35·23	41·41

[From *The Book of Normals* (M.O. 236)]

the official convention we shall use the term " general rainfall " as connoting the space-average of rainfall over a wide area. The " general average rainfall " means the time-average of the general rainfall over a period of years. For the comparison of the average rainfall of one place with that of another it is essential that the averages should refer to the same period of years. The adopted standard period is the thirty-five years 1881 to 1915. Comparatively few of the existing stations have actual records covering the standard period of thirty-five years but there are well-recognized methods of applying corrections to the results for other periods, to reduce them to the standard period.

The general average rainfall of an area such as England, or the British Isles as a whole, can only be calculated after the average rainfall at a large number of individual stations has been determined and charted. The annual average rainfall chart for the British Isles is shown on a rather small scale in Fig 24. From such a chart the general average annual rainfall can be determined by planimetering the areas included between successive isohyetal lines, or by arithmetical computation from the values read off at a large number of equally-spaced points. The values arrived at in this way for the British Isles and its major divisions are given in the last line of Table XIV. The monthly values were derived by similar methods from monthly charts.

We see that the British Isles as a whole has an annual rainfall of 41·4 inches ; the Isle of Man and Ireland are the areas which approach the general average most closely ; in both Scotland and Wales the general fall slightly exceeds fifty inches ; in England it is only 32·7 inches, or about three-fourths of the general average for the whole area.

A glance at the map (Fig. 24) shows that the distribution of the annual average rainfall is mainly determined by the configuration ; the mountainous areas of the west and north are areas of high rainfall and the flat plains of the east and south are areas of low rainfall. A more detailed study shows, however, that the relationship between rainfall and altitude is not so close as appears at first sight. We find, for example, that in Inverness-shire and Argyllshire, in the west of Scotland, certain areas at an altitude of about 1,000 feet have an annual rainfall exceeding eighty inches, while areas at a similar elevation in the east of Scotland have an annual rainfall of under forty inches. In general, if we consider similar altitudes, rainfall is greater in the west than in the east, but the local topography also enters into the question. Thus the rainfall is higher on a mountain-range at right-angles to the prevailing south-westerly winds than on a range running parallel to the prevailing winds, and in the latter circumstance low rainfall extends for a greater distance up the valleys.

A very large proportion of central and eastern England has an annual total of less than thirty inches ; in fact this value is only exceeded on moorlands or hill-ranges such as the Yorkshire moors, the Yorkshire and Lincolnshire wolds, the Chilterns and the downlands of the southern counties. Narrow strips on the east coasts of Scotland and Ireland also have an annual fall of under thirty inches ; and there is a curious little patch in the centre of Ireland to which this statement applies. In many parts of these areas the annual total is under twenty-five inches; and there is a small area round the Thames estuary in which the average falls slightly below twenty inches.

At the other end of the scale, there are large areas in Scotland, the northern Pennines, the English Lake District, Wales, the Devon-Cornwall peninsula and western Ireland with annual totals of more than sixty inches. In the west of Scotland there is a considerable area, comprising parts of Argyllshire and Inverness-shire, where the fall exceeds 100 inches; this value is also reached over small areas in Cumberland and north Wales. Within these areas there are five small regions which call for special notice.

39. The wettest places. *Snowdonia.* A number of rain gauges are situated on the eastern side of the Snowdon massif. The highest of these is at Glaslyn (2,500 feet), about 1,000 feet below the summit. This gauge recorded the enormous total of 242 inches in 1909 and the computed annual average for the standard period is 198 inches. It seems probable that the annual total for a small area near the summit of Snowdon exceeds 200 inches.

Ben Nevis. An observatory on the summit of Ben Nevis (4,406 feet) recorded an annual average of 161 inches during the twenty years 1885-1904 and the average for the standard period is estimated to be 165 inches. It is probable that on the east side of the final peak the annual average is about 175 inches.

Ben Alder (Inverness-shire, twenty miles east of Ben Nevis). The rain gauge at Lochan Sgoir (2,300 feet), about half a mile to the north-east of the summit, shows an annual average of 111 inches; the maximum rainfall on the mountain is estimated to be about 130 inches.

Head of the River Garry (Inverness-shire). At Loan, Loch Quoich (650 feet), the annual average is 165 inches. It is estimated that the average at Sgurr na Ciche (3,140 feet), from which flow the head-waters of the River Garry, may exceed 200 inches.

The English Lake Disrtict. There is a very wet district extending from Seathwaite (Borrowdale) across the Stye to Scafell and Scafell Pikes. At Seathwaite (423 feet) the annual average is 129 inches; at the Stye it is 175 inches. Lower totals are found at Stye Head Tarn (1,472 feet) and Sprinkling Tarn (1,985 feet) but Dr. J. Glasspoole, to whom the estimates given in this paragraph are due (19), considers that the maximum in this region may be of the order of 185 inches. The rain gauge at the Stye recorded 250 inches in 1928, 247 inches in 1923 and 244 inches in 1872.

The wettest inhabited places in the British Isles appear to be Pen-y-

Gwrhyd Hotel (Snowdonia), Seathwaite Farm and Kinlochquoich Lodge (Inverness-shire), at each of which the average annual fall is from 125 to 130 inches.

40. The driest places. The area with an annual average of under twenty inches is restricted to a small region, about fifty-three square miles in extent, mainly on the Essex coast, bordering the River Thames estuary. On the other side of the river, a narrow strip of the Kent coast has a rainfall of about twenty inches. The driest spot appears to be the village of Great Wakering, near Shoeburyness (Essex), where the computed annual average is 18·4 inches. For Shoeburyness itself an average of 18·9 inches has been published, but a careful examination of the available data indicates that an average of about twenty inches is more nearly correct. Other places with an annual average of under twenty inches are Dagenham Sanatorium (19·3 inches) and Southend (The Cliffs) (19·7 inches). The dry coastal strip may be said to extend up the Essex and Suffolk coasts at least as far as the estuary of the River Orwell, for the annual average is no more than 20·5 inches at Clacton-on-Sea and 20·3 inches at Felixstowe Aerodrome.

Another dry patch is found in the fenland district south of The Wash. Within this area we find annual averages of under twenty-one inches at Upwell (20·6 inches) and Stanground Sluice (20·3 inches) in Cambridge-shire and at Market Deeping (20·9 inches) and Fishtoft School (20·8 inches) in Lincolnshire.

In Scotland there are two conspicuously dry coastal areas, bordering the Firth of Forth and the Moray Firth. In the former we have the islands of Fidra and Inchkeith with annual averages of 21·0 inches and 21·8 inches, and on the mainland East Fortune (23·5 inches) and North Berwick (24·1 inches). In Edinburgh the rainfall varies from about twenty-four inches at the City Observatory to twenty-seven inches at Blackford Hill—that is to say, it is about the same as that of London.

On the northern side of the Moray Firth, Tarbetness, Fortrose and Fearn have annual averages of from twenty-three to twenty-four inches ; on the southern side, the driest place appears to be Nairn (24·5 inches).

41. Areas of rainfall zones. Table XV gives the areas of different main divisions of the British Isles having rainfall between stated limits. It will be seen that rather more than half of England has a rainfall of under thirty inches; the zone 30–40 inches accounts for about two-thirds of the remainder, leaving only about one-sixth of the entire country with an annual fall exceeding forty inches. In Wales, only a very small area has under thirty inches and about forty-five per cent. of the entire area has more than fifty inches. In Scotland, more than 2,000 square miles has an average of under thirty inches but an equal area has more than eighty inches. The rainfall of Ireland is more uniformly distributed; about 26,000 out of the 32,000 square miles of that country is accounted for by the 30–40 inches and 40–50 inches zones. Of the remainder, only 500 square miles has less than thirty inches and this is nearly all comprised in a patch on the east coast running north from Dublin.

TABLE XV

AREAS OF THE RAINFALL ZONES OVER THE BRITISH ISLES

Average Annual Rainfall	England	Wales (and Monmouth)	Isle of Man	Scotland	Ireland	British Isles
	sq. miles	sq. miles	sq. miles	sq. miles	sq. miles	sq. miles
Less than 20 in.	53	—	—	—	—	53
20–25 ,,	5,610	—	—	220	—	5,830
25–30 ,,	21,970	230	—	1,940	500	24,640
30–40 ,,	14,670	1,705	105	8,860	13,680	39,020
40–50 ,,	4,840	2,590	110	7,540	12,510	27,590
50–60 ,,	1,970	1,740	15	5,180	3,210	12,115
60–80 ,,	880	1,270	—	4,280	2,110	8,540
80–100 ,,	190	340	—	1,370	423	2,323
100–150 ,,	120	121	—	739	7	987
More than 150 ,,	7	4	—	11	—	22
Total area	50,310	8,000	230	30,140	32,440	121,120

(From the *Rainfall Atlas of the British Isles*)

It is of interest to note that over the British Isles as a whole about 1,000 square miles has an annual average fall exceeding 100 inches. About three-fourths of this area is in Scotland and nearly all the remainder is shared between England and Wales in equal proportions.

42. The fluctuations of annual rainfall. The rainfall of any place, measured over consecutive calendar years, shows a very considerable degree of fluctuation from year to year. Apart from their climatological interest these fluctuations are of great importance to engineers responsible for the maintenance of water supplies, and they have been the subject of much study. We will begin our consideration of the subject by examining the range of fluctuation of the general rainfall of the

British Isles and its major divisions. The data in regard to the driest and wettest years from 1863 to 1935 are shown in Table XVI.

Over the British Isles as a whole 1887 was the driest year and 1872 was the wettest ; the former year gave a rainfall twenty-three per cent. below normal and the latter gave a rainfall thirty-seven per cent. above normal. The total range of fluctuation during this period of seventy-three years was thus sixty per cent. of the normal value. Taking England and Wales as a separate unit the fluctuations in both directions were

TABLE XVI

RANGE OF FLUCTUATIONS OF GENERAL RAINFALL, 1863–1935

	England and Wales	Scotland	Ireland	British Isles
Rainfall in driest year - -	(1921) 24·66 in.	(1887) 40·26 in.	(1887) 33·34 in.	(1887) 31·89 in.
Per cent. of standard average -	70	80	77	77
Rainfall in wettest year -	(1872) 50·73 in.	(1872) 67·43 in.	(1872) 55·42 in.	(1872) 56·73 in.
Per cent. of standard average -	144	134	128	137
Total range of fluctuation per cent. - -	74	54	51	60

considerably greater ; 1921, the driest year, gave thirty per cent. below normal and 1872 gave forty-four per cent. above normal, a total range of seventy-four per cent. In Scotland, on the other hand, the extreme fluctuations were smaller and in Ireland they were smaller still. We notice that the extreme positive fluctuations exceeded the extreme negative fluctuations, and this is also found to be true for any individual station. Rainfall, in fact, furnishes an example of a skew frequency distribution, arising from the fact that its range of variation is definitely limited to zero in one direction but is more or less unlimited in the other direction. In a given month, for example, the rainfall cannot be more than 100 per cent. below normal, but it may be 200 or 300 per cent., or even more, above normal.

We show in Fig. 25 a graph of the variations which have occurred over England and Wales from 1863 to 1935. Deviations below the

F

standard average (1881-1915) are shaded; those above this average are
unshaded. The details of this graph are of some interest. At the commencement we have two successive dry years, 1863 and 1864, in the
second of which the rainfall was more than twenty per cent. deficient ;
then come two moderately wet years followed by two years of nearly
normal rainfall. Next comes another very dry year, 1870, then a normal
year, followed by the " record " wet year 1872, in which the rainfall
exceeded, by the large margin of six inches, anything recorded in the

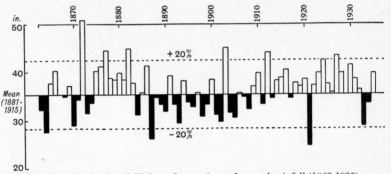

FIG. 25.—England and Wales ; fluctuations of annual rainfall (1863-1935).

following sixty-three years. After two moderately dry years we have a
remarkable run of wet years lasting from 1875 to 1886, with only one
interruption. We then have the very dry year 1887, which gave the
lowest fall on record in all divisions of the British Isles except England
and Wales. After three more moderately dry years we begin, in 1891, a
curious sequence in which a wet year is followed by two dry years. This
quasi-periodicity goes on for no less than eighteen years, including the
very wet year 1903. In 1909 we begin a long series of mainly wet years,
broken, however, in 1921 by the " record " dry year. Near the end of
the period comes the recent very dry year 1933, and finally the year 1935
with a rainfall substantially above normal. In looking at this diagram
we must, however, remember that the average refers to the standard
period, 1881-1915. If the whole period of seventy-three years had been
used the average would have been higher, owing to the predominance
of wet years in the periods before 1881 and after 1915.

43. Annual fluctuations at individual stations. If we examine the
yearly totals at an individual station with a long record we naturally
find that the fluctuations are relatively greater than those found in the
annual values of general rainfall over a large area. As an example we

may take the readings at the Radcliffe Observatory, Oxford, which are continuous from 1815 to the present day. From this record we find that the annual total has fluctuated between 14·94 inches in 1921 (fifty-nine per cent. of the average, 25·56 inches) and 40·73 inches in 1852 (159 per cent. of the average). In Fig. 26 the " dispersion " of the annual totals is exhibited in the form of a curve showing how often during the 116 years 1815 to 1930 a given rainfall was exceeded. The observed fre-

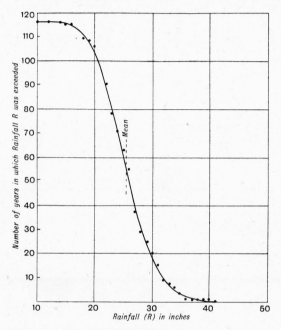

Fig. 26.—Annual rainfall at Oxford (Radcliffe Observatory), graduation curve.

quencies are marked as points on the diagram and the curve was drawn through them freehand. A good deal of mathematical research work has been done on the theoretical form of these " graduation curves " as they are called ; the interested reader may consult a discussion by Doodson and Bigelstone of the Bidston Observatory record, on these lines (20). The mathematical treatment has for one of its objects the determination of the probability that a given rainfall will be exceeded. For example, the extreme annual rainfall found at Oxford in a period of 116 years was 40·73 inches ; is this fall to be expected about once in a hundred years, or once in a thousand years ? Unfortunately there is some disagreement among the mathematicians themselves in regard to the answers to problems such as these, and the subject is, in any case, outside the scope of this book.

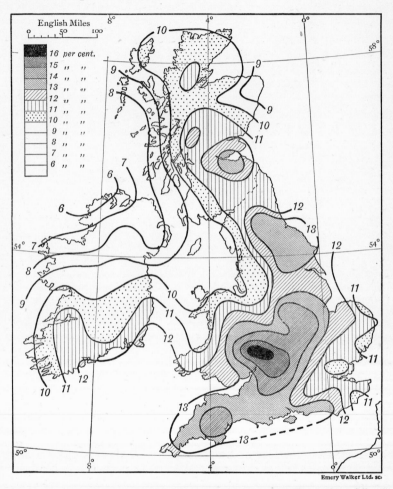

FIG. 27.—Mean percentage deviation from the normal of annual rainfall.
(After J. Glasspoole.)

If we take our freehand curve in Fig. 26 as a reasonably exact representation of the Radcliffe rainfall, we find that it intersects the mean value, 25·56 inches, at the point representing fifty-five years; in other words, the rainfall exceeded the average in fifty-five years and was less than the average in sixty-one years. The mean deviation from normal, taken without regard to sign, is about fifteen per cent. of the normal.

J. Glasspoole (21) has determined the mean deviation during the period 1881 to 1915, from the average for that period, at a considerable number of stations, and has shown that this quantity has a definite geographical distribution, unrelated to the general distribution of rainfall. We give in Fig. 27 a chart, taken from his paper, showing the distribution. The reader should clearly understand that the figures attached to the lines represent the mean deviation expressed as a *percentage* of the local normal. A chart showing the mean deviation in actual inches of rain would look very different. We see from Fig. 27 that the greatest percentage variability of annual rainfall is found in the Midland counties, where the mean deviation exceeds fourteen per cent. over a large area. This region extends roughly from Nottinghamshire to the Bristol Channel, and includes a patch over Herefordshire where the value is as high as seventeen per cent. There are two other patches, one over Yorkshire and a smaller one centred near Edinburgh, where the mean deviation exceeds thirteen per cent. The smallest mean deviations are found over northern Ireland and the western seaboard of Scotland. On the coast of Donegal the value is as low as six per cent. In the south of Ireland, however, we have values increasing from ten per cent. in the latitude of Dublin to twelve per cent. on the south coast. This geographical variation in the variability of rainfall is also seen in the recorded extremes at stations with long records. We have already seen that at Oxford (Radcliffe Observatory) the range of variation is from fifty-nine per cent. to 159 per cent. of the average. This station is situated near the region of maximum variability. At Armagh Observatory, northern Ireland, which is near the region of minimum variability, the variations during the 86-year period 1936-1921 ranged only between seventy per cent. in 1870 and 129 per cent. in 1845.

44. Three driest consecutive years. At the Radcliffe Observatory, Oxford, the rainfall was 23·61 inches in 1900, 22·27 inches in 1901 and 16·66 inches in 1902. The total for the three years is 62·54 inches, and the mean 20·85 or eighty-two per cent. of the long-period average. No drier sequence of three successive years is to be found in the whole record. For the purpose of estimating the reliable annual yield of a catchment area engineers have adopted the figure of eighty per cent. as the mean rainfall in the three driest consecutive years. The Oxford record confirms this value, but it is not quite correct for all parts of the kingdom. In northern Ireland the variation is so small that the three driest consecutive years yield about ninety per cent. of the long-period average, and a similar value has been found for Kilmarnock in the south-west of Scotland. There is, on the other hand, evidence that in parts of England the value may fall slightly below eighty per cent. On the whole, however, the adopted value of eighty per cent. may be regarded as near enough to the truth for the practical purposes of the water engineer.

45. Monthly rainfall. Average values of the monthly rainfall for the British Isles and its major divisions have already been given in Table XIV. These show that April is, on the whole, the driest month and December the wettest, the rainfall in that month being nearly twice as great as in April. The figures in the last column of Table XIV do not, however, show a regular and smooth progression from the minimum to the maximum. After increasing from April to August the value drops sharply in September, increases substantially in October, drops slightly again in November and then rises to the December maximum, after which it falls fairly regularly to the April minimum. The month with the minimum rainfall is not the same in all parts of the kingdom ; it is May in Wales and June in Scotland. Also, we note that the maximum occurs in October in England. It is also of interest to note that the range of the annual variation is distinctly greater in Scotland and Wales than in England or Ireland.

Fig. 28 is a "diagrammatic table" showing the percentage of the year's total which falls in each of the twelve months in the various climatological districts of the British Isles. This diagram may be regarded as a table in which the breadth of the columns is varied in proportion to the percentage of rainfall. The horizontal line at the top of the diagram shows what the breadths of the columns would be if the mean daily rainfall were the same in all months. The months are not of equal length, consequently the successive divisions in this " index line " are not all the same. One use to which this diagram may be put is to estimate the percentage of the year's total fall between 1st January and any given date, or between two given dates. The percentages are most uniform in the month of April, which yields about six per cent. of the annual total in all parts of the kingdom. On the other hand, July gives ten per cent. in north-eastern and eastern England but only $6\frac{1}{2}$ per cent. in northern Scotland. October, November and December yield a high percentage in all districts but January shows considerable variation, from seven per cent. in north-east England to eleven per cent. in northern Scotland. The September subsidiary minimum occurs in all districts but is particularly prominent in Scotland east, England north-east and north-west, and in Ireland.

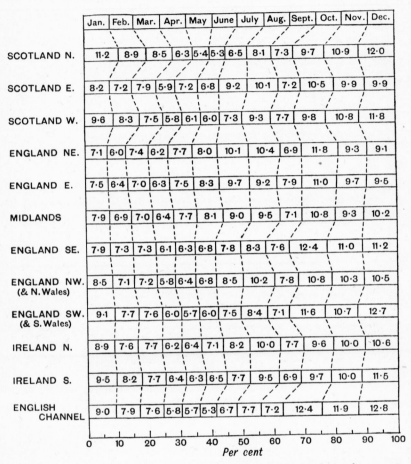

	Jan.	Feb.	Mar.	Apr.	May	June	July	Aug.	Sept.	Oct.	Nov.	Dec.
SCOTLAND N.	11·2	8·9	8·5	6·3	5·4	5·3	6·5	8·1	7·3	9·7	10·9	12·0
SCOTLAND E.	8·2	7·2	7·9	5·9	7·2	6·8	9·2	10·1	7·2	10·5	9·9	9·9
SCOTLAND W.	9·6	8·3	7·5	5·8	6·1	6·0	7·3	9·3	7·7	9·8	10·8	11·8
ENGLAND NE.	7·1	6·0	7·4	6·2	7·7	8·0	10·1	10·4	6·9	11·8	9·3	9·1
ENGLAND E.	7·5	6·4	7·0	6·3	7·5	8·3	9·7	9·2	7·9	11·0	9·7	9·5
MIDLANDS	7·9	6·9	7·0	6·4	7·7	8·1	9·0	9·5	7·1	10·8	9·3	10·2
ENGLAND SE.	7·9	7·3	7·3	6·1	6·3	6·8	7·8	8·3	7·6	12·4	11·0	11·2
ENGLAND NW. (& N.Wales)	8·5	7·1	7·2	5·8	6·4	6·8	8·5	10·2	7·8	10·8	10·3	10·5
ENGLAND SW. (& S.Wales)	9·1	7·7	7·6	6·0	5·7	6·0	7·5	8·4	7·1	11·6	10·7	12·7
IRELAND N.	8·9	7·6	7·7	6·2	6·4	7·1	8·2	10·0	7·7	9·6	10·0	10·6
IRELAND S.	9·5	8·2	7·7	6·4	6·3	6·5	7·7	9·5	6·9	9·7	10·0	11·5
ENGLISH CHANNEL	9·0	7·9	7·6	5·8	5·7	5·3	6·7	7·7	7·2	12·4	11·9	12·8

0 10 20 30 40 50 60 70 80 90 100
Per cent

FIG. 28.—Diagrammatic table showing the rainfall of each month expressed as a percentage of the annual average.

An interesting fact brought out by this diagram is that the rainfall in the English Channel district (which comprises the Channel Isles and Scilly) for the three months October to December is very nearly equal to the aggregate fall during the whole of the summer half-year, April to September.

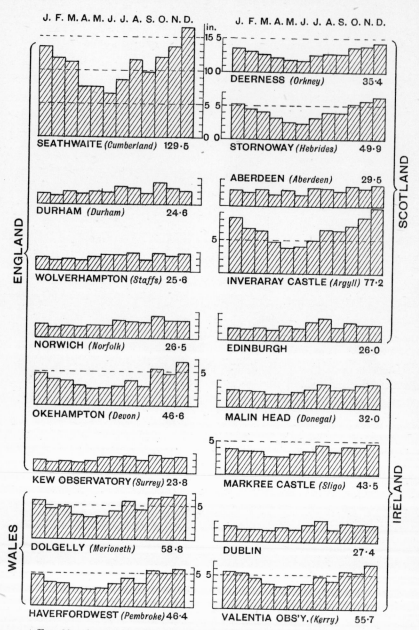

Fig. 29.—Average monthly and annual rainfall at representative stations.

Monthly percentage values similar to those shown in Fig. 28 can, of course, be calculated for individual stations; if this is done for a large number of stations, maps can be constructed showing the variation over the British Isles of the monthly percentages. A series of such " isomeric maps," as they are called, was constructed by H. R. Mill and M. de C. S. Salter (22), and they have been used to a considerable extent for the purpose of determining the monthly averages for a given station whose annual average has been estimated from the annual chart.

Monthly averages of rainfall in inches, for a representative selection of stations, are shown in Fig. 29. The three stations, Deerness (Orkney), Stornoway (Hebrides) and Inveraray Castle (Argyll), show a very good approach to a simple annual rhythm with a summer minimum and a winter maximum. The curve for Seathwaite (Cumberland) is almost as simple, but the continuity is broken by the subsidiary maximum in August. The drier stations show little tendency towards a regular seasonal variation; in several cases, and particularly at Aberdeen, the alternations of dry and wet month give the diagrams a profile like that of an embattled wall. Edinburgh, Malin Head, Dublin and Wolverhampton all show a maximum in August, a feature which we were hardly led to expect from Fig. 28.

The *Rainfall Atlas of the British Isles* (23), published by the Royal Meteorological Society, contains an admirable series of monthly rainfall maps referring to the standard period 1881 to 1915. An examination of these maps shows that the main features of the annual distribution, as displayed in Fig. 24, are repeated in each of the twelve months; there is no month in which we fail to find the driest areas in the eastern half of England, and the wettest areas in the mountainous districts of the west and north. We have seen, however, that the monthly percentages are not the same in all districts, and these variations are sufficient to make it worth while examining the resultant variations in the isohyetal pattern from month to month. The variations we have in mind are not easily seen in a series of detailed monthly charts, and we therefore present in Fig. 30 a simplified set of charts suited to this purpose. In these charts black indicates a monthly rainfall exceeding four inches; grey, two to four inches; and white, under two inches.

Starting with January we see that the white (dry) area covers the whole of eastern England from the Thames valley to the Humber, northward of which it extends, though with considerable interruptions, in the form of a coastal strip right up to the Moray Firth. There is also a large dry patch over the Avon valley. The black (wet) area covers

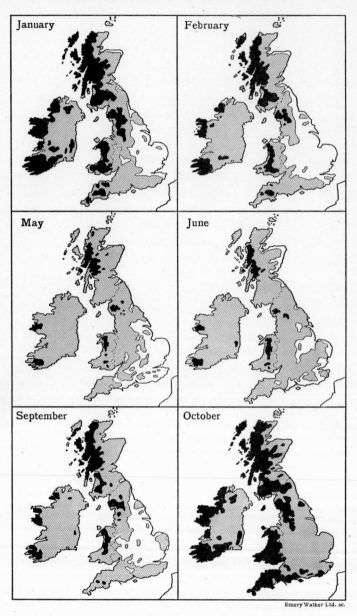

FIG. 30.—Monthly charts of average rainfall. Black, over four
(Based on charts in the *Rainfall Atlas of the British*

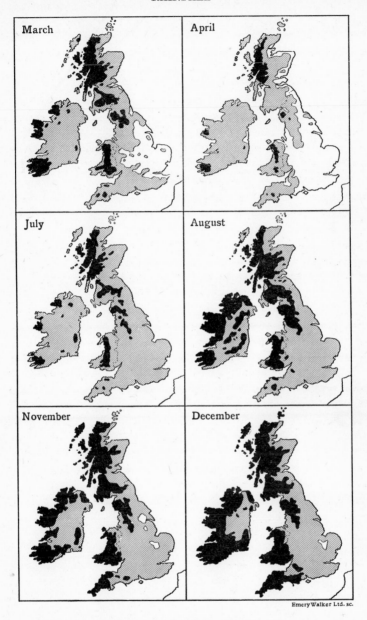

inches ; shaded, two to four inches ; unshaded, less than two inches.
Isles, published by the Royal Meteorological Society.)

very nearly the whole of western Scotland and the western islands, the
English Lake District and the Pennines, most of Wales, Cornwall and
Devon, and the high ground in Ireland. In February the white area
has extended westward to the Irish Sea, and the coastal strip in north-
east England and eastern Scotland is nearly continuous ; the black area
has shrunk very considerably. In March the white area has diminished
again, and has nearly disappeared from Scotland ; the black area shows
little change. April shows a great advance by the white area which now
covers a very large proportion of England and a wide strip along the
east coast of Scotland ; also, a white patch has appeared on the east
coast of Ireland, near Dublin. The black area has shrunk very markedly,
being confined now to the highest parts of Scotland, Ireland, the Lake
District, Cross Fell, the Welsh mountains, Dartmoor and Exmoor. In
May the white area has contracted once more but it still covers all but
the hilliest portions of eastern and southern England ; the black area
remains very small. June shows some curious changes ; the white area
is greatly diminished over England but reappears as a coastal strip in
the east of Scotland ; the black area has decreased to its minimum size.
The predominant rainfall amount for the month of June is therefore two
to four inches, only small areas having a fall less than or exceeding this
range.

July is marked by the total disappearance of the white area and a
very marked expansion of the black area. In August the white area
remains absent and the black area has regained its January status over
Great Britain ; in Ireland, black is the predominating tint. September
shows an abrupt change, the white area reappearing over the Midlands
and eastern England ; it should be noted, however, that there is a large
grey patch over Norfolk and Suffolk. In regard to the black area, the
distribution is very similar to that of March. In October the white
area disappears once more ; the black area is similar to that of January
in Scotland, Ireland and northern England. In the south, however, it
now covers practically the whole of Wales, Devon and Cornwall, as well
as large patches over the high ground in the south of England. We
may notice also that the Yorkshire moors are defined by a black patch.
In November the black patches have mostly disappeared from the south
of England and small white areas reappear in eastern England December shows a general increase in the black area, more particularly in
Ireland, and white is confined to one small patch over Cambridgeshire.

The more detailed maps show that monthly averages below 1·5 inches
occur in the drier areas of eastern England during the months January

to May, while in the wettest parts of Scotland, Cumberland and Wales averages exceed ten inches in all months except April, May and June. In December the wettest places, detailed in paragraph 39, receive an average fall exceeding twenty inches.

46. Fluctuations of monthly rainfall. As an example of the fluctuations of monthly rainfall observed during a period exceeding 100 years we give in Fig. 31 a diagram referring to Oxford (Radcliffe Observatory).

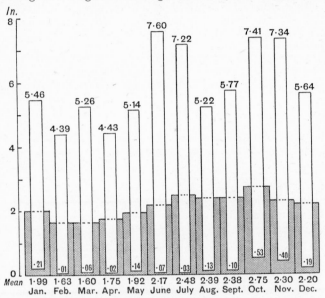

FIG. 31.—Oxford (Radcliffe Observatory); means and extremes of monthly rainfall (1815-1930).[1]

In this diagram the shaded columns represent the averages for the period 1815-1930; the tops and bottoms of the superposed white columns represent the highest and lowest totals observed in each month during the whole period.* The lengths of the white columns therefore represent the observed range of variation. The extreme monthly rainfall, 7·60 inches, occurred in June 1852 and amounted to 350 per cent. of the average for June. No month during the period of 116 years yielded absolutely no rain, though the February minimum, which occurred in 1891, is only 0·01 inch. The diagram brings out clearly a point that has already been mentioned, namely that the positive deviations from the normal are numerically greater than the negative deviations, since the

[1] The extremes are correct to 1935, except May, 1932, 5·46 in.

latter are limited definitely by the zero line. Another point to notice is that the extreme falls in different months vary over a wide range. The extremes for June, July, October and November are outstanding and are of about the same order of magnitude; February and April show the lowest extremes, and these are also of the same order of magnitude, about 4·4 inches. The remaining six months all show extremes lying between 5·1 and 5·8 inches.

In Fig. 32 the dispersion of the fluctuations in the driest month,

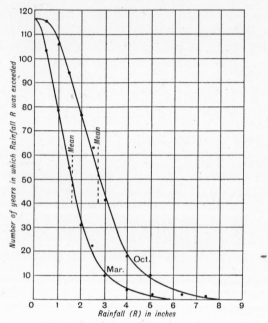

Fig. 32.—Oxford (Radcliffe Observatory); rainfall in March and October, graduation curves.

March, and the wettest month, October, are shown by means of curves similar to those of Fig. 26. The curves are of generally similar shape, which suggests that if the deviations were expressed as percentages of the monthly means the curves would not differ much. J. Glasspoole (24) has investigated the deviations from normal of monthly rainfall during the period 1881 to 1915 at a string of six stations extending from Buncrana in Donegal to Tenterden in Kent. The mean of the six stations gave an average deviation of forty-five per cent. of the normal rainfall in February and September, with lower values in other months, the minimum, thirty-one per cent., occurring in November. A more detailed investigation for the months of January and July showed that the geographical distribution of the variability of monthly rainfall was generally similar to that of annual rainfall. In either month the mean deviation from normal was found to vary from about twenty-five per cent. on the north-western seaboard to about forty-five per cent. over most of England, with patches over the south coast of England and the central portions of northern England in which the variability slightly exceeded fifty per cent. Glasspoole also found, on examining the records for a number of stations in England and Wales, that in about one month out of three the rainfall was within twenty-five per cent. of the normal. Months with a rainfall twenty-five per cent. or more below normal were slightly more frequent than months with a rainfall twenty-five per cent. or more above normal.

47. Very dry and very wet months. It is uncommon in the British Isles for a period as long as thirty or thirty-one days to produce no rain at all in a particular area. When such a period does occur, the chances that it will include the whole of a calendar month are very slender ; consequently the occurrence of 0·00 inch as the rainfall total for the month at any station is decidedly rare. The following is a list of occasions of no rainfall over considerable areas during the past sixty years :

February 1891. About 3,300 square miles, mainly in the centre and south-east of England, received no rain.

April 1893. During the famous spring drought of 1893 a considerable area in the south-east of England received no rain for fifty days ; locally the drought lasted two months, from 17th March to 16th May.

September 1894. The driest September on record in Scotland ; a few stations, *e.g.* Corsewall and Moffat, recorded no rain.

February 1895. No rain in parts of south-west England, *e.g.* Ashburton on Dartmoor.

July 1911. A small area in Wiltshire received no rain.

April 1912. No rain in parts of Berkshire and Sussex.

June 1921. Nearly as dry as June 1925 and February 1891 ; no rain in parts of Kent, Sussex, Hampshire, south-west Wales and extreme south of Ireland.

June 1925. Probably the driest month on record in England ; about 6.400 square miles in various parts of England received no rain.

March 1929. No rain over the Lea valley.

February 1932. This month ranks as the driest on record over the

British Isles generally ; many stations in the west of England, Wales and Scotland recorded no rain.

In considering exceptionally wet months we naturally expect to find the highest recorded totals in places such as Snowdonia, where the normal fall in a winter month may exceed twenty inches. We find, indeed, that monthly totals of the order of fifty inches have occasionally been recorded in these small areas, but the values can hardly be regarded as remarkable when considered in relation to the average fall in these districts. It is of more interest, therefore, to consider the rainfall as a percentage of the local average. An examination on these lines indicates that September 1918 was the wettest month in the British Isles since comparable records began in 1870. In that month the whole of England and Wales and nearly the whole of Ireland had more than twice the normal for September ; over a considerable part of this area in England and Wales the fall exceeded three times the normal and at Garforth, near Leeds, it slightly exceeded four times the normal. In Scotland the excess was not so marked and a large area in the west had less than one and a half times the normal. It has been computed that in this one wet month the amount of water which fell was sufficient, if it could be stored, to supply the whole population of the British Isles with an allowance of thirty-six gallons a day (the amount utilized in London, per head) for about twenty years.

48. Sequences of dry or wet months. From the point of view of the water engineer an entire failure of rain in a single month is not a serious matter, because the supply of water stored in his reservoirs is available to tide over the deficiency. Anxiety does, however, arise when a shortage of rainfall persists for a long period; it is important, therefore, to ascertain the minimum amount of rain likely to occur in runs of one, two, three, four, . . . months. The complementary question of the *maximum* amount to be expected in similar runs of months is also of interest, but it is of practical importance in relation to drainage rather than to water supplies. The results given here are taken from a paper by J. Glasspoole (25), using data up to the year 1927. Since that date there have been two severe droughts—one in 1929 and the other spreading over 1933 and 1934, in one or other of which new " records " of persistent deficiency of rainfall were established in many areas. Also, during the last three months of 1929 there was a very remarkable wet period which set up new records for wetness in many places. The values for minimum rainfall quoted below are therefore a little on the high side, and those for maximum rainfall are a little on the low side.

TABLE XVII

MEANS OF THE EXTREMES OF RAINFALL AS RECORDED AT FORTY STATIONS
IN THE BRITISH ISLES FOR VARIOUS PERIODS (EACH EXTREME BEING
EXPRESSED AS A PERCENTAGE OF THE AVERAGE ANNUAL FALL)

Country	No. of stations	Number of consecutive months											
		1	2	3	4	5	6	7	8	9	10	11	12
		%	%	%	%	%	%	%	%	%	%	%	%
		(a) Least values											
England -	15	0·1	2·0	6·7	10	15	20	25	32	37	44	52	60
Wales - -	5	0·2	2·8	7·1	12	19	21	27	35	42	51	58	65
Scotland -	11	0·6	3·4	7·7	12	17	22	30	36	44	51	58	63
Ireland -	9	0·4	3·3	7·3	13	17	24	31	38	44	53	60	67
British Isles -	40	0·3	2·8	7·2	11	17	22	28	35	44	49	56	63
		(b) Greatest values											
England -	15	29	46	60	72	86	98	107	116	126	137	147	158
Wales - -	5	27	42	56	69	83	93	104	115	124	133	140	151
Scotland -	11	27	44	58	70	81	93	102	111	121	130	141	154
Ireland -	9	25	43	55	69	81	92	103	111	120	130	139	148
British Isles -	40	27	44	58	71	83	94	104	114	123	133	143	154

The data used by Glasspoole covered a period of fifty-eight years.
He found that the maximum and minimum values at different stations
showed a considerable degree of resemblance when expressed as percentages of the annual average. Taking the means of the stations in
each area he obtained the results set out in Table XVII. Graphs of the
mean values for the British Isles are given in Fig. 33. It is important to
remember that these curves refer to the " average individual station ",
not to the area as a whole ; it should also be emphasized that the data
refer to calendar months. It would obviously be possible to find higher
or lower extremes in periods of thirty or thirty-one days commencing
on an arbitrary date, than in calendar months ; this consideration is
likely, however, to affect the shorter periods more than the longer periods.
In Fig. 33 we have added, as a matter of interest, two broken lines
showing the greatest and least percentages that would arise from normal
rainfall, using the values given in Table XIV, last column.

We see from Table XVII that both drought periods and flood periods
are more intense in England than in other parts of the British Isles.

G

In England, six successive months have given as little as one-fifth, and nearly as much as the whole, of the average year's rain. These figures are an understatement when we pick out the individual station at which

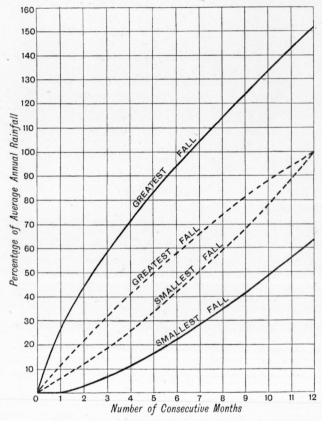

Fig. 33.—*Full lines*—Greatest and least recorded amounts of rain in a given number of consecutive calendar months (averages for forty stations, after J. Glasspoole).

Broken lines—Highest and lowest totals for sequences of calendar months, using normal monthly values (1881-1915).

(In each case the rainfall is expressed as a percentage of the annual average.)

the most extreme conditions have been recorded. The famous drought of 1921 was particularly severe in the south-eastern corner of England, and we give in Table XVIII details of conditions in the Isle of Thanet. It will be seen that in 1921 the driest six months yielded only one-sixth of the annual average, and the whole twelve months yielded less than half of the annual average. Similarly, we find that at Rothbury, in Northumberland, the wettest period of twelve consecutive months has yielded as much as 180 per cent. of the normal annual total for that station.

TABLE XVIII

RAINFALL OF THE DRIEST CONSECUTIVE MONTHS OF
1921 IN THE ISLE OF THANET

	Months	Rainfall	
		Inches	Per cent. of annual average
1	July - - -	0·1	0·5
2	June–July - -	0·3	1·5
3	May–July - -	1·2	5
4	April–July - -	2·3	10
5	May–September -	3·1	13
6	May–October - -	3·8	16
7	April–October -	5·0	21
8	March-October -	6·0	25
9	February–October -	6·7	28
10	February–November	8·4	35
11	February–December	9·7	41
12	January–December -	11·2	47

49. Conditions associated with abnormally wet or dry periods. Three types of rainfall are commonly recognized: (a) the orographic type, due to the dynamic cooling of moist air which is forced to move up an inclined solid surface; (b) cyclonic rain, which is caused, on current theory, by the ascent of moist air over cold air masses; and (c) thunderstorm rain, in which the dynamic cooling of the moist air is due to convection. These three divisions of rainfall are by no means sharply separated ; they merge into one another to such an extent that no one could go through a year's return of rainfall from a single station, say Eskdalemuir Observatory, and put on (a), (b) or (c) against each day's entry with certainty and confidence. The rainfall in the south-westerly wind forming the warm sector of a depression is subject to orographic action as much as any other rain, giving greater amounts on the high ground than on the low ground. We can say, however, that when heavy falls of rain occur over low-lying areas remote from hill-slopes, they are of cyclonic or thunderstorm origin. They may pertain to both, because thunderstorms giving heavy rains occur not infrequently in association with shallow depressions.

An abnormally wet period is definitely due, therefore, to an unusual intensification or prolongation of the conditions giving rise to one or more of the three types of rain. A study of the weather charts during the period would naturally provide the clue to the predominating cause, but a good deal can be deduced from the monthly rainfall charts, especially those in which the rainfall is represented as a percentage of the local normal. Orographic rains would naturally be increased by an intensification of the normal flow of air from between south and west. Such an intensification would result from an increase in the mean pressure gradient from north-west to south-east, giving strong and persistent moist winds from the Atlantic. When monthly mean pressures are relatively low in the north, and normal, or only slightly different from the normal, in the south, we should expect to find abnormally heavy rains on the high ground in the west and north, rather than in the low-lying areas in the east. The rainfall map would, indeed, show an exaggerated version of the ordinary distribution.

Exceptional cyclonic activity occurs when the main low-pressure and high-pressure " centres of action " are displaced far to the southward of their normal position. In these circumstances high pressure becomes established in the latitude of Iceland and the Azores anticyclone recedes towards the equator. A corridor for the passage of depressions is thus established across the British Isles, and the resulting abnormal rainfall is distributed more or less uniformly. In these circumstances the averages of pressure for the month will show negative deviations from the normal in all districts. If the paths of depressions lie sufficiently far to the southward, stations in the far north may show only small deviations from the normal rainfall, and the percentage rainfall chart would show the main areas of excess over the southern half of the kingdom. September 1918 provided a striking example of this type of distribution. Occasionally a single depression of unusual intensity may produce an abnormal amount of rain in a single day, over a relatively small area. Such an occurrence took place on 28th June, 1917, over the Quantock Hills in Somerset and the enormous total of 9·56 inches was recorded at Bruton (Sexey's School). The famous Norfolk floods of August 1912 were also caused by a cyclonic rain amounting near Norwich to eight inches in about twenty hours, spread over the two rainfall days 25th-26th August. In that storm more than four inches fell over an area of no less than 1,660 square miles. This was an outstanding example of a cyclonic rain entirely uncomplicated by orographic effects.

Thunderstorm rains, though often of great intensity, do not often produce total amounts of rainfall, even at individual stations directly in their path, of the same order of magnitude as are observed when intense cyclonic rains are augmented by orographic action. An exception occurred on 18th August, 1924, when a thunderstorm produced 9·4 inches of rain at Cannington, Somerset. Of this amount fully eight inches fell in about five hours. The area receiving more than four inches was, however, no more than ten square miles in extent, and that fact leads us to observe that when high monthly totals are mainly due to thunderstorms, the monthly rainfall chart presents an irregular appearance, with patches of high percentages of normal, having no relation to ground contours.

Turning now to abnormally dry periods—that is to say, periods of drought—it is natural to find that they occur under conditions diametrically opposite to those which produce heavy and widespread rainfall. Two sets of circumstances may be recognized: (a) an exceptional persistence of anticyclonic conditions over our area; (b) the reversal, for long periods, of the normal pressure gradient, as a result of which the flow of air is predominantly from an easterly point instead of from a westerly point. Thus the very dry year 1921 was characterized by an unusual prevalence of anticyclones; and the same statement is true in regard to the famous droughts of 1864, 1868, 1880, 1887, 1893 and 1896. In February 1932, some details of which have already been given, the mean pressure for the month was from fifteen millibars to twenty-five millibars above normal in all parts of the kingdom and northerly to easterly winds were unusually persistent. This month, which was the driest on record over the British Isles generally, thus showed both types of conditions favourable to drought. The recent dry year 1933 was remarkable for the abnormally low frequency of south-westerly winds, and a correspondingly high frequency of easterly and north-easterly winds.

When drought conditions are caused by anticyclones the deficiency of rain is usually general ; when a predominance of easterly winds is the cause it is common to find that the deficiency, reckoned as a percentage of the normal, is more marked in the west than in the east. In this connection it is worthy of comment that in the dry year 1933 a small area in north-east England actually received a normal year's rainfall. Quite often, however, the two effects are intermingled, as we noted in the case of February 1932.

At this stage the discerning reader is likely to remark that when we speak of the " causes " of abnormally wet or dry periods in terms of cyclones, anticyclones and so forth, we have really only pushed the in-

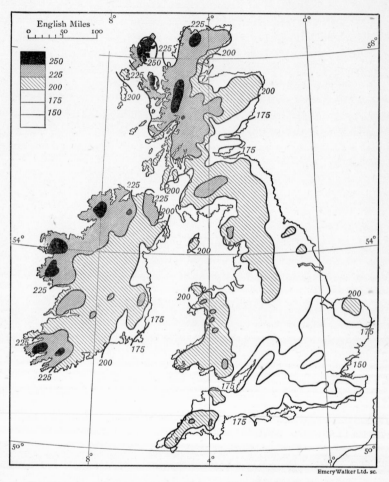

FIG. 34.—Annual average number of days with rain (after J. Glasspoole).

quiry back a stage further. Questions immediately arise as to why periods running into months should be distinguished by sequences of anticyclones or by a southward displacement of the tracks of depressions. The answers to such questions cannot yet be given, but it seems clear that we must seek for the answers by a study of atmospheric circulation on a world-wide scale. Investigations related to these problems are being pursued by many workers ; the reward of success is great, for if the causes of these abnormal periods could be clearly made out, the possibility of predicting them would present itself.

50. Days of rain. A " rain-day " or " day of rain " is defined in this country as one on which the measurement of rain, or its equivalent of snow, hail, etc., is 0·01 inch (0·2 mm.) or more. The geographical distribution of the total number of rain-days in the average year is illustrated in Fig. 34. It will be observed that there is a superficial resemblance between this chart and the average annual rainfall chart (Fig. 24), the number of rain-days being large in the western and northern areas, where the annual rainfall is high, and small in the east and south-east, where the annual rainfall is low. The range in the annual number of rain-days is from about 150 in the south-east to over 260 in the north-west. The areas where rain-days are most frequent thus receive some rain on nearly five days out of seven, while the driest areas have rain on only about three days out of seven.

A closer examination shows, however, that the resemblance between the rainfall chart and the rain-day frequency chart is not so exact as appears at first sight. We find, for example, that the west coast of Ireland, the Hebrides and the Orkneys and Shetlands have a very high frequency of rain-days, but these are not the areas of heaviest rainfall. Data for individual stations in close proximity show that the annual number of rain-days is similar though the annual average amount of rain may be very different. For example, the annual rainfall at Fort William is, roughly, seventy-eight inches, while at the summit of Ben Nevis the annual fall exceeds 160 inches ; the average number of rain-days is 240 in the one case and 263 in the other, a difference of only ten per cent. One may regard the rain-day frequency chart as an expression of the experience of different areas in relation to the frequency with which one or other of the causes of rain was in operation. In respect to cyclonic rain and thunderstorm rain, we should not expect large variations over small areas ; in respect to orographic rain, although the neighbouring valleys would share in the precipitation initiated by the neighbouring slopes, there would nevertheless be a number of occasions when precipitation of small amount took place on the hill-sides only. The aggregate number of rain-days would thus be somewhat higher on high ground than on neighbouring low ground, but the ratio of the number of rain-days in the two places would be smaller than the ratio of the total amounts of rain.

In Fig. 35 will be found diagrams showing the average number of rain-days in each month at a few selected stations. We see that the number of rain-days varies over a relatively small seasonal range at all stations. June is, on the whole, the month of fewest rain-days, while the

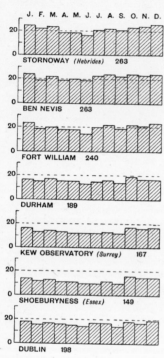

maximum number occurs in December or October. At Valentia and Stornoway the frequency is as high as twenty-six in December. At Shoeburyness, which is in the driest area of the British Isles, there are, on the average, only ten days of precipitation in June, July and September. The relatively low frequency in June and July as compared with August, in all districts, is a matter of interest to holiday-makers. Data for other stations will be found in the Appendix.

51. The frequency-distribution of daily rainfalls exceeding stated values. We give in Table XIX data in regard to the percentage frequency of daily rainfalls exceeding certain limits. Data of this kind are available for very few stations, and those given in the table are quoted from an article in *British Rainfall*, 1932 (26). The first column of figures refers to days with 0·04 inch or more—that is to say, "wet days" as defined for the purposes of *British Rainfall*. Their number exceeds

Fig. 35.—Monthly and annual averages of the number of days with rain at representative stations.

fifty per cent. at Strontian and nearly reaches that value at Markree Castle. At most of the stations on the eastern side of Great Britain the frequency of wet days is round about thirty-three per cent. or one day in three. It will be observed that at all stations the percentage frequency decreases rapidly as we go from left to right across the table. For example, at Kew Observatory twenty-nine per cent. of all days have 0·04 inch or more but only eleven per cent. have as much as 0·2 inch, and only four per cent. have as much as 0·4 inch. There is a rather surprising degree of similarity between the results for certain widely separated stations. For example, the figures in the first three columns are all higher at Deerness, Orkney, than at Kew Observatory, but in the remaining columns the figures are very similar for the two stations. Also it will be noted that the frequency of days with 1·0 inch or more is between 0·4 and 0·5—that is, four to five days per thousand—at a considerable number of stations, including Aberdeen, Kew and the four Irish stations.

These data show an interesting form of frequency-distribution. If frequency is plotted on a logarithmic scale and rainfall on an ordinary linear scale the resulting curve is very nearly a straight line, as will be seen from Fig. 36, where the data for six stations are plotted. In other words, the frequency n is related to the rainfall r by an equation of the form $\log n = a - br$, where a and b are constants varying from station to station.

In regard to the seasonal distribution of daily falls, we may quote the following remarks from the original article :

" At all stations the lowest frequency of wet days occurs either in spring or summer. At nearly all stations falls with a lower limit of 0·2, 0·4 or 0·6 inch are markedly less frequent in spring than at other seasons. At certain stations, more particularly in the northern and western parts of the British Isles, the minimum frequency under each heading throughout the table occurs in spring but in the eastern half of Great Britain the frequency of heavy falls, *e.g.* 1·0 inch or more, tends to be lowest in winter.

" At stations in south-eastern, north-eastern and eastern England, at Plymouth, Glasgow, Kilmarnock and the Irish stations, the highest frequencies of rains of one inch or more are found in the summer season. At Falmouth, Churchstoke, Douglas and the stations in northern Scotland, such rains occur most frequently in the autumn, the preponderance being particularly striking at Deerness and Braemar. At Strontian, a wet station in Argyllshire, the heavy falls are slightly more frequent in winter than in autumn and are least frequent in summer."

52. Some outstanding daily rainfalls. In Table XX will be found a list of the recorded daily rainfalls of six inches or more during the period 1865 to 1935. The list is arranged by counties and contains only one entry for the same county on a given date. The list would have been very much longer if we had included all the individual measurements exceeding six inches—for example, nearly twenty stations in Norfolk recorded more than six inches on 26th August, 1912. It will be noticed that certain dates, *e.g.* 3rd November, 1931, have yielded extreme falls in more than one county. The number of different dates is thirty-four.

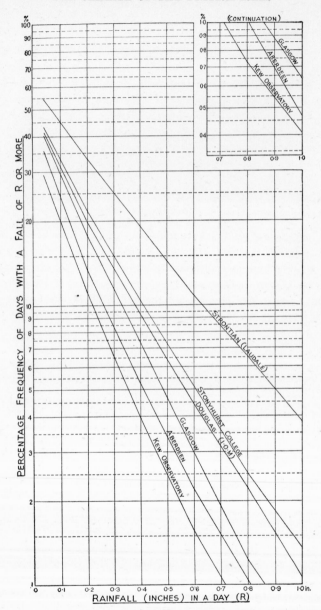

Fig. 36.—Percentage frequency of days with rainfall exceeding stated amounts.
(From *British Rainfall*, 1932)

TABLE XIX   107

PERCENTAGE FREQUENCY OF DAILY RAINFALL AMOUNTS (WHOLE YEAR)

Station and Period	Percentage number of days with falls not less than									Annual Average Rainfall
	0·04 in.	0·2 in.	0·4 in.	0·6 in.	0·8 in.	1·0 in.	1·2 in.	1·6 in.	2·0 in.	in.
SCOTLAND										
Deerness (*Orkney*) - 1886–1921	45·9	17·5	5·31	1·91	0·78	0·33	0·17	0·04	0·01	35·4
Dunrobin Cas. (*Sutherland*) 1880–1910	38·6	15·4	5·41	2·09	0·87	0·44	0·24	0·06	0·01	31·7
Braemar (*Aberdeen*) - 1880–1910	37·5	15·7	6·40	2·92	1·45	0·75	0·43	0·13	0·08	35·4
Aberdeen (*Aberdeen*) - 1871–1930	35·7	13·4	5·16	2·18	1·03	0·47	0·26	0·07	0·01	29·5
Dundee (*Angus*) - - 1880–1912	32·9	12·0	4·57	2·21	1·05	0·46	0·29	0·09	0·03	27·4
Strontian (*Argyll*) - 1879–1909	54·4	33·4	19·00	10·80	6·54	3·84	2·24	0·70	0·20	77·8
Glasgow (*Lanark*) - 1886–1920	40·5	17·9	7·27	2·95	1·23	0·64	0·29	0·08	0·03	37·2
Kilmarnock (*Ayr*) - 1902–1930	45·8	20·2	7·90	3·03	1·10	0·41	0·27	0·05	0·03	37·3
ISLE OF MAN										
Douglas, 1878–1931 -	41·2	19·8	9·18	4·40	2·21	1·06	0·54	0·16	0·06	41·2
ENGLAND										
Morpeth (Cockle Park) 1900–1931	33·9	12·2	4·91	2·13	1·04	0·57	0·33	0·12	0·06	28·7
Scarborough (*Yorks.*) - 1881–1906	32·3	11·5	3·96	1·65	0·79	0·44	0·22	0·08	0·03	25·8
Hillington (*Norfolk*) - 1877–1910	32·8	12·7	4·38	2·00	1·01	0·46	0·24	0·08	0·02	27·9
Cambridge (*Cambs.*) - 1900–1931	28·2	9·5	3·14	1·31	0·60	0·28	0·12	0·04	0·01	21·8
London (Kew Observatory), 1871–1931	29·4	11·2	3·91	1·56	0·73	0·41	0·19	0·04	0·01	23·8
Southampton (*Hants.*) 1878–1931	32·5	14·7	6·33	2·82	1·32	0·62	0·35	0·12	0·05	30·9
Plymouth (*Devon*) - 1893–1910	36·0	16·4	7·25	3·45	1·72	0·82	0·36	0·08	0·02	36·7
Falmouth (*Cornwall*) - 1871–1931	41·8	20·9	9·96	4·84	2·36	1·29	0·60	0·20	0·07	43·6
Stonyhurst College - (*Lancs.*) 1884–1931	43·5	21·9	10·30	5·15	2·50	1·37	0·70	0·20	0·07	46·5
WALES										
Churchstoke (*Montgomery*), 1876–1900	34·7	14·2	5·27	2·36	1·05	0·53	0·27	0·12	0·04	30·8
IRELAND										
Armagh Observatory (*Armagh*), 1871–1931	40·4	15·0	5·12	1·94	0·83	0·42	0·30	0·07	0·02	31·7
Markree Castle (*Sligo*) - 1876–1931	49·8	21·9	7·46	2·86	1·10	0·45	0·24	0·07	0·02	43·5
Dublin (Phœnix Park) 1871–1931	35·4	12·2	4·17	1·90	0·89	0·49	0·26	0·10	0·04	27·6
Birr Castle (*Offaly*) - 1873–1931	41·0	15·6	5·45	2·09	0·87	0·39	0·21	0·07	0·02	32·6

(From *British Rainfall*, 1932)

TABLE XX

DAILY RAINFALLS OF SIX INCHES OR MORE, 1865–1935

			Inches
ENGLAND			
Norfolk - -	- Brundall (Blofield Rd.) - -	- 26th Aug., 1912	- 7·31
Wiltshire - -	- Stourhead Gardens - -	- 28th June, 1917	- 6·50
Somerset - -	- Bruton (Sexey's School) -	- 28th June, 1917	- 9·56
	Cannington (Brymore House)	- 18th Aug., 1924	- 9·40
Lincoln - -	- Boston (Black Sluice) - -	- 8th Aug., 1931	- 6·10
Yorks. (W.R.) -	- Doncaster (Pumping Station)	- 17th Sept., 1913	- 6·06
Cumberland -	- Borrowdale (Seathwaite) -	- 12th Nov., 1897	- 8·03
	„ „ -	- 29th Oct., 1911	- 7·00
	„ „ -	- 30th Sept., 1890	- 6·79
	„ „ -	- 8th May, 1884	- 6·78
	„ „ -	- 13th Nov., 1869	- 6·70
	„ „ -	- 4th Dec., 1864	- 6·47
	„ „ -	- 30th May, 1865	- 6·41
	„ „ -	- 16th Nov., 1866	- 6·38
	„ „ -	- 28th Jan., 1906	- 6·15
	„ „ -	- 24th Aug., 1891	- 6·14
	Buttermere (Hassness) - -	- 26th Dec., 1924	- 6·05
Westmorland -	- Dungeon Ghyll - - -	- 9th Feb., 1920	- 6·81
	Skelwith Bridge - - -	- 12th Nov., 1897	- 6·35
	Dungeon Ghyll - - -	- 8th Jan., 1921	- 6·10
	„ „ - - -	- 15th Feb., 1935	- 6·16
WALES			
Glamorgan -	- Rhondda (Lluest Wen Res.) -	- 11th Nov., 1929	- 8·31
	„ „ „ -	- 3rd Nov., 1931	- 6·38
Carmarthen -	- Llynyfan Fach (Nant Coch) -	- 3rd Nov., 1931	- 6·52
Cardigan - -	- Abergwesyn (Nantneuadd) -	- 18th July, 1926	- 6·05
Brecon - -	- Trecastle (Blaenau-hydfer) -	- 3rd Nov., 1931	- 7·25
	Swansea W.W. (Bwlch) -	- 10th Dec., 1909	- 6·14
Merioneth -	- Blaenau Festiniog (Oakley Q.)	- 28th June, 1928	- 7·77
	„ „ (Llechwedd Q.) -	- 27th Aug., 1927	- 6·00
Carnarvon -	- Snowdon (Llydaw Copper M.)	- 28th June, 1928	- 7·25
	„ (Pen-y-Gwryd) -	- 8th Aug., 1914	- 6·35
	Lake Eigiau (Dam Site) -	- 3rd Nov., 1931	- 6·20
SCOTLAND			
Argyll - -	- Lochbuie - - - -	- 9th Dec., 1909	- 6·32
Inverness - -	- Loch Quoich (Kinlochquoich)	- 11th Oct., 1916	- 8·20
	Ben Nevis Observatory - -	- 6th Feb., 1894	- 7·74
	„ „ „ - -	- 2nd Oct., 1890	- 7·29
	Loch Quoich (Kinlochquoich)	- 2nd Feb., 1909	- 6·46
	„ „ „ -	- 9th Feb., 1920	- 6·28
Ross and Cromarty	- Loch Carron (Dunhulladale) -	- 2nd April, 1933	- 6·50
Sutherland -	- Tongue - - - - -	- 7th Sept., 1870	- 6·00

Note.—In this list, if two or more stations in the same county recorded more than six inches on the same day, only the highest reading is included.

(From *British Rainfall*, 1935)

In seventy-one years there were $71 \times 365 + 17$ or 25,932 days. It appears, therefore, that one day out of 762 yields a fall exceeding six inches somewhere in the British Isles. That is about once in two years. The

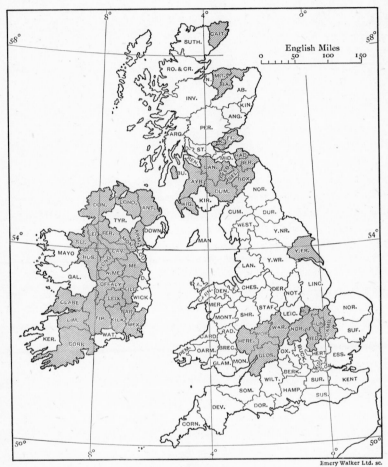

Fig. 37.—Counties (shaded) in which a daily rainfall of four inches has never been exceeded.

detection of one of these falls naturally depends on there being a rain-gauge (read daily) on the spot where it occurs. There are very few daily rain-gauges in the wettest areas of the British Isles and it is probable, therefore, that the actual frequency of fall exceeding six inches is rather greater than the list implies.

The list includes two readings exceeding nine inches and five exceeding eight inches. Only a few of the English counties are represented and there are no entries at all for Ireland. The record fall for Ireland is 5·71 inches at Glen-na-Smoel (county Dublin) on 25th August, 1905. In Fig. 37, counties which have never recorded a fall of as much as four inches in a day are shown by shading on the chart. In Scotland these comprise three groups of counties on the east coast and practically all the southern counties. In England, apart from Yorkshire (East Riding), the counties which appear to be immune from these heavy rains form a very distinct belt running from the Bristol Channel to The Wash. In Ireland the area in which the maximum fall is under four inches greatly exceeds the area where this limit has been passed. We may say that Ireland is distinguished by frequent rains rather than by falls which reach a large total on any individual day. In the counties of Clackmannan and Kinross in Scotland, and Wexford, Offaly, Longford, Roscommon, Sligo, Armagh and Londonderry in Ireland, no fall of as much as three inches has been recorded. In London, only one fall has exceeded the four-inch limit, namely 16th June, 1917, when a severe thunderstorm gave a total of 4·65 inches at Kensington in less than 2½ hours. For details of the extreme falls which have occurred in all the British counties reference should be made to an article in *British Rainfall*, 1934 (27).

The following is a list of falls in which an amount exceeding nine inches has been spread over two or more successive rainfall days :

Days			Inches
2	Aug. 24-25, 1891.	Borrowdale (Seathwaite) *Cumberland* -	10·24
2	Nov. 2-3, 1931.	Trecastle (Blaenau-hydfer), *Brecon* -	9·61
2	Dec. 16-17, 1932.	Borrowdale (The Moraine), *Cumberland*	9·23
3	Oct. 25-27, 1888.	Wythburn, *Cumberland* - - -	10·92
4	July 20-23, 1930.	Castleton, *Yorks., N.R.* - - -	11·97
4	Oct. 18-21, 1908.	Portland (H.M. Breakwater), *Dorset* -	9·34
4	May 6-9, 1913.	Glen Prosen (Balnaboth Gdns.), *Angus*	9·09

To these we may add, on account of its special interest as occurring in a normally dry area :

Aug. 25-26, 1912. Sprowston School, *Norfolk* -   -   - 8·25

This was the highest reading during the great Norfolk rainstorm, to which reference has previously been made. Practically the whole fall occurred on the civil day, 26th August, 1912, but it occupied parts of two " rainfall days " which are regarded as covering the period of twenty-four hours, 9 a.m. to 9 a.m. In regard to total volume of rain this storm remains unsurpassed in our rainfall annals. It caused great dislocation of traffic and immense damage to property, roads and bridges in East Anglia. A full account of the storm will be found in an article by H. R. Mill in *British Rainfall*, 1912 (28).

A day's rainfall is officially classed as " heavy " if the amount is not less than either (*a*) 2·5 inches or (*b*) 7½ per cent. of the year's total at the station. Falls of this order of magnitude are not very common at any individual station, but when the whole kingdom is brought into the reckoning they are fairly frequent. In 1935 they occurred on forty-two dates, giving an average of nearly once per week. Here again we have to remember that we are without daily readings of rainfall for many moorlands and mountain areas, where the rain gauges are, as a rule, only read monthly.

53. Duration of rainfall. As explained in Chapter I, our data in regard to the duration of rainfall are obtained from the records of self-recording rain-gauges. These vary in sensitivity, and difficulty also arises from the fact that during periods of drizzle it is difficult to determine, from the record, exactly when the rainfall began and ended. If an attempt is made to determine the total duration of rain, inconsistent results are obtained, and it has been found better to tabulate only the duration of fall exceeding a definite rate. The rate selected is 0·004 inch (0·1 millimetre) per hour, and the figures we shall quote refer to that standard. It has been estimated at Kew Observatory that the duration of rain, so defined, is about fifteen per cent. less than the duration of " recordable " rain. In addition it has been found that certain types of slight rain or drizzle do not reach a recordable level of intensity. In other words, occasions exist when the record of the autographic gauge gives no indication that precipitation was occurring but the observer has nevertheless logged " drizzle " or " slight rain " from his personal perceptions. By counting up the occasions when this has happened it is possible to estimate by how much the tabulated duration of rain falls short of the true duration of " perceptible rain " (or snow, or sleet). Such calculations give the surprising result that at Kew Observatory the tabulated duration is only about half the true duration. We need not be unduly concerned about this discrepancy ; the important point is that we should remember that the tabulated values refer to a rate of rainfall well above the limit of perception.

Table XXI shows the monthly and annual averages of " tabulated duration " for a selection of stations. The averages refer to the ten years

TABLE XXI

Average Duration of Rainfall in each Month and the Year

(Daily mean in italics)

Station	Height above M.S.L.	Average annual rainfall	Average duration of rain in hours												
			Jan.	Feb.	Mar.	Apr.	May	June	July	Aug.	Sep.	Oct.	Nov.	Dec.	Year
	ft.	in.													
SCOTLAND															
Lerwick (*Shetland*)	269	38	**102**	69	66	61	40	43	47	55	63	88	88	101	823
			3·3	*2·5*	*2·1*	*2·0*	*1·3*	*1·4*	*1·5*	*1·8*	*2·1*	*2·9*	*2·9*	*3·3*	*2·25*
Glenleven (*Argyll*) (Black-water Dam)	1,072	84	**203**	108	106	105	84	99	105	118	113	186	160	164	1,551
			6·5	*3·9*	*3·4*	*3·5*	*2·7*	*3·3*	*3·4*	*3·8*	*3·8*	*6·0*	*5·3*	*5·3*	*4·11*
Aberdeen (*Aberdeen*)	48	29	61	54	52	69	49	45	50	44	56	75	**76**	69	700
			2·0	*1·9*	*1·7*	*2·3*	*1·5*	*1·5*	*1·6*	*1·4*	*1·9*	*2·4*	*2·5*	*2·2*	*1·93*
Eskdalemuir (*Dumfries*)	794	56	**157**	93	92	81	69	85	90	91	81	138	123	117	1,217
			5·1	*3·3*	*3·0*	*2·7*	*2·2*	*2·8*	*2·8*	*2·8*	*2·7*	*4·4*	*4·1*	*3·8*	*3·33*
ENGLAND															
Nottingham (*Notts.*)	83	23	44	31	26	39	36	28	26	27	31	39	**55**	40	422
			1·4	*1·1*	*0·9*	*1·3*	*1·2*	*0·9*	*0·8*	*0·9*	*1·0*	*1·3*	*1·8*	*1·3*	*1·16*
London (Camden Sq.)	111	24	43	39	44	31	29	30	27	28	25	45	47	**49**	437
			1·4	*1·4*	*1·4*	*1·0*	*1·0*	*1·0*	*0·9*	*0·9*	*0·8*	*1·5*	*1·6*	*1·6*	*1·20*
Falmouth (*Cornwall*)	167	44	99	64	64	63	50	45	41	44	55	89	**101**	94	809
			3·2	*2·3*	*2·1*	*2·1*	*1·6*	*1·5*	*1·3*	*1·4*	*1·8*	*2·9*	*3·4*	*3·0*	*2·22*
Southport (*Lancs.*)	39	32	68	53	70	49	55	41	45	58	45	63	61	**77**	685
			2·2	*1·9*	*2·3*	*1·6*	*1·8*	*1·4*	*1·5*	*1·9*	*1·5*	*2·0*	*2·0*	*2·5*	*2·21*
WALES															
Holyhead (*Anglesey*)	26	35	78	52	53	41	49	49	38	54	46	68	**81**	77	686
			2·5	*1·9*	*1·7*	*1·4*	*1·6*	*1·6*	*1·2*	*1·7*	*1·5*	*2·2*	*2·7*	*2·5*	*1·88*
Cray Reservoir (*Brecon*)	1,044	c. 65	**154**	103	86	90	81	91	89	101	86	132	146	135	1,294
			4·9	*3·7*	*2·8*	*3·0*	*2·6*	*3·0*	*2·9*	*3·5*	*2·9*	*4·2*	*4·9*	*4·3*	*3·54*
IRELAND															
Armagh (*Armagh*)	209	32	**95**	64	64	66	53	60	58	71	63	84	80	90	848
			3·1	*2·3*	*2·1*	*2·2*	*1·7*	*2·0*	*1·9*	*2·3*	*2·1*	*2·7*	*2·7*	*2·9*	*2·32*
Valentia (*Kerry*) (Cahirciveen)	30	56	96	62	71	50	57	73	62	73	64	78	89	**100**	875
			3·1	*2·2*	*2·3*	*1·7*	*1·8*	*2·4*	*2·0*	*2·3*	*2·1*	*2·5*	*3·0*	*3·2*	*2·40*

1926 to 1935, except at Camden Square and Southport, where previously published averages for longer periods have been used. Average daily mean values are also given. It will be observed that the figures show seasonal variations similar to those of rain-days, with summer minima and winter maxima. The daily mean for the whole year varies from about 1·2 hour at the driest stations, Nottingham and London, to over four hours at Glenleven (Blackwater Dam) in Argyllshire. In individual months we have a variation from less than one hour per day during the driest month in London and Nottingham to 6·5 hours in January at Glenleven.

In computing the daily means we have simply divided the total duration by the number of days in the month, as is done in the case of sunshine. It is of some interest, however, to determine the average duration per rain-day—that is to say, the average duration on days when it rains at all. The results for three stations are given below :

AVERAGE DAILY DURATION, PER RAIN-DAY, IN HOURS

	Jan.	Feb.	Mar.	Apr.	May	June	July	Aug.	Sep.	Oct.	Nov.	Dec.	Year
Aberdeen - - -	3·4	3·2	2·6	4·1	2·9	3·0	3·0	2·4	3·3	3·7	4·0	3·6	3·3
London (Camden Sq.) -	2·7	3·0	3·1	2·4	2·4	2·5	2·3	2·1	2·1	2·7	2·9	2·9	2·6
Valentia - - -	4·0	2·9	3·4	2·6	3·2	4·3	2·9	3·3	3·6	3·5	3·9	3·8	3·5

It will be seen that the means for the whole year are not very different for the three stations. For Glenleven or Cray Reservoir the yearly mean would work out at about six hours per rain-day. The monthly values given above are very irregular, due no doubt to the fact that only ten years were used in computing the averages of duration for Aberdeen and Valentia. It is difficult to recognize any sort of regular seasonal variation at these stations and it may be inferred that there is, in the long run, not much difference from month to month in the mean duration of rain per rain-day. For Camden Square the results indicate that rainfall is more prolonged in winter months than in summer months.

During the year 1934, at Kew Observatory, there were :

> 56 days with duration of rain 0·1 to 1·0 hour
> 36   ,,   ,,   ,,   1·1 to 2·0 hours
> 61   ,,   ,,   ,,   2·1 to 6·0   ,,
> 7   ,,   ,,   ,,   6·1 to 12   ,,
> 2   ,,   ,,   ,,   more than 12 hours

The corresponding figures for Eskdalemuir Observatory (Dumfries-shire) were 39, 34, 89, 55 and 25 days respectively. These figures may serve to give some idea of the difference in rainfall persistence at a dry station and a wet station—Kew had only nine days with more than six hours of rain but Eskdalemuir had eighty such days. Even in London, however, prolonged rains occur occasionally. The " record " was set up in June 1903, when at Camden Square rain fell continuously

H

TABLE XXII

RAINFALLS OF VERY RARE INTENSITY LASTING FOR ONE HOUR OR LESS

Year	Date		Station	Amount	Duration		Rate per hour
				in.	h.	m.	in.
1893	Aug.	10	Preston, Corporation Offices -	1·25 ?	0	5 ?	15·00 ?
1927	Sept.	23	Chagford, Dartmoor Sanatorium -	1·30	0	10	7·80
1914	Aug.	14	Guernsey, St. Martin's Road -	1·50	0	15	6·00
1875	Aug.	7	Canterbury, Harbledown - -	2·12	0	20	6·36
1932	Aug.	20	Malvern, Free Library - - -	1·86	0	20	5·58
1878	June	23	St. Pancras, Camden Square -	1·82	0	20	5·46
1897	June	24	Luton, Pumping Station - -	1·65	0	20	4·95
1920	May	29	Leyland, Worden Hall -	1·65	0	20	4·95
1933	June	24	Silchester House - - - -	2·50	0	25	6·00
1934	July	18	Stratford-on-Avon, Milcote - -	2·25	0	25	5·40
1878	June	23	St. Pancras, Camden Square -	2·30	0	28	4·93
1880	July	22	Cowbridge, Ash Hall - - -	2·90	0	30	5·80
1915	July	4	Abergavenny, The Chain - -	2·20	0	30	4·40
1933	July	21	Chatham, Woolman's Wood -	2·13	0	30	4·26
1918	July	17	Shad Thames Pumping Station -	2·07	0	30	4·14
1895	June	27	Middleton-in-the-Wolds - -	2·00	0	30	4·00
1902	Sept.	10	Surbiton, Vronvelin - - -	2·00	0	30	4·00
1931	June	14	Cannock Sewage Works - -	2·35	0	38	3·71
1920	May	25	Hatfield, Broad Oak, Barrington -	2·79	0	45	3·72
1933	June	21	Temple Combe Rectory - -	2·75	0	45	3·67
1904	July	27	Cooling, Broomy Farm -	2·66	0	45	3·55
1909	Sept.	29	Ilfracombe Reservoir - - -	2·50 ?	0	45	3·33 ?
1895	June	26	Marlborough - - - -	2·71	0	50	3·25
1915	June	30	Mildenhall - - - -	2·63	0	50	3·16
1903	July	18	Crewe, Betley Hall - - -	2·53	0	50	3·04
1905	July	9	Enfield, Carisbrooke - - -	2·44	0	50	2·93
1911	May	31	Epsom, Ashley Road - -	2·44	0	50	2·93
1901	July	29	Wadhurst, Lower Cousley Wood -	3·25 ?	0	55	3·55 ?
1913	June	17	Elvedon Hall - - - -	2·85	0	58	2·95
1901	July	12	Maidenhead, Lowood - -	3·63	1	0 ?	3·63 ?
1903	May	30	Beddington Corner - - -	3·50	1	0	3·50
1911	May	26	Fareham, The Mount - - -	3·00	1	0	3·00
1897	July	21	Ipswich, Bishops Hill - - -	2·95	1	0	2·95
1932	July	11	Cranwell Aerodrome - -	2·93	1	0	2·93
1895	June	26	Worcester, Diglis Lock - -	2·75	1	0	2·75
1934	July	13	Wrexham, W.W. Office - -	2·75	1	0	2·75
1909	June	1	Carsphairn, Shiel - - -	2·71	1	0 ?	2·71 ?
1873	July	28	Fettercairn - - - -	2·60	1	0	2·60
1889	June	7	Tonbridge, Ferndale - -	2·60 ?	1	0 ?	2·60 ?
1886	July	25	Sale, Brooklands - - -	2·58	1	0	2·58
1899	July	22	Dorchester Water Works -	2·56	1	0 ?	2·56 ?
1875	July	22	Trowbridge, Sunnyside -	2·53	1	0	2·53
1875	June	29	Cardington - - - -	2·50	1	0	2·50
1886	July	25	Wakefield, Stanley Vicarage -	2·50	1	0	2·50
1935	June	25	Melksham, Beechfield - -	2·50	1	0	2·50

(From *British Rainfall*, 1935)

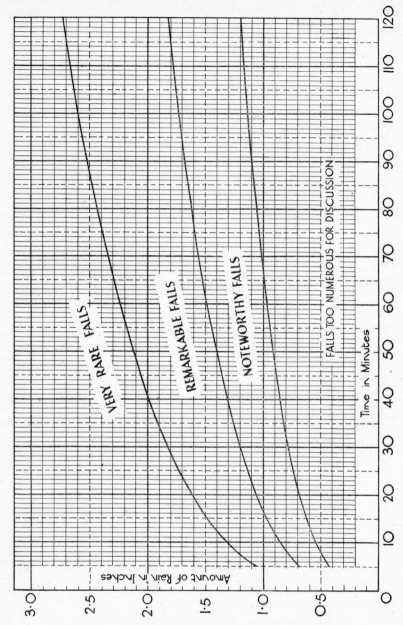

FIG. 38.—Curves showing the classification of heavy falls of rain in short periods.

(From *British Rainfall*, 1935)

from 1 p.m. on 13th to 11.30 p.m. on 15th—a total duration of $58\frac{1}{2}$ hours.

54. Heavy falls in short periods.   Under this heading we have to consider rainfalls in which the intensity or rate of fall is exceptional, rather than the total amount. In the drier areas of the British Isles the " record " daily rains in summer months are more often than not of this type; in other words, a rain which is remarkable for intensity is often also remarkable for total amount.   Our attention is, however, for the moment focussed on what happens in a matter of minutes, or an hour or two, rather than on large amounts spread over a whole day.

A list of some of the most intense falls lasting one hour or less is given in Table XXII. These falls are included in the " very rare " category, according to a classification which will be described shortly. The data depend partly on eye-observations by observers whose equipment consists simply of an ordinary rain-gauge plus a watch or clock for timing the fall, and partly on measurements of the traces of self-recording rain-gauges.   Neither method is entirely satisfactory. Without a recording rain-gauge, data in regard to the duration of heavy falls occurring in the night hours, or when the observer was not personally present to time the fall, would be lacking ; but even when a recording rain gauge is available, the trace may be so congested as to make it difficult to determine the exact time occupied by the most intense portion of the fall.   To meet this latter difficulty, F. J. W. Whipple (29) has recently introduced a new type of rain recorder in which the amount falling in every minute during intense rains is accurately registered.

A large number of observations of intense rainfalls, usually occurring in thunderstorms, have been recorded year by year in the volumes of *British Rainfall*.   It is impossible, however, from these data to arrive at any estimate of the frequency with which a fall of stated intensity may be expected to occur at a given place.   Data of this kind are of great value to drainage engineers and in recent years the problem has been tackled from a new angle (30).   At certain stations equipped with recording rain-gauges the traces have been systematically examined, and all occasions when falls of 0·2 inch, 0·4 inch and 1·0 inch occurred within specified times have been noted.   In this way the data set out in Table XXIII have been obtained.   There are two points which it is necessary to make clear: (*a*) the three falls of 0·2 inch in six minutes or less at Camden Square are included in the twenty-one falls of 0·2 inch in fifteen minutes or less, and these are in their turn included in the forty falls of 0·2 inch in thirty minutes or less, and so on throughout the table ;

(*b*) a fall entered under 0·2 inch in six minutes or less may be part of a fall giving an entry under the heading " 0·4 inch in fifteen minutes or less " ; the same fall may therefore give rise to entries in several of the columns.

TABLE XXIII

Total Number of Days on which Specified Amounts of Rain fell in Specified Times during the Ten Years 1925 to 1934

County	Place	Average Annual Rainfall in.	0·2 inch				0·4 inch				1 inch			
			6 min. or less	15 min. or less	30 min. or less	60 min. or less	15 min. or less	30 min. or less	60 min. or less	2 hours or less	1 hour or less	2 hours or less	5 hours or less	24 hrs. or less
London -	Camden Square	24·5	3	21	40	77	4	10	16	25	3	3	4	13
Surrey -	Croydon - -	26·7	9	20	51	96	1	6	14	37	0	1	4	25
,,	Kew Observatory	23·8	16	28	44	85	6	13	18	34	4	4	5	15
Kent -	Lympne - -	28·5	10	24	57	113	7	12	15	38	0	0	6	27
Hants. -	Calshot - -	25·5	6	18	42	94	6	11	20	31	0	2	7	26
,,	South Farnborough -	26·1	12	29	58	97	4	9	19	39	2	2	4	25
Suffolk -	Felixstowe -	20·3	9	20	41	65	4	6	14	24	1	1	3	8
Devon -	Mount Batten -	33·1	6	16	43	117	3	7	15	41	0	1	8	44
Lincoln -	Cranwell - -	23·2	9	16	36	64	2	5	8	23	2	2	3	12
Lancashire	Southport -	32·0	7	18	40	106	4	5	8	30	0	1	2	25
Flint -	Sealand - -	26·0	7	18	29	73	4	5	10	27	1	1	2	16
Anglesey -	Holyhead -	34·9	4	19	48	121	0	3	11	44	0	0	5	36
Dumfries	Eskdalemuir Observatory -	56·3	10	28	82	243	3	9	25	111	1	1	21	141
Renfrew -	Renfrew (Abbotsinch)	37·0	9	17	38	110	5	7	10	40	0	1	4	37
Fife -	Leuchars -	25·7	11	19	32	65	4	7	10	25	1	1	3	26
Aberdeen	Aberdeen Observatory -	29·5	6	18	35	89	1	2	6	19	0	0	7	29
Co. Kerry	Valentia Observatory -	55·7	4	16	66	194	3	4	16	75	0	0	5	80
Co. Armagh	Armagh - -	31·7	6	26	42	84	3	11	15	26	1	1	4	14
Mean for England and Wales (12) - - - - -		27·0	8·2	20·6	44·1	92·3	3·8	7·7	14·0	32·7	1·0	1·5	4·4	22·7
Mean for Scotland and Ireland (6) - - - - -		39·3	7·7	20·7	49·2	130·8	3·2	6·7	13·7	49·3	0·5	0·7	7·3	54·5
Mean for British Isles (18) -		31·1	8·0	20·6	45·8	105·2	3·6	7·3	13·9	38·3	0·9	1·2	5·4	33·3

(From *British Rainfall*, 1935)

It will be noticed that the data entered in this table vary considerably from station to station. The first three lines refer to stations in the London area, within which some degree of uniformity might have been expected. We observe, however, that during the ten years in question Camden Square recorded only three falls of 0·2 inch within six minutes, while Croydon recorded nine and Kew sixteen such falls. Again, under the heading "one inch in one hour or less" we find a zero entry for Croydon, but four for Kew Observatory. In the columns representing falls of 0·2 inch within sixty minutes, 0·4 inch within two hours, and one inch within twenty-four hours the entries for the two stations Eskdalemuir and Valentia are outstanding. Both of these stations have a high annual rainfall and the inference is that rains of only moderate intensity are more frequent in the wetter areas of the country, as might be expected. The table indicates, on the other hand, that the frequency of the more intense rains is not related to the annual rainfall, and we should indeed expect the frequency to be related, rather, to the annual frequency of thunderstorms. Apart from this rough generalization no definite variation with place can be made out with certainty, and it is perhaps legitimate to take the mean values for England and Wales, which exclude the two wet stations, as the best available approximations to the frequencies of rains in the various categories at the "average station". It is found that these averages accord closely with values computed from the formula

$$\log n = 0 \cdot 0952 + \log t - 3 \cdot 55 \log (r + 0 \cdot 1),$$

where t = time in hours, r = rainfall in inches and n = number of occurrences in ten years.

TABLE XXIV

COMPUTED AMOUNTS OF RAIN FALLING IN STATED TIMES

Frequency		n	5 min. or less	10 min. or less	15 min. or less	20 min. or less	30 min. or less	45 min. or less	60 min. or less	90 min. or less	120 min. or less
			in.	in.	in.	in.	in.	in.	in.	in.	in.
One day in a year	-	10	0·18	0·23	0·28	0·31	0·36	0·41	0·46	0·52	0·58
One day in 2 years	-	5	0·24	0·31	0·36	0·40	0·46	0·52	0·58	0·66	0·72
One day in 5 years	-	2	0·33	0·43	0·49	0·55	0·62	0·71	0·78	0·88	0·98
One day in 10 years	-	1	0·43	0·54	0·62	0·68	0·77	0·88	0·97	1·10	1·20
One day in 20 years	-	0·5	0·54	0·68	0·78	0·85	0·97	1·10	1·20	1·36	1·47
One day in 40 years	-	0·25	0·68	0·85	0·97	1·06	1·19	1·35	1·48	1·67	1·82
One day in 160 years	-	0·0625	1·06	1·31	1·49	1·61	1·82	2·06	2·24	2·52	2·73

(From *British Rainfall*, 1935)

By computation from this formula we arrive at the values shown in Table XXIV. The graphs of the values corresponding to one day in ten years, one day in forty years and one day in 160 years are shown in Fig. 38. For the purpose of tabulation in *British Rainfall*, from 1st

January, 1936, records representing a frequency of less than once in ten years are classed as " noteworthy ", less than once in forty years as " remarkable ", and less than once in 160 years as " very rare ". As these curves represent rainfalls of considerable intensity of short duration they are regarded, on the evidence of Table XXIII, as applying all over the British Isles. This assumption is almost certainly not strictly true but it will be many years before we are able to state the frequency of intense rains in various parts of the kingdom with any degree of certainty.

It will be observed that all the rains of very rare intensity tabulated in Table XXII occurred during the months May to September inclusive. During the fifty years 1878 to 1927 there were twenty-eight occasions when an inch of rain occurred within a period of five hours at Kew Observatory ; of these, two occurred in May, seven in June, six in July, six in August, six in September, one in October and none in any of the other months. Very intense rains are definitely a summer phenomenon, and they nearly always occur in association with thunderstorms. The reason for this summer incidence becomes clear when we consider that rainfall is due to the dynamic cooling of moist air. The amount of water vapour present in a given volume of saturated air increases very rapidly with the temperature ;[1] consequently the weight of water set free when saturated air is cooled by a given amount, say 10° F., is very much greater when the initial temperature is high than when it is low. If saturated air at 70° F. is cooled 10° F. about five grams of water will be condensed out of every cubic metre of air ; cooling from 40° F. to 30° F. would, however, produce only about two grams of condensed water. Added to this we have the fact that the convectional processes associated with thunderstorms are far more vigorous in the summer than in the winter, as is shown, for example, by the fact that large hailstones occur only in the summer half-year.

BIBLIOGRAPHY

(19) J. Glasspoole, " The wettest places in the British Isles," *Water and Water Eng.*, 1931, p. 560.

(20) A. T. Doodson and H. S. Bigelstone, " The frequency-distribution of rainfall at Bidston Observatory, Liverpool," *Q.J.R. Meteor. Soc.*, 1934, pp. 403-412.

(21) J. Glasspoole, " The fluctuations of annual rainfall," *British Rainfall*, 1921, pp. 288-300. (H.M.S.O.)

(22) H. R. Mill and M. de C. S. Salter, " Isomeric rainfall maps of the British Isles," *Q.J.R. Meteor. Soc.*, **41**, 1915, pp. 1-39.

[1] See Fig. 68, p. 208.

(23) *The Rainfall Atlas of the British Isles*, Royal Meteorological Society.

(24) J. Glasspoole, " The fluctuations of monthly rainfall," *British Rainfall*, 1922, pp. 234-259. (H.M.S.O.)

(25) J. Glasspoole, " The reliability of rainfall over the British Isles," *Trans. Inst. Water Engineers*, **35**, 1930.

(26) E. G. Bilham and A. C. Lloyd, " The frequency-distribution of daily rainfall," *British Rainfall*, 1932, pp. 268-277. (H.M.S.O.)

(27) J. Glasspoole, " Heavy falls on rainfall days, 1865 to 1934," *British Rainfall*, 1934, pp. 266-283. (H.M.S.O.)

(28) H. R. Mill, " The great rainstorm of August 25-26, 1912," *British Rainfall*, 1912, pp. 28-47. (H.M.S.O.)

(29) F. J. W. Whipple, " A ' minute-by-minute ' rain gauge," *Meteorological Magazine*, 1934, p. 157. (H.M.S.O.)

(30) E. G. Bilham, " The classification of heavy falls in short periods," *British Rainfall*, 1935, pp. 262-280. (H.M.S.O.)

See also :

M. de C. S. Salter, *The Rainfall of the British Isles*, (London University Press).
C. E. P. Brooks and J. Glasspoole, *British Floods and Droughts* (Benn).
The Book of Normals (M.O. 236, Sec. I and Sec. V). (H.M.S.O.)

CHAPTER VI

EVAPORATION AND PERCOLATION

55. Measurements of evaporation. Although meteorological literature abounds in references to evaporation, the subject has been curiously
neglected in the British Isles. Luke Howard, the " father of British
meteorology ", included a description of an evaporimeter, and a series of
readings taken therewith, in his *Climate of London*, published in 1818.
Howard's evaporimeter, consisting merely of a shallow pan, five inches
in diameter, two-thirds filled with water and " placed near the ground,
in a situation where it may be sheltered from rain and have the sun's
rays without reflection ", was not a very good instrument. It recorded
a mean annual evaporation of the order of twenty inches in the London
district. Modern observations made with a tank of the kind described
in Chapter I, which holds about 450 gallons of water, give a substantially
lower average, and we may ascribe the difference mainly to the fact
that the water in Howard's small pan became strongly heated in
the sun's rays and thus evaporated more rapidly. Even the modern
tank is a microscopically small vessel in comparison, say, with the
Queen Mary Reservoir at Littleton, but experience shows that observations made on such a tank agree surprisingly well with the evaporation which actually occurs from comparatively large sheets of
water.

Apart from observations on an experimental concrete tank at
Valentia Observatory no readings of evaporation are made at official
meteorological stations. Data from certain voluntary stations are,
however, published in the annual volumes of *British Rainfall* and from
these we are in a position to draw certain conclusions in regard to the
annual amount of evaporation and its seasonal variation.

56. Annual evaporation. Table XXV gives the annual averages of
evaporation at stations with relatively long records. It will be observed
that these averages vary only over a relatively short range, from about
15·3 inches at London and Talla Water (Peebles) to about $19\frac{1}{2}$ inches
at Otterbourne and Harrogate. The excess of annual rainfall over
annual evaporation varies from about nine inches at London to about

thirty-one inches at Talla Water. So far as can be judged from the small number of observations available, there is no definite relationship between the mean annual evaporation at any place in the British Isles and the mean annual rainfall at that place ; nor does there appear to be any definite geographical distribution of evaporation analogous with what we find in the case of rainfall, sunshine and other meteorological elements. At Camden Square the total annual evaporation has varied between 12·60 inches (eighty-one per cent. of the mean) in 1888 and 19·69 inches (127 per cent. of the mean) in 1921. The year 1921 was a dry, hot year which gave the lowest recorded annual rainfall at Camden Square. 1888 was also a dry year over England and Wales as a whole, but it gave a slight excess of rainfall at Camden Square, and the evaporation was low in the summer months, which were very wet. In

TABLE XXV

ANNUAL AVERAGES OF EVAPORATION (1908–1935)

London (*Camden Square*) - - - -	15·33 inches
Otterbourne (*Hants.*) - - - -	19·67 ,,
Kennick (*S. Devon*) - - - - -	18·60 ,,
Ardsley (*Yorkshire, W.R.*) - - - -	17·59 ,,
Harrogate (*Yorkshire, W.R.*) - - - -	19·43 ,,
Southport (*Lancs.*) - - - - -	15·62 ,,
Talla Water (*Peebles*) - - - -	15·28 ,,

(From *British Rainfall*, 1935)

general we may say that the evaporation is low in wet years, particularly in years with wet summers, and high in dry years. The coefficient of correlation between annual evaporation and annual rainfall is, however, only − 0·36 ; between annual evaporation and annual number of rain-days the coefficient has a distinctly higher value, namely − 0·62.

Very occasionally the annual evaporation has exceeded the annual rainfall at Camden Square. In 1921 evaporation exceeded rainfall by 5·09 inches, and in 1933 by 1·7 inches. These were both drought years with very dry summers. In view of the tendency for evaporation to be more or less the same all over the kingdom, while rainfall varies greatly with altitude and place, it would be practically impossible for a year's evaporation to exceed a year's rainfall anywhere outside the driest areas of the British Isles.

57. Monthly averages for Camden Square and Southport. At 62 Camden Square, London, N.W., observations of evaporation have been maintained for more than fifty years, this being the longest record

available in the kingdom. A monthly summary of the results is given
in Table XXVI A, with rainfall averages, and values of the average
difference, rainfall minus evaporation. Graphs of the averages of rainfall
and evaporation are shown in the upper portion of Fig. 39. Unlike rainfall, evaporation shows a beautifully regular variation with a maximum

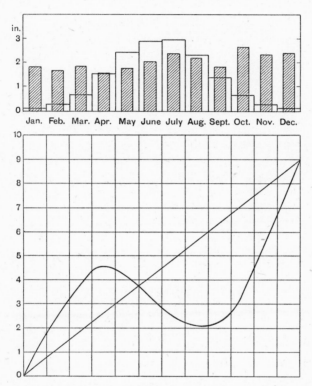

Fig. 39.—(*At top*) Normal rainfall and evaporation at Camden Square,
London. Rainfall, shaded columns ; evaporation, unshaded columns.

(*Below*) Normal variation of level in a tank due to the combined effects of
rainfall and evaporation.

in midsummer and a minimum in midwinter. The regularity of the
curve is even more apparent when, as in Fig. 40, the values are expressed
in the form of daily means ; this is probably as close an approach to a
simple " sine wave " with a maximum at the summer solstice and a
minimum at the winter solstice as it is possible to find in the whole of
meteorology.

TABLE XXVI

A. Monthly Averages of Evaporation (1885–1919) and Rainfall (1881–1915) at London (Camden Square)

Month	Evaporation					Rainfall mean	Rainfall *minus* evaporation
	Mean	Extremes (1885-1935)					
		Largest	Date	Smallest	Date		
	in.	in.		in		in.	in.
January - -	0·10	0·26	1903	c. 0·17	1924	1·86	1·76
February - -	0·25	0·64	1895	0·01	1893	1·67	1·42
March - -	0·66	1·03	1926	0·30	1909, '16	1·83	1·17
April - - -	1·51	2·34	1912	0·85	1920	1·54	0·03
May - - -	2·43	3·25	1901	1·56	1898	1·76	−0·67
June - - -	2·91	3·85	1901	1·70	1909	2·02	−0·89
July - - -	**2·97**	**4·60**	1911	1·44	1888	2·38	−0·59
August - -	2·33	3·78	1899	1·58	1925	2·21	−0·12
September - -	1·38	2·38	1906	0·68	1896	1·82	0·44
October - -	0·62	0·93	1934	0·36	1892	**2·63**	2·01
November - -	0·25	0·43	1888	0·02	1892	2·36	2·11
December - -	0·09	0·32	1913	c. 0·14	1897	2·39	**2·30**
Year - -	15·50	19·69	1921	12·60	1888	24·47	8·97

c. denotes condensation.

B. Monthly Averages of Evaporation (Twenty Years) and Rainfall (1871–1930) at Southport (Lancs.)

Month	Evaporation	Rainfall	Rainfall *minus* evaporation
	in.	in.	in.
January - - -	0·04	2·80	2·76
February - - -	0·20	2·12	1·92
March - - -	0·68	2·22	1·54
April - - -	1·57	1·79	0·22
May - - -	2·36	2·17	−0·19
June - - -	**3·11**	2·19	−0·92
July - - -	2·97	3·01	0·04
August - - -	2·32	3·72	1·40
September - -	1·40	3·13	1·73
October - - -	0·65	**3·77**	3·12
November - -	0·22	3·26	3·04
December - -	0·10	3·24	**3·14**
Year - - -	15·62	33·42	17·80

At midsummer the mean daily evaporation is about one-tenth of an inch, and about thirty times as great as at midwinter ; in other words, about as much evaporation occurs in a day at midsummer as in a month at midwinter.

The lower part of Fig. 39 shows how, in the " average year ", the water level in the tank at Camden Square would vary from 1st January to 31st December under the combined influences of rainfall and evaporation. Starting from the zero level on 1st January, rainfall would raise

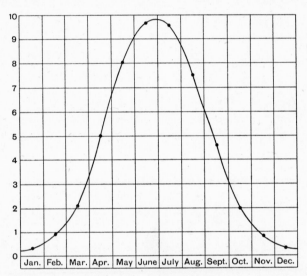

Fig. 40.—Annual variation of mean daily evaporation at Camden Square, London. (Unit, 0·01 inch.)

the level by 1·86 inches during January, but evaporation would lower it by 0·10 inch ; consequently the water would stand 1·86 – 0·10 or 1·76 inches higher on 1st February than on 1st January. February would raise the level by 1·67 – 0·25 or 1·42 inches and the water would thus have risen a total distance of 1·76 + 1·42 or 3·18 inches by the end of February. Proceeding in this way we find that the level would rise for the first three months, become nearly stationary in April and then fall to a minimum at the end of August. It would then rise rapidly, finally attaining a level of nine inches above the zero level. Suppose now arrangements were made to draw off this " net yield " of nine inches uniformly throughout the year. The amount drawn off up to any given date would be represented by the corresponding point on the straight line drawn on

Fig. 39, and the height (positive or negative) of the water surface above the zero level (which we will assume to be well above the bottom of the tank) would be represented by the difference of the ordinates of the points on the curve and on the straight line for that date. We can thus derive a fresh curve showing how the level would vary under the combined effects of rainfall, evaporation and drainage or withdrawals. The curve arrived at in this way is shown by the full line in Fig. 41. It will be seen that this curve has a maximum at the end of March and a minimum at the end of September, with an annual range of 6·3 inches. Two other curves are drawn on Fig. 41 ; we shall refer to these later.

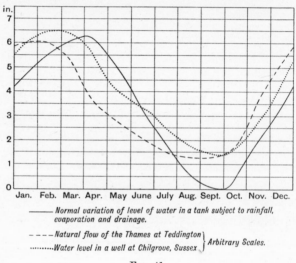

———— Normal variation of level of water in a tank subject to rainfall, evaporation and drainage.

– – – – Natural flow of the Thames at Teddington ⎱ Arbitrary Scales.
··········Water level in a well at Chilgrove, Sussex ⎰

Fig. 41.

In Table XXVIᴮ monthly averages of evaporation and rainfall are given for Southport (Lancashire). It will be seen that there is a very remarkable similarity between the average of evaporation at the two stations ; in most months the values are indeed nearly identical, a curious result in view of the fact that one station is in a London back-garden while the other is in a public park at a Lancashire seaside resort.

58. Percolation. For a few stations records are available of the amount of water percolating through a definite thickness of soil, with or without vegetation growing upon it. These records are obtained from " percolation gauges " which consist essentially of blocks of soil, characteristic of the neighbourhood, isolated by being surrounded by impervious walls and provided with a perforated bottom through which the percolating water can trickle into a vessel for measurement.

From the climatological point of view the interest of percolation measurements lies mainly in the fact that they provide a means of estimating the loss by evaporation from natural soil. The results of percolation measurements have not been summarized in any systematic way, but an idea of the sort of results obtained is given in Table XXVII, where the data for the year 1935 obtained from evaporation and percolation gauges have been brought together. It will be noticed that the mean evaporation calculated from the percolation records agrees pretty well with the mean value calculated from the tank records. Consideration shows, however, that there is no special reason why they should agree, and we find, indeed, that the tank readings differ widely from the percolation readings at the one station (Harrogate) where both types of record are maintained. In a percolation gauge, the difference between the amount of water falling on the gauge, *i.e.* the rainfall, and the amount discharged from the gauge is only a measure of the evaporation so long as the moisture content of the soil remains the same. We may assume this condition to be satisfied while the gauge is actually discharging water, because the soil must then be saturated. After a period of dry weather, however, percolation ceases and no water will be discharged until the soil becomes saturated again. In a normal year little or no percolation occurs from about May to August or September, because the rate of evaporation during this period normally exceeds the rate at which moisture due to rainfall can penetrate the soil. During such periods of no percolation the " calculated evaporation " is obviously equal to the rainfall. We have noted, however, that in evaporation tanks in dry areas like Camden Square, London, evaporation normally exceeds rainfall in summer months. Consequently it must be a matter of accident if the annual total evaporation from percolation gauges comes to about the same figure as the annual total evaporation from tanks. In very dry years, such as 1921, we should expect to find very low values of " calculated evaporation " in dry areas, because the calculated evaporation must be less than the rainfall. Actually, in that year, the calculated evaporation at Rothamsted was only about nine inches, while the tank evaporation at Camden Square was 19·7 inches.

59. Evaporation in nature. Evaporation is the process by which the moisture which falls as rain or snow, or condenses as dew or frost, is returned to the atmosphere. The results of observations of evaporation are therefore of great importance in meteorology. In general, however,

TABLE XXVII

Observations of Evaporation and Percolation in 1935

A. *Measurement of Evaporation from Open Water Surfaces in Tanks*

	inches
London (Camden Square) - - - -	17·11
Otterbourne (*Hants.*) - - - - -	22·10
Petersfield (*Hants.*) - - - -	18·77
Ormesby St. Michael (*Norfolk*) - - -	19·46
Kennick (*S. Devon*) - - - -	17·30
Bartley (*Warwickshire*) - - -	20·31
Revesby (*Lincolnshire*) - - -	15·95
Southport (*Lancs.*) - - - -	16·60
Ardsley (*Yorks., W.R.*) - - -	21·49
Lower Laithe (*Yorks., W.R.*) - - -	17·68
Harrogate (*Yorks., W.R.*) - - -	23·35
Talla Water (*Peebles*) - - - -	13·65
Glencorse (*Midlothian*) - - -	14·38
Mean of thirteen records - - -	18·31

B. *Measurement of Percolation and Calculated Evaporation*

		Rainfall	Percolation	Calc. evap.
		in.	in.	in.
Compton (*Sussex*)	3 ft. soil - - - - -	43·96	27·91	16·05
Rothamsted (*Herts.*)	20 inches soil - - - -	29·44	16·85	12·59
,, ,,	40 ,, ,, - - - -	,,	17·81	11·63
,, ,,	60 ,, ,, - - - -	,,	17·27	12·17
Farlington (*Hants.*)	24 inches chalky marl - - -	37·43	19·93	17·50
,, ,,	36 ,, ,, ,, - - -	,,	17·08	20·35
,, ,,	48 ,, ,, ,, - - -	,,	15·28	22·15
,, ,,	36 inches sand - - - -	,,	16·86	20·57
,, ,,	36 inches chalk - - - -	,,	16·03	21·40
Harrogate (*Yorks.*)	3 ft. soil - - - - -	33·64	21·19	12·45
Craibstone (*Aberdeen*)	40 inches soil, unmanured - -	41·07	19·51	21·56
,, ,,	40 ,, ,, manured - - -	,,	20·55	20·52
,, ,,	40 ,, ,, manured and limed -	,,	18·50	22·57
Mean of thirteen records - - - -				17·81

(From *British Rainfall*, 1935)

such observations do not receive much attention except from biologists, agriculturists and persons interested in questions of water supply. Here we shall discuss the subject of evaporation only from the latter point of view. To some extent the interests of agriculturists and water engineers are antagonistic, because moisture drawn from the soil by growing plants and transpired into the air represents a large proportion of the " loss " on the debit side of the water engineer's balance sheet.

Let us consider briefly what happens to a fall of rain after it has reached the ground. Some part of it will fall on house-roofs, tarred roads and other impervious surfaces. This portion will run off down gullies, drains and watercourses into streams, rivers or lakes and finally reach the sea after experiencing some loss from evaporation. The type of evaporation-loss will resemble that measured in a tank, because a free liquid surface is exposed to the air all the time. In addition, some water may percolate through fissures or fall directly into rivers, lakes, etc. Another portion of the rain will fall on soil, into which it will soak unless the soil is already saturated. The history of this portion will depend very much on the geology of the area and on the condition of the soil in respect to dryness. If the soil is very dry the rain will wet only the upper layers, and this will be re-evaporated either directly or through the medium of vegetation ; it will contribute nothing either to the re-plenishment of subsoil water or to the discharge of streams. If, however, the surface soil is already moist, water will penetrate the upper layers and go into storage. The storage may be only temporary, because it is the slow drainage from water thus held in the soil that maintains the flow of streams and rivers during dry periods. If the catchment area of a stream contains a large proportion of pervious rocks the flow will be maintained at a usefully high value for long periods of dry weather, and it will only fail entirely after very exceptional periods of drought. Also, since a large amount of natural storage is provided, the stream will not be excessively augmented for brief periods by the sudden run-off of heavy rains. If, on the other hand, the catchment area consists largely of impervious rocks, such as granites, the stream will be " flashy ", spates occurring immediately after heavy rains, subsiding quickly to very low dry-weather flows. When the precipitation is in the form of snow, the slow melting of the latter imparts to the catchment area a character similar to that provided by pervious rocks.

Finally, a portion of the rain may fall on pervious formations of great depth. Some of this may be lost by evaporation of the type measured in a percolation gauge, but the remainder will percolate down and form

I

a contribution to deep-seated water supplies. Over large areas of southern England the chalk forms such a reservoir, so to speak, for the natural storage of rain. This rock is so pervious that there is hardly any surface run-off. Streams are few and nearly the whole of the rainfall is either lost by evaporation or is absorbed by the chalk, whence it can be withdrawn for use by means of wells.

60. Underground water. It will be realized from the concluding remarks in the last paragraph that a percolation gauge provides a close analogy with the natural economy of underground water supplies. The analogy is not quite complete, because when rain falls on to soil in a percolation gauge which is already saturated it may overflow and be completely lost, or it may be retained by the rim and subsequently percolate. Neither of these processes can occur in nature on a considerable scale. Nevertheless we should expect a percolation gauge to give a very fair idea of the water available for the replenishment of underground supplies, and this has been found to be the case, in relation to the chalk formation. In Fig. 41 the dotted curve shows the mean annual variation of water level in a well at Chilgrove, Sussex, in the chalk, drawn on an arbitrary scale (the range of the anuual variation is actually about fifty feet). It will be observed that this curve strongly resembles the full-line curve showing the normal variation of level in a tank subject to rainfall, evaporation and drainage. It is true that tank observations of evaporation were used in drawing this curve, but its shape would have been very nearly the same if we had used observations from a percolation gauge. The shape of the curve is in fact determined entirely by the fact that the annual variation of rainfall *minus* evaporation has a winter maximum and a summer minimum.

The form of curve yielded by the Chilgrove well is typical of curves obtained from well-gaugings in almost any district. The shape is not quite so regular as the simple sine wave calculated from rainfall and evaporation data. A characteristic feature is the slow descent from the maximum about February to the autumn minimum and the relatively rapid rise thereafter. This sort of variation is shown in most years, but if a dry winter is followed by a wet spring the maximum level may be attained in summer. It will be realized that the response of the water-level in a deep well to rainfall must usually be slow; also, even heavy rains occurring after hot, dry periods in the summer may produce little or no percolation, because the water is simply taken up and re-evaporated by the surface layers.

61. The flow of rivers. Water flowing in a river consists partly of direct run-off from impervious surfaces, and partly of drainage from pervious soil [1] ; during dry periods it must consist entirely of the latter and the rate of discharge must therefore depend on the natural storage capacity, and on the state of replenishment of the water so stored, in the catchment area. Surface run-off is subject to direct loss by evaporation, and the water stored in the soil must also be depleted by evaporation from the soil itself and by transpiration of moisture by vegetation. Some estimate of the total loss by evaporation may be obtained by comparing the measured discharge of the river with the amount of water deposited on the catchment area in the form of rain. To get a correct answer it is necessary to make an allowance for water which percolates through deep pervious formations and is thus lost, so far as the flow of the river is concerned. The magnitude of the latter loss may be very difficult to estimate.

As the question is of some climatological interest we shall give here some results for the River Thames, taken in part from a paper read at an agricultural conference in 1934 (31). No attempt has been made to assess the value of the correction mentioned at the end of the last paragraph and we shall simply refer to the difference between the rainfall and the run-off as the " loss ". The total flow of the river (*i.e.* the run-off) is regularly gauged at Teddington Weir, and the results are published in the Annual Reports of the Metropolitan Water Board. The rainfall is determined in the Meteorological Office from charts based on the readings of a large number of rain-gauges in the catchment area draining to Teddington, and in adjacent areas. In this way the " general rainfall " of the catchment area is obtained. The year adopted by the Metropolitan Water Board comprises the twelve months ending 31st March, and our data refer to these periods.

62. Rainfall and run-off of the River Thames basin. The mean annual rainfall is 28·2 inches and the mean annual run-off, expressed as inches of depth over the whole catchment area, is 9·4 inches, exactly one-third of the rainfall. In other words, of every inch of rain that falls over the Thames catchment area, only one-third of an inch finds its way to Teddington Weir. In a normal year the loss is thus equal to 18·8 inches. From the similarity of this figure to the values of mean evaporation given in Table XXV we may judge that nearly the whole of the loss is due to evaporation. The extent of the fluctuations from year to year,

---

[1] These remarks refer to conditions due to natural causes ; in practice the flow may be affected appreciably by human activities, *e.g.* discharge of sewage or trade effluents.

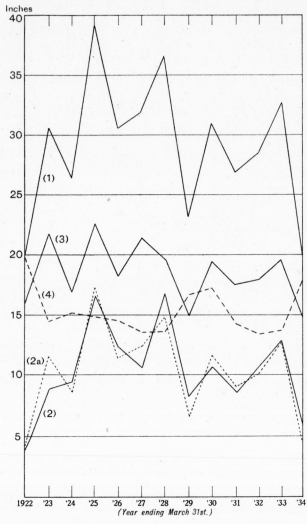

Fig. 42.

(1) Rainfall, Thames valley (R).
(2) Run-off, measured at Teddington Weir (F).
(2a) Run-off, calculated from $F = 0.67R - 9.1$.
(3) Loss (rainfall minus run-off).
(4) Evaporation at Camden Square, London.

and their relation to rainfall and evaporation, may be judged from the graphs in Fig. 42, which cover a period of thirteen years. In this diagram rainfall is shown by graph 1, run-off by graph 2, loss (rainfall *minus* run-off) by graph 3, and evaporation measured at Camden Square by graph 4.

These graphs show a number of interesting features. The loss curve (3) shows no resemblance at all to the Camden Square evaporation curve (4). We may assume that Camden Square gives a fair indication

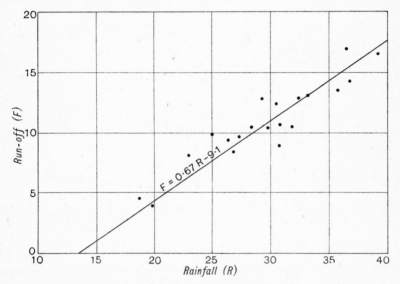

FIG. 43.—Correlation of rainfall and run-off in the Thames basin.

of the general evaporation from open water surfaces in the catchment area and we must conclude, from the dissimilarity of graphs 3 and 4, that losses by evaporation from surface run-off, and from the free water surfaces in the river and its tributaries, are not an important component of the total loss. We observe, on the other hand, that there is a very marked parallelism between the loss curve (3) and the rainfall curve (1). From this we may deduce that the major part of the loss is due to evaporation of water from the soil and from plants ; we have already seen that this form of loss by evaporation must be larger in wet years than in dry years.

In order to investigate the correlation between rainfall and run-off, the dot diagram (Fig. 43) was constructed, using data for twenty years.

Each dot represents the run-off and rainfall of a twelve months' period. It will be seen that the dots cluster around a straight line. Calling the run-off in inches F and the rainfall R, this straight line is represented by the equation [1]

$$F = 0.67R - 9.1,$$

which may be expressed, approximately, as : " run-off equals two-thirds of the rainfall *minus* nine inches ". To test how well this equation really represents the annual run-off, we may use it to compute the run-off for past years. By this process we obtain graph 2a and it will be seen that this agrees very well, on the whole, with the observed graph 2. It may be presumed that an even better fit would have been obtained if the summer rainfall and winter rainfall had been treated separately, because the effect on the flow produced by one inch of winter rainfall is definitely greater than the effect of one inch of summer rainfall.

From the formula given above we may make some important deductions in regard to the effect on the annual run-off of fluctuations in the annual rainfall. By calculating the value of F for different values of R we obtain the following results :

If rainfall is 10 per cent. below normal, run-off is 16 per cent. below normal

,,	,,	20	,,	,,	,,	,,	36	,,	,,	,,
,,	,,	30	,,	,,	,,	,,	56	,,	,,	,,
,,	,,	40	,,	,,	,,	,,	77	,,	,,	,,
,,	,,	50	,,	,,	,,	,,	99	,,	,,	,,

and finally, if the rainfall is 13·6 inches (fifty-two per cent. below normal), the run-off is nil.

Roughly speaking, if the rainfall is reduced by a given percentage, the run-off is reduced by double that percentage, in the case of the River Thames. In actual practice, the lowest recorded rainfall over the Thames catchment area in a twelve months' period ending 31st March was 18·63 inches in 1933-34. This represents a fall thirty-four per cent. below normal and the mean discharge of the Thames was about half the normal. A rather lower discharge (56·5 per cent. below normal) was measured during the year 1921-22. During the twelve months August 1933 to July 1934 the rainfall was deficient by rather more than forty per cent. and the discharge was sixty-four per cent. below normal.

---

[1] Since this was written, the equation representing the relation between F and R during the period 1914-1936 has been computed by the method of least squares ; the revised equation is $F = 0.57R - 6.05$. For moderate values of R the calculated values of F do not differ much from those given by the earlier equation.—E. G. B.

This figure, representing drought conditions which we may reasonably regard as extreme, is rather better than the formula would indicate.

These figures are of interest in so far as they show how it is that a serious water shortage may result from a deficiency of rainfall that does not at first sight appear to be alarming. If we had considered a catchment area with a higher annual yield than that of the Thames, we should still have found that a given percentage deficiency of rainfall resulted in a larger percentage deficiency in the yield, but the rate of decrease would not have been so rapid as in the case of the Thames. It is obviously advantageous, therefore, whenever possible, to utilize the run-off from a normally wet area, rather than a dry area, for purposes of public water supply.

63. The Thames under normal and under drought conditions. A curve showing the normal monthly discharge of the Thames has been added to Fig. 41. It is drawn on an arbitrary scale and the purpose of including it in the diagram is to show how a typical run-off curve resembles, and how it differs from, other curves relating to rainfall, evaporation and drainage. The main difference in the case of the Thames curve is that the maximum occurs decidedly earlier in the year. We may attribute this to the contribution made by surface run-off, which is an important factor in the winter. In the summer the flow is maintained to a large extent by the drainage of water stored in the soil and the minimum naturally coincides with the minimum found for well-levels and with that to be anticipated from calculation.

In Fig. 44 we are able to see the effect of severe drought conditions on the flow of the river. The dotted graphs in the two portions of the diagram represent the normal monthly values of flow and rainfall. The shaded columns represent the actual records for the two years 1933 and 1934. The tops of the columns in the upper portion of the diagram represent the " natural flow " at Teddington ; the heavily shaded portions show the amount abstracted by the Metropolitan Water Board above the weir. The lightly shaded portions therefore show how much water actually flowed over the weir. It will be seen that the flow began to be markedly deficient in August 1933 after three dry summer months. The flow remained below the normal summer value until the end of the year, owing to the very deficient rains in October, November and December. January 1934 produced a normal rainfall and there was a considerable increase in the flow, though it remained very much below normal. February was very dry but the rains of March and April were above normal. The fact that the flow remained very much below normal during these months may be attributed to the low levels to which the ground water had subsided as a result of the deficiency of winter rainfall. Another dry summer followed and the flow decreased

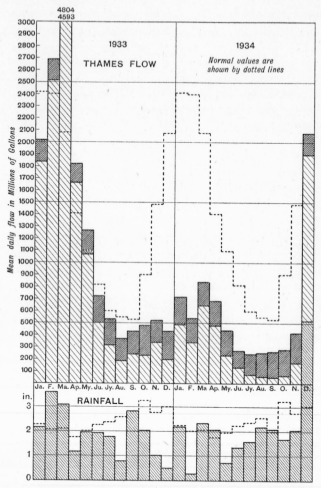

Fig. 44.—Rainfall and run-off of the River Thames basin in 1933 and 1934. (Normal values are shown by dotted lines.)

to a value insufficient for the needs of the population. Severe restrictions were imposed on the use of water and considerable quantities had to be abstracted from the storage reservoirs. Rainfall and flow remained deficient until December 1934, when a very heavy rainfall restored the flow of the river to its normal value.

From these graphs we may judge how near the flow of the Thames may approach to complete failure. The Thames is a relatively large river and its catchment area has a large natural storage capacity for the maintenance of the flow in dry weather. Many smaller streams, with lesser reserves of subsoil water to draw upon, did actually cease to flow during the worst period of the 1933-34 drought.

64. "Dew ponds." We have already referred to the fact that on the chalk formation which covers a large portion of southern England there is very little surface run-off. Public water supplies are therefore drawn from deep wells. The lack of surface water may be regarded as the chief reason for the existence in these areas of so-called "dew ponds". These are shallow artificial ponds constructed mainly in depressions on the downlands, and their main purpose is to provide a supply of drinking water for flocks and herds. Their presence in regions where no surface water is otherwise to be seen has led to the belief that some peculiar agency is concerned in their maintenance, and the name by which they are known implies the existence of an idea that they are replenished by dew. It has often been pointed out that the dew-fall, as measured by rain-gauges or by special devices, is utterly inadequate to contribute any appreciable amount of water to a pond. The absurdity of the idea was conclusively demonstrated by E. A. Martin (32), who found that on clear nights when dew deposited freely on the grass, the water temperature in the ponds was practically always higher than the air temperature and above the dew-point. There was no possibility, therefore, that moisture would condense out of the air on to the water. Martin thought that the ponds received some replenishment from moisture deposited from mists, and other writers have expressed the same idea. In considering this possibility we have to remember that its advocates are trying to explain how a pond would receive more moisture, per unit area, than an adjacent rain-gauge. We are concerned, therefore, with precipitation at a rate well below the "recordable" limit; also, since the ponds are supposed to possess a mysterious power of maintaining a supply of water during long spells of dry, warm weather, we may confine attention to summer months. Thick, wet mists are not observed on downlands on every summer night but let us suppose that they occurred, on an average, for twenty hours per week from April to September, giving an aggregate of 500 hours. The rate of precipitation would be unlikely to exceed one-thousandth of an inch per hour; the

aggregate precipitation during the whole summer would thus only amount to 0·5 inch, an insignificant quantity in relation to ordinary rainfall. Even if we doubled this quantity it would still be negligible.

So far as is known to the present writer no satisfactory evidence has been produced to show that a so-called " dew pond " is anything more than a water-tight vessel exposed to the combined influences of rainfall and evaporation. From their elevated situations the ponds receive a relatively high rainfall, and, moreover, they usually have wide shelving margins which provide an extended catchment area for rain. Evaporation would prevent much contribution from the margins during light rains, but they would yield a substantial run-off from heavy rains. Let us consider a pond with a mean area of 500 square yards, sited in a region with an annual rainfall of thirty-five inches. One inch of rain is equivalent to 4·7 gallons of water per square yard. The total volume of rain collected during an average year would therefore be $500 \times 35 \times 4·7$ or 82,100 gallons. To this we may add, say, twenty-five per cent. to represent the run-off from the sloping margins, bringing the total up to 102,800 gallons. Taking the loss by evaporation as eighteen inches per annum, we have to subtract $18 \times 500 \times 4·7$ or 42,300 gallons, giving a net annual yield of $102,800 - 42,300$ or 60,500 gallons, *i.e.* 166 gallons per day. We thus get about one-third of a gallon from every square yard of pond surface per day. The yield of a pond in a wetter district would naturally be greater.

If a quantity of water equal to the average daily yield were removed every day from the pond, its surface would show an annual variation of level similar to that of the full-line curve in Fig. 41 and a depth of only a few inches would suffice to prevent its drying up in an average year. How long the supply would hold out during a drought, assuming the rate of withdrawal to remain constant, would naturally depend entirely on the depth of the pond. Suppose the mean depth, measured from the mean surface level, to be eighteen inches ; then the total amount of water in the pond would be $500 \times 9 \times 1·5$ or 6,750 cubic feet, which is equivalent to 42,000 gallons. To the daily withdrawal of 166 gallons we must add the equivalent of about one-tenth of an inch per day to allow for evaporation. This amount of evaporation is equivalent to 235 gallons per day. In round figures the total daily depletion thus amounts to 400 gallons per day. The store of 42,000 gallons would therefore last for $\dfrac{42,000}{400}$ or 105 days—that is, about three months—*if there were no rain at all*. This is a possibility that we need not consider ;

for practical purposes we should take the data given in Table XVIIA
showing the actual amounts of rain falling during the worst periods of
drought. We then get the following figures :

	Withdrawals and loss by evaporation, galls.	Gain by rainfall, galls.	Total depletion, galls.
After 3 months of worst drought	36,000	5,500	30,500
,, 4 ,, ,, ,,	48,000	8,200	39,800
,, 5 ,, ,, ,,	60,000	12,300	47,700
,, 6 ,, ,, ,,	72,000	16,500	55,500

The water in the pond would thus be exhausted only after about
four and a half months of the worst drought conditions, assuming
evaporation to remain at the value of 0·1 inch per day throughout the
period. The drying up of the pond would be a very rare event, and its
occurrence would obviously be still rarer if the pond were deeper.
The rarity of the event is probably the basis of the popular belief that
" dew ponds never dry up ".

BIBLIOGRAPHY

(31) E. G. Bilham, "Evaporation—A brief review of methods and results," *Report
     of the Agricultural Meteorological Conference,* 1934. (London : Ministry of
     Agriculture and Fisheries).

(32) Edward A. Martin, *Dew Ponds.* (T. Werner Laurie.)

See also :

Annual Reports of the Metropolitan Water Board.

R. C. S. Walters, *The Nation's Water Supply.* (Ivor Nicholson & Watson.)

Inland Water Survey in the British Isles (British Association Reprints, N.S.,
     No. 31).

CHAPTER VII

TEMPERATURE OF THE AIR

65. Factors causing variations of temperature. The following types of variation of temperature are readily recognizable, even without the aid of instruments :

(*a*) A regular daily variation with a minimum in the early hours of the morning and a maximum in the afternoon.

(*b*) A regular annual variation with a minimum in the winter and a maximum in the summer.

(*c*) Casual variations, generally associated with changes of wind direction, causing irregular changes of temperature from day to day or during the course of the same day.

There are other types of variation of temperature, including cyclical variations of long period and secular changes, some of which may be vaguely perceived by persons with long memories, but which can only be established in a scientific sense by a mathematical analysis of a long instrumental record. Their combined effect is, however, small in comparison with the effects of the diurnal variation (*a*), the annual or seasonal variation (*b*), and the non-periodic variations (*c*).

For the purpose of determining the magnitude of the regular diurnal variation it is necessary to measure the temperature at very frequent intervals, and this is done most conveniently by making use of the records furnished by a self-recording instrument. The general practice at meteorological observatories is to tabulate hourly values ; in this country the values are measured at each hour of Greenwich Mean Time. From such tabulations the mean for the day is derived, to a high degree of accuracy, by taking the mean of the tabulated hourly values, with an adjustment to allow for any difference in the value at the two midnights, which we need not be concerned about here. At the end of a month, averages may be taken of the values at 0 h., 1 h., 2 h., etc., on all days, and in this way the average form of the diurnal variation during the month may be made out. By repeating this process over a long period of years, and averaging the hourly values for each month, we may assume that the effects of casual variations have been eliminated and we are

140

finally left in possession of data which show how the temperature would vary from hour to hour in each month, if there were no disturbing factors. By subtracting the mean for the month from the mean for each hour, the annual variation is eliminated ; similarly, by taking averages of the daily mean in each month we eliminate the diurnal variation and are left with a series of twelve monthly averages for the purpose of studying the annual variation.

The process which has thus been briefly described is a mathematical artifice for separating out and isolating factors (a) and (b), but it also gives information having a definite physical significance. The diurnal variation represents the response of the atmosphere to the effects of solar and terrestrial radiation, effects which vary according to the environment of the place and the time of year and which are of definite climatological importance. The annual variation represents the integrated effects of solar and terrestrial radiation plus certain effects due to environment, among which the effects of the general flow of air are conspicuous. Having ascertained the normal diurnal variation at all times of the year, and the form of the normal annual variation, we are in a position to judge of the extent to which the temperature is influenced at any given moment by the prevailing meteorological circumstances.

The mean annual temperature of the place is the grand mean of all the hourly observations over a long period of years, or, what amounts to the same thing, the mean of all the daily means. It is only at a few specially staffed and specially equipped observatories that our data in regard to temperature can be obtained in this rather laborious manner. As explained in Chapter I, it is the practice at ordinary climatological stations to derive the mean for the day as the arithmetical average of the readings of self-registering maximum and minimum thermometers. From these readings we can compute the monthly and annual averages with sufficient accuracy for practical purposes ; also, by taking differences between the mean daily maximum and the mean daily minimum we obtain information in regard to the " mean daily range " in the different months of the year. We shall see later, however, that this is not the same thing as the " range of the mean diurnal variation ", or " mean diurnal range ", derived from the means of hourly values. Averages of the values of dry-bulb temperature at the fixed hours of observation do, however, give us some data in regard to the diurnal variation if these exceed one or two per day and are suitably spaced over the twenty-four hours.

For the purpose of studying temperature as a separate element in the climate of the British Isles we shall find it convenient to begin by considering the mean annual temperature, proceeding thence to the discussion of the annual variation and the diurnal variation. We shall then be in a position to consider the records of maximum and minimum temperature, which include the effects of casual variations.

66. Mean annual temperature. At stations near sea level the mean annual temperature, derived from observations during the period 1906 to 1935 (33), varies from 45° F. in the Shetlands to rather more than 52° F. in the extreme south-west of England, Scilly and the Channel Islands, a total range of 7° F. The mean values for a selection of individual stations are given in the climatic tables in the Appendix. The Meteorological Office has published averages for a very large number of stations, and it is found that in a few instances the annual mean is less than 45° F. on the mainland. The stations where this occurs are at high levels, and we are thus brought in contact with the fact that altitude enters as a complicating factor into any discussion of the distribution of mean temperature. The value adopted internationally for the mean lapse-rate of temperature up to the average height of the stratosphere is $6 \cdot 5°$ C. per kilometre, which is equivalent to 1° F. per 280 feet. During the period 1884-1903 the mean temperature at the summit of Ben Nevis (4,405 feet) was found to be $31 \cdot 5°$ F. At Fort William (171 feet), near the base of the mountain, the mean value was $47 \cdot 2°$ F. This gives a mean lapse-rate of $15 \cdot 7°$ F. in 4,234 feet or 1° F. per 270 feet, agreeing fairly closely with the international value. Individual monthly means for Ben Nevis and Fort William showed that the mean lapse-rate was greater in summer than in winter, but the variations from the mean were not substantial. For many years past it has been the practice to reduce mean temperatures to sea level by assuming a lapse-rate of 1° F. per 300 feet. As it is rather exceptional to have to deal, in the British Isles, with readings from stations at altitudes exceeding 1,000 feet, small errors in the value assumed for the lapse-rate are obviously of little consequence. It should be emphasized that the reduction to sea level is merely an artifice for eliminating the complicating effects of altitude when it is desired to discuss the geographical distribution of mean temperature. It would be quite unjustifiable to reduce an individual observation to sea level by the same process, because the actual value of the difference of temperature between two points, one near sea level and the other at an elevation of a few hundreds of feet, may vary very greatly from the mean, according to the time of day and the presence or absence of wind and cloud.

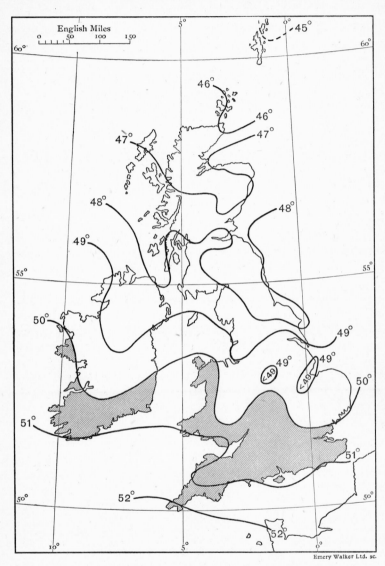

FIG. 45.—Mean temperature reduced to sea level; whole year (1906-1935).
(Areas with mean temperature above 50° F. are shaded.)

A chart showing the distribution over the British Isles of the mean annual temperature (1906-1935) reduced to sea level is given in Fig. 45. Isotherms are drawn for each whole degree Fahrenheit, and it will be seen that they have a general west-east trend, with bulges towards south where they cross the land masses. This is seen most clearly over Ireland, where the effect of the bulging towards south is to make the mean temperature of the central inland districts about one degree lower than it would be if the isotherms ran straight across the country. There is also a tendency for the isotherms to dip towards east, with the result that places on the west coast are in general substantially milder than places on the east coast in the same latitude. The isotherms are fairly regularly spaced from north to south, the mean interval being 110 miles per degree Fahrenheit. We may judge the general mean values to be about 47·5° F. over Scotland, 50° F. over England and Wales, and 49·5° F. over Ireland.

From this chart it is possible to estimate the mean annual temperature at any place whose altitude, h feet, is known, by first reading off the sea-level value from the chart and then subtracting the quotient of h divided by 300. Thus we may judge the mean annual temperature at the top of Snowdon (3,570 feet) to be $50·2° - 3,570/300$, i.e. 38·3° F. Another point we may notice is that the general pattern of the isotherms is independent of altitude. By subtracting 1° F. from the numbers attached to the isotherms we get the temperature distribution appropriate to a height of 300 feet, and so on. Differences of temperature between one part of the country and another, indicated by the isotherms at sea level, are assumed to remain the same at all heights; thus we may say that at any given height the temperature on the Welsh mountains is about 3° F. higher than on the Grampians or on the Western Highlands.

It is of interest to try and picture what an unreduced map of mean annual temperature would look like. The portions of the isotherms which cross the sea, or which cross land areas only a few feet above sea level, would be the same as in Fig. 45. In all other areas the course of the isotherms would be determined mainly by the land contours. Within the small island of Rum, south of Skye, which is barely visible on the scale to which Fig. 45 is drawn, we should have to crowd eight one-degree isotherms, because there is a peak on the island rising to over 2,500 feet. Similarly, we should have enormous thermal gradients everywhere in our islands where there are steep orographical gradients. It would be impossible to indicate the distribution of temperature over areas like Scotland, except in the broadest outline. Those are good reasons for preferring, in a book of this kind, to give charts of the distribution reduced to sea level, supplemented by tables of the actual temperatures at observing stations.

67. Fluctuations of mean annual temperature. The variations of mean annual temperature from the long-period average are relatively small in all parts of the British Isles. In the long record of the Radcliffe Observatory, Oxford, which dates from the year 1815, the lowest annual mean, 45·6° F. in 1879, differs by only 3·4° F. from the average, 49·0° F.; and the highest annual mean, 51·4° F. in 1921, differs by only 2·4° F. from the average. In most years the mean value differs by less than 1° F. from the average; the standard deviation, *i.e.* the

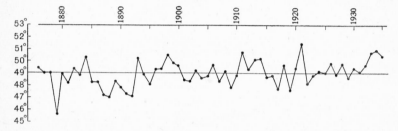

Fig. 46.—Fluctuations of mean annual temperature at Oxford (Radcliffe Observatory) during the sixty years 1876-1935.

(The long-period average, 49·0° F., is indicated by the horizontal line.)

root mean square of all the deviations, is only 1·1° F., and the " probable error " of a single yearly mean, regarded as an estimate of the long-period average, is less than 0·8° F. Fig. 46 is a graphical representation of the fluctuations during the sixty years 1876-1935. We may note in this graph some indications of a tendency for cold and warm conditions to occur in spells spread over several years—for example, all the values from 1885 to 1892 are below the average and all the values from 1896 to 1900 are above the average.

An examination of the records from other stations shows that the conditions which give rise to high or low values of the mean annual temperature tend to affect very large areas simultaneously. We may say, therefore, that the graph of fluctuations revealed by the Oxford record is fairly applicable to England and Wales as a whole, in respect to the " ups and downs ". There is a high correlation between the variations of annual temperature at any pair of individual stations within the area of the British Isles.

K

The extreme range of variation of the annual mean at Oxford is 51·4 – 45·6 or 5·8° F. The following are the corresponding values at certain other stations, based on records covering a period of at least fifty years :

SCOTLAND—

Sumburgh Head and Lerwick (*Shetland*)	46·3 – 43·1 = 3·2° F.
Deerness (*Orkney*) - - - -	46·7 – 43·5 = 3·2° F.
Stornoway (*Hebrides*) - - - -	47·7 – 43·7 = 4·0° F.
Fort William (*Inverness*) - - -	48·6 – 45·3 = 3·3° F.
Aberdeen (*Aberdeen*) - - - -	48·1 – 44·2 = 3·9° F.
Leith (*Midlothian*) - - - -	49·7 – 45·3 = 4·4° F.
Rothesay (*Isle of Bute*) - -	49·2 – 45·1 = 4·1° F.
Glasgow Observatory (*Lanark*) - -	48·9 – 44·3 = 4·6° F.

ENGLAND AND WALES—

Douglas (*Isle of Man*) - - - -	50·2 – 45·4 = 4·8° F.
North Shields and Tynemouth (*North'd*)	47·2 – 43·6 = 3·6° F.
Yarmouth (*Norfolk*) - - - -	51·2 – 45·4 = 5·8° F.
Cambridge (*Cambs.*) - - - -	51·5 – 46·2 = 5·3° F.
Buxton (*Derby*) - - - -	47·7 – 42·5 = 5·2° F.
Greenwich (*London*) - - - -	52·7 – 46·8 = 5·9° F.
Kew Observatory (*Surrey*) - -	52·5 – 46·6 = 5·9° F.
Dungeness (*Kent*) - - -	51·3 – 47·7 = 3·6° F.
Southampton (*Hants.*) - - -	52·7 – 47·0 = 5·7° F.
Southport (*Lancs.*) - - -	50·5 – 45·6 = 4·9° F.
Stonyhurst (*Lancs.*) - - - -	49·9 – 45·3 = 4·6° F.
Holyhead (*Anglesey*) - - -	51·8 – 47·9 = 3·9° F.
Falmouth Observatory (*Cornwall*) -	53·5 – 49·0 = 4·5° F.
Scilly (St. Mary's) - - - -	54·5 – 50·5 = 4·0° F.

IRELAND—

Dublin (*City*) - - - - -	52·1 – 47·3 = 4·8° F.
Armagh (*Armagh*) - - . - -	50·3 – 44·7 = 5·6° F.
Valentia Observatory (*Kerry*) - -	52·6 – 49·3 = 3·3° F.

These values are, on the whole, remarkably concordant. Most of the coast stations show a variation of the order 3° to 4° F., and the inland stations 5° to 6° F. The year 1879 which gave the lowest mean at Oxford also gave the lowest mean at most of the stations in the above list whose record began prior to that date. 1892 was the coldest year at Stornoway, Aberdeen and Stonyhurst, 1888 at Shetland, Deerness and Dungeness (comm. 1886), 1881 at Southport and 1917 at Scilly. Similarly, 1921 was the warmest year at most of the stations but the highest value occurred in 1894 at Shetland, 1884 at Deerness, 1898 at Leith, Glasgow (term. 1920) and Dungeness, and 1911 at Rothesay. It will be noticed that most of the years mentioned also gave substantial departures from the mean at Oxford.

68. The annual variation of temperature. The seasonal change from the cold of winter to the warmth of summer is perhaps the most familiar of all meteorological periodicities; its measurement is one of the main purposes for which climatological stations are established. It is necessary, however, to have a long series of observations before the exact shape of the annual curve can be accurately determined. The monthly and annual averages in current use refer to a period of thirty years but it is preferable for this particular purpose to examine records covering a period of sixty years or more. In Fig. 47 are shown graphs of the monthly values of mean temperature at ten typical stations with long records. Except in the case of Oxford the values shown are the arithmetical averages of mean daily maximum and mean daily minimum temperatures; with one or two exceptions they were specially computed for the present purpose and are set out in Table XXVIII.

All these curves show a very strong family resemblance; a characteristic feature of all of them is the beautifully smooth and regular ascent from the minimum to the maximum and descent back to the minimum. Closer examination of the curves, or of the figures in the table, show that there are, however, some rather important points of difference from station to station. The most conspicuous of these is the range of variation from the minimum to the maximum. At Deerness the annual range is 15 degrees and at Valentia 14·5 degrees, as compared with nearly 23 degrees at Oxford, 23·2 degrees at Kew and 22·4 degrees at York. There are also some differences in the dates of occurrence of the maxima and minima; at most stations the maximum occurs in July but August gives slightly the higher mean at Valentia and Falmouth, and the values in the two months are nearly identical at Deerness. January is the coldest month nearly everywhere but February is slightly colder at Deerness and Valentia. On the south-west coasts, and also in the extreme north, the phase of the variation therefore seems to be retarded as compared with other districts. Unfortunately we have no long records from other stations on the western seaboard but the averages for the period 1906 to 1935 indicate that August is the warmest month and February the coldest month over most of Ireland, south-west England, and northern Scotland. In Wales, February is slightly colder than January but July tends to be rather warmer than August at most stations.

We find the clue to the explanation of this retardation in phase on the western coasts in the data relating to sea temperature. In Fig. 48

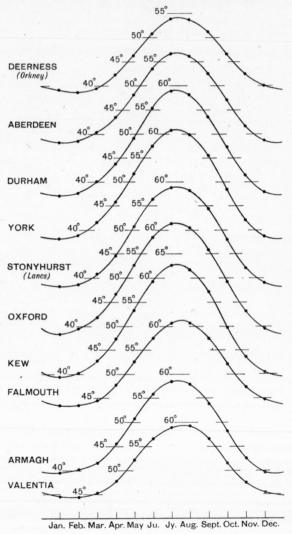

FIG. 47.—Annual variation of mean temperature (Oxford, 1815-1930; others, 1871-1930).

we have graphs of the average temperature of the sea surface off various parts of the coast, based on data covering a period of more than sixty

years, published in the *Marine Observer*, 1926. It will be noted that the
minimum occurs in February in the Orkneys region and in the North
Sea but is postponed until March at the mouth of the English Channel
and off the west coast of Ireland. In each district the maximum occurs
in August. The temperature observed at any place inland at a given
moment is the resultant of several factors, the most important of which
are solar and terrestrial radiation and the transport of warm or cold
air by wind. Solar radiation depends upon the declination of the

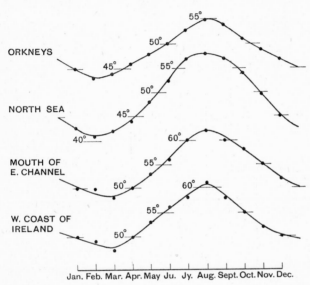

Fig. 48.—Annual variation of temperature of British coastal waters
(1855-1917).

sun and tends to produce a maximum of temperature at the summer
solstice—that is to say, near the end of June. Cooling due to terrestrial
radiation exceeds the warming due to solar radiation in winter and tends
to produce a minimum of temperature at the winter solstice—that is
to say, near the end of December. Even if solar and terrestrial radiation
were the only factors involved we should expect some lag in the response
of the atmosphere to these influences, because the warming and cooling
of a large mass of air is a cumulative process which takes time. This
fact is illustrated during anticyclonic periods in winter and summer,
when effects due to air movement are more or less in abeyance and the
results of radiation are conspicuous. In winter, when these conditions

prevail, the temperature tends to become progressively lower from day to day; in summer the temperature tends to become progressively higher from day to day.

If the effects of radiation were absent our annual curves would be similar to those of Fig. 48. The combined effects of radiation and advection produce the results actually observed. All winds, except

TABLE XXVIII

MONTHLY AVERAGES OF MEAN TEMPERATURE FOR LONG PERIODS

Station	Jan.	Feb.	Mar.	Apr.	May	June	July	Aug.	Sep.	Oct.	Nov.	Dec.	Year
SCOTLAND													
Deerness (*Orkney*) 1871–1930	39·2	38·9	39·5	42·3	46·4	50·8	**53·9**	53·8	51·3	46·8	42·5	40·0	45·5
Aberdeen (*Aberdeen*), 1871–1930	38·2	38·5	40·2	43·5	48·1	53·5	**56·7**	56·3	52·7	47·3	41·9	38·7	46·3
ENGLAND AND WALES													
Durham (*Durham*) 1871–1930	37·3	37·9	40·1	43·9	49·1	55·1	**58·9**	58·0	53·9	47·3	41·5	37·9	46·7
York (*Yorks.*) - 1871–1930	38·2	39·0	41·5	45·9	51·7	57·3	**60·6**	59·8	55·5	48·6	42·3	38·6	48·3
Stonyhurst (*Lancs.*) 1871–1930	38·3	38·7	40·7	44·9	50·7	56·1	**58·9**	58·2	54·5	48·1	42·3	38·9	47·5
Oxford (*Oxon.*) - 1815–1930	38·4	39·5	41·9	46·5	52·6	58·4	**61·3**	60·4	56·1	49·5	43·1	39·9	49·0
Kew Observatory (*Surrey*) 1871–1930	39·5	40·3	42·7	47·3	53·5	59·1	**62·7**	61·7	57·2	49·9	43·5	40·3	49·8
Falmouth (*Cornwall*), 1871–1930	43·6	43·8	44·5	47·9	52·5	57·3	60·5	**60·6**	57·6	52·3	47·5	44·9	51·1
IRELAND													
Armagh (*Armagh*) 1871–1930	39·6	40·3	41·7	45·5	50·7	55·8	**58·4**	57·9	54·0	48·1	42·8	39·7	47·9
Valentia (*Kerry*) - 1871–1930	44·7	44·6	45·2	47·9	52·3	56·5	58·9	**59·1**	56·5	51·7	47·3	45·3	50·9

purely local winds, which blow over the British Isles, have to cross a stretch of sea, and in doing so the air in contact with the sea tends to take up the sea-surface temperature. Westerly winds come nearest to doing so because they have to cross very long stretches of water. As westerly winds are, on the whole, the most frequent we should expect the form of annual variation of temperature on the west coasts to approximate to that of the surface waters in the Atlantic. As the air moves eastward its temperature is modified in increasing degree by the effects of radiation, and we thus find that the annual maxima and

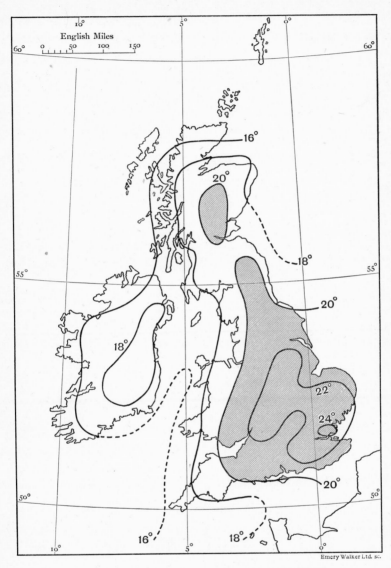

FIG. 49.—Annual range of mean temperature (1906-1935).
(Areas with an annual range exceeding 20° F. are shaded.)

minima of temperature occur distinctly earlier on the eastern side of Ireland and Great Britain than on the western side of those islands. For similar reasons we should expect to find the minimum range of the annual variation on the western coasts and the maximum range on the eastern sides of the land areas. In Fig. 49 we have a chart showing the geographical distribution of the average annual range of mean temperature during the period 1906 to 1935, and it will be seen that the distribution accords very well with these principles. The highest annual ranges are found in the Midland counties, in East Anglia and in southeast England ; several stations in the latter areas have ranges of about 23° F., and the maximum occurs at Southend, 24·3° F. Round the western and northern seaboard from Valentia to the Shetlands the annual range is less than 15° F.

In Chapter III it was stated that autumn is a milder season than spring, even when allowance is made for the lag of air temperature behind the sun's variations in declination. Justification for this statement is to be seen in the shapes of the curves drawn in Fig. 47. These look at first sight like regular " sine " curves, but closer examination shows that the descending portions of the curves, representing conditions during the autumn months, are differently shaped from the ascending portions, representing conditions in the spring months. The rate of ascent from the winter minimum is relatively slow compared with the rate of descent towards the minimum. At Kew Observatory the minimum appears to occur accurately in the middle of January, and the mean temperatures are similar in December and February ; but March is 0·8° F. colder than November and April is 2·6° F. colder than October. Similar differences are seen if the data for other stations are examined.

69. Irregularities in the annual variation—" Buchan's periods ". In Fig. 47 the annual variation of temperature at various stations is represented as a smooth curve drawn through twelve points, which were obtained by averaging the monthly mean temperatures over long periods. Strictly speaking, a curve drawn in this manner cannot be used for the purpose of defining the average temperature on a given date. Suppose, for example, we take a point on the Stonyhurst curve, midway between the points representing April and May ; the value is 47·8° F. and at first sight it might appear that that figure represents the mean temperature at the end of April. We cannot, however, make that assertion ; the curve is a curve of monthly means and all we are entitled to assume is that the value mentioned, 47·8° F., is a close estimate of the mean temperature, at Stonyhurst, of a month, say thirty days, centred at the end of April. A curve constructed from a series of monthly means is, in fact, a highly " smoothed " representation of the annual variation. It will occur to the reader that this process of smoothing must result in some reduction in the apparent amplitude of the oscillation ; that is true, but it has been shown that this reduction is too small to be a matter of much concern. But we have to consider the question of whether the annual march of temperature is, in fact, really a smooth and regular progression of the kind pictured in Fig. 47.

The obvious method of settling this question is to compute the average temperature for each individual day of the year, and construct a fresh curve from the daily averages so obtained. When that is done, it is found that the successive daily averages do not, by any means, fit together as points on a simple, regular curve. As illustrations of the sort of results obtained, we show in Fig. 50 three graphs of daily averages for the month of December. The first two refer to Kew Observatory and Aberdeen and are based on thirty-year averages ; the third refers to

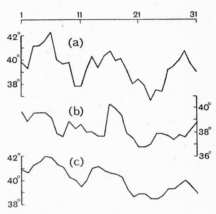

Fig. 50.—Variation of daily average temperature in December.

(a) Kew Observatory, 1871-1900.
(b) Aberdeen, 1871-1900.
(c) Greenwich, 1841-1934.

the Royal Observatory, Greenwich, and is based on averages for the long period of ninety-four years. It will be seen that these graphs present a very irregular appearance, and that the range of variation is quite substantial. From the curves in Fig. 47 we should expect a fairly steady drop of about 2° F. between the first and last days of the month. We find, however, that the highest value does not occur at the beginning of the month, nor the lowest value at the end of the month. In the Greenwich and Kew graphs there are three distinct maxima and two minima. At Kew the major maximum occurs on the 6th and the minimum on the 23rd ; the difference of average temperature on these two days is nearly 6° F. After the 23rd the average temperature rises to a value 4° F. higher on the 29th; there are also increases of the order of 3° F. between the 2nd and 6th, and between the 11th and 15th. The

Aberdeen curve is less striking, but the rise of nearly 3° F. from the 15th to the 16th is worthy of notice.

The Greenwich curve shows less " movement " than the Kew curve, but there is a very striking degree of similarity between them in respect to the dates of incidence of the maxima and minima.

The graphs for the whole year, constructed in a similar manner, show that irregularities of the kind which occur in December also occur in every other month. The " pattern " varies from month to month, but there is no period during which an upward or downward movement is maintained for more than a few days at a time.

The question at once arises as to whether these irregularities represent real and permanent features of the annual variation of temperature, as distinct from mere deviations arising from the imperfect elimination of chance fluctuations. It is a familiar fact that our weather tends to be made up of cold and warm spells. In a single month we may experience a warm spell with temperature ten degrees above normal, followed by a cold spell with temperature well below normal, or *vice versa*. The graph of a month's daily readings of temperature invariably shows a substantial amount of up-and-down movement ; if we average thirty or forty such graphs for months of the same name, we can hardly expect that the irregularities will completely cancel out, leaving a smooth curve. Are the irregularities shown by the daily averages anything more than the " residue " of this incomplete cancellation of warm and cold spells, occurring fortuitously?

This question has engaged the minds of many meteorologists, beginning with that famous secretary of the Scottish Meteorological Society, Dr. Alexander Buchan. Buchan examined a number of records from Scottish stations and came to the conclusion that certain humps and hollows in the annual curves were due to a tendency for warm or cold periods to occur round about the same dates in most years. The periods which he considered to have this property of recurrence are as follows :

Cold Periods	Warm Periods
1. February 7-14.	1. July 12-15.
2. April 11-14.	2. August 12-15.
3. May 9-14.	3. December 3-14.
4. June 29-July 4.	
5. August 6-11.	
6. November 6-13.	

This work of Dr. Buchan's (34) attracted a very considerable amount of attention, and " Buchan's cold periods " in particular may be said to have become a part of the weather lore of this country. It is difficult to see why cold or warm spells, which result from quite definite causes, such as a " break through " of polar air or a flow of warm air from the south, should tend to occur on particular dates (it must be remembered that the words " cold " and " warm " are not used here in an absolute sense, but merely in relation to the normal conditions for the time of year). The question has been examined by C. E. P. Brooks and S. T. A. Mirrlees (35) by the following method : curves of daily average temperature for Kew Observatory were drawn for two separate periods, 1871-1900 and 1901-1929. The irregularities shown by these two curves were then compared and it was assumed that if at any season of the year there was a real tendency for a warm or cold period to recur at about the same date, the fact would be revealed by the presence of a hump or hollow on *both* curves. The authors found no such tendency for recurrence at any time of year and summed up their conclusions in the following words :

" On the whole it seems improbable that there exists in our climate an abiding tendency for any part of the year to be either abnormally warm or abnormally cold for the season. It does seem, however, that such tendencies may spring up suddenly, persist for ten or twenty or thirty years, and as suddenly and mysteriously vanish. Any positive conclusions as to these spells are valid only for the time and place of their occurrence, and cannot be applied to other times and places. Thus, while Buchan's cold or warm spells were probably true for Scotland in the eighteen-sixties, they are certainly not true for London in the twentieth century. As Sir Richard Gregory remarked in his Presidential Address to this Society [1] in January 1930, ' Such an assumption is quite unwarranted and Buchan, if he were alive to-day, would be the first to reject it.' "

That is the most recent pronouncement on the subject, but many people will no doubt be very unwilling to consign the Buchan periods to the realm of the unreal. In particular the " May frosts " associated with Buchan's third cold period had established a firm position as a recurrent climatic feature, not only in the British Isles but in Continental countries, for centuries before the time of Buchan. Even, however, if we admit that Buchan's work was based on insufficient data, it is nevertheless a fact that quite appreciable variations—" irregularities " is hardly the right word—appear in the curve even when the data cover

[1] The Royal Meteorological Society.

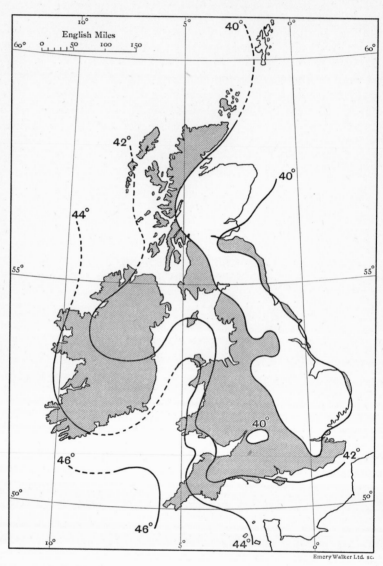

FIG. 51.—Mean temperature reduced to sea level, January (1906-1935).
(Areas with mean temperature above 40° F. are shaded.)

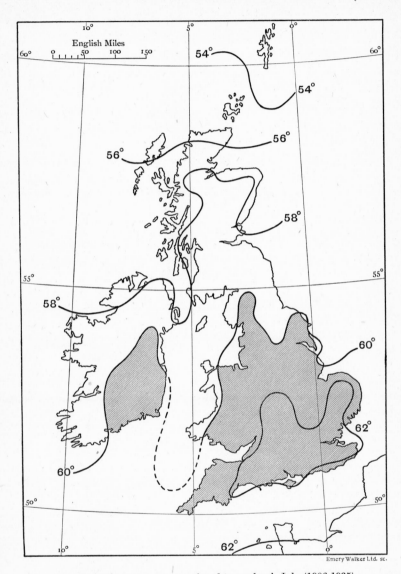

FIG. 52.—Mean temperature reduced to sea level, July (1906-1935).
(Areas with mean temperature above 60° F. are shaded.)

a period of nearly a hundred years. When one looks at graphs (*a*) and (*c*) of Fig. 50 it is difficult to believe that these waves are purely fortuitous. There appears, in short, to be a case for further investigation.

70. The distribution of mean temperature in winter and summer. The distribution of mean temperature, reduced to sea level, in January and July is shown in Fig. 51 and Fig. 52. The most conspicuous feature of the January chart is the region extending from the Shetlands southward over Scotland and eastern England into Kent, within which the reduced value of the mean temperature is below 40° F. The general run of the isotherms is from north to south and it may be said, therefore, that in the middle of winter temperature decreases from west to east, across the British Isles, rather than from south to north. It must not be forgotten, of course, that we have to allow for the decrease due to altitude (taken as 1° F. per 300 feet) when using this chart to compare the mean temperatures of any two places. Taking places near sea level, however, the following January means may be quoted to show how little is the difference of temperature between the north and south in winter : Baltasound (Shetlands), 39·2° F. ; Fort William (Inverness), 39·2° F. ; Aberdeen,[1] 39·0° F. ; York, 39·5° F. ; Cambridge, 39·3° F. ; Clacton (Essex), 39·1° F. ; Kew Observatory, 40·5° F. Hampstead, London (450 feet), is slightly colder in January than Edinburgh (Blackford Hill, 441 feet), the mean temperature at the two stations being 38·8° F. and 39·1° F. respectively. These facts are so much at variance with popular impressions that they deserve to be carefully noted by the reader.

The mildest winter temperature is found in the Scilly Isles, where the January mean during the period 1921-1935 was 46·7° F. Values slightly above 44° F. are found at points on the west coast of Ireland, Anglesey, the south-west corner of Wales, the Cornish coast and the Channel Islands. At Penzance the mean temperature for January is 45·2° F., and this appears to be the mildest spot in winter on the mainland of the British Isles.

The distribution of mean temperature in July, shown in Fig. 52, is altogether different from the distribution in January. In July the warmest regions are very definitely found in the south ; the isotherms run more or less from west to east, with northward protrusions over the land masses. At sea level a considerable area in the southern half of England has a mean temperature exceeding 62° F., while in the Shetlands

---

[1] Values quoted here refer to the thirty years 1906-1935 ; they differ in some cases from the long-period averages given in Table XXVIII.

a value below 54° F. occurs. At Camden Square (110 feet) in London the July mean is as high as 64·3° F., and values only slightly below 64° F. are found in other parts of London. Even on the coast we find a mean of 63° F. at Southend (Essex).

It is clear from these charts that the summer temperature is really the major factor in determining the difference between north and south in respect to mean annual temperature. London is a warmer place than the Shetlands mainly because the summers are warmer, not because the winters are warmer. It is not difficult to understand why that should be so; in winter our mildest conditions tend to occur in general south-westerly wind currents. These blow off the sea with a temperature approximating to 50° F., and they produce similar temperatures generally over the British Isles. They are at least as frequent in the north as in the south. Northerly winds produce colder weather in the north than in the south but they are infrequent, and to balance their effect we have the fact that low temperatures due to night radiation in calm weather tend to occur more often in the low-lying inland areas of the Midlands, east and south-east England than elsewhere. Thus we should not expect to find large differences in winter between the mean temperatures in the north and south of Great Britain.

In summer, on the other hand, solar radiation is the dominating factor in determining the mean temperature, and the effects of solar radiation are dependent on the " continentality " of the place, that is to say, on its remoteness from the sea and on its position in relation to the main continental land mass. We thus expect to find considerably higher temperatures in the southern parts of Great Britain, especially inland, than in the northern parts, which are not only narrower and more broken up by sea inlets, but are also divided by broader seas from the continental land mass.

71. Fluctuations of monthly mean temperature. Speaking broadly, the annual variation of temperature is repeated in successive years with considerable fidelity. In individual months there may, however, be substantial deviations from the normal value and it is of interest to examine the extreme variations shown by long records. In Fig. 53 the broken lines are graphs of the largest positive and negative deviations from the normal monthly means at Oxford (Radcliffe Observatory) during the period 1815 to 1935. The full lines give similar data for Glasgow Observatory during the period 1871 to 1920. Considering first the Oxford data, we observe that the maximum positive deviation (7·4° F. above the mean) occurred in January, and that deviations nearly as large have occurred in May, June and December. The smallest values of the extreme positive fluctuations occurred in April (5·3° F.), March (5·4° F.), August (5·5° F.) and September (5·6° F.). There is thus some indication of a tendency for abnormally mild weather to occur in winter and early summer rather than at other periods. The largest negative deviation (11° F.) occurred in February, and it is very noticeable that other large departures from the normal have been

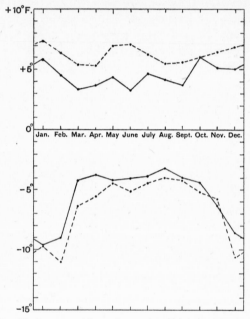

Fig. 53.—Maximum positive and negative deviations of monthly mean temperature.
Full line—Glasgow, 1871-1920.
Broken line—Oxford, 1815-1935.

confined to the winter months. Between March and November the curve shows little variation. The smallest value of the extreme negative deviation (4·0° F.) occurred in August. The curve for Glasgow representing the negative fluctuations is very similar to that for Oxford, but there is little resemblance between the curves for the two stations representing the positive deviations. In nearly all months the extreme deviations, both positive and negative, are larger for Oxford than for Glasgow.

In Table XXIX the actual values of the highest and lowest monthly mean temperatures at Oxford are given, and in the last line we have the range of variation represented by the difference between the highest and lowest values. From these figures we see that the winter months December to February show the greatest range of variation, while August and September show the smallest range. Perhaps the most striking facts brought out in Fig. 53 and Table XXIX are the tendency for the maximum deviations to occur in winter, and for the largest observed deviations to have a negative sign. In other words, the most striking form of thermal abnormality to which our climate is liable is a spell of very cold weather in winter. By comparison, the warmest recorded month in summer represents a far lower degree of abnormality.

TABLE XXIX

OXFORD (RADCLIFFE OBSERVATORY) HIGHEST AND LOWEST MONTHLY
MEAN TEMPERATURES, 1815–1935

	Jan.	Feb.	Mar.	Apr.	May	June	July	Aug.	Sep.	Oct.	Nov.	Dec.
	° F.	° F.	° F.	° F.	° F.	° F.	° F.	° F.	° F.	° F.	° F.	° F.
Highest monthly mean -	45·8	45·9	47·3	51·8	59·6	65·5	67·5	65·9	61·7	55·5	49·6	46·8
Year -	1916	1869	1822	1865	1833	1846	1921	1911	1929	1831	1818	1852
Deviation from normal -	7·4	6·4	5·4	5·3	7·0	7·1	6·2	5·5	5·6	6·0	6·5	6·9
Lowest monthly mean -	28·7	28·5	35·5	40·9	48·2	53·3	56·9	56·4	51·9	44·3	37·3	29·2
Year -	1838	1895	'45'83	1837	1817	1909	1879	1920	1877	1919	1923	1890
Deviation from normal -	− 9·7	− 11·0	− 6·4	− 5·6	− 4·4	− 5·1	− 4·4	− 4·0	− 4·2	− 5·2	− 5·8	− 10·7
Range of variation -	17·1	17·4	11·8	10·9	11·4	12·2	10·6	9·5	9·8	11·2	12·3	17·6

It is of interest to notice what would be the result if every month were liable to exhibit extreme variations, both positive and negative, equal to the extreme negative deviation, 11° F., observed in February. The highest value for January would become 49° F. and would be about equal to the lowest value for August. The highest value for July would become nearly 73° F., exceeding the highest mean recorded up to the present in July by 5° F.

Data for Kew Observatory, similar to those given in Table XXIX for Oxford, are included in Table XXXI.

Various explanations might be advanced to account for the peculiarities in respect to winter months revealed by our data. Perhaps the simplest way to look at the matter is to consider that in normal circumstances the prevalence of westerly winds blowing over a warm sea gives our islands a winter climate which is abnormally mild for their latitude. We live, in fact, on the edge of a continental area whose winter climate

L

we do not ordinarily share, but which we are liable to share when the warming agency, the westerly wind-stream, breaks down. Winter is quite definitely the season of greatest contrast between the climate of the British Isles and the climates of the land areas which lie to eastward. Consequently when our air supply is drawn from those areas, or from a northerly point, instead of from the west, a large fall of temperature is to be expected. In winter, moreover, solar radiation has little effect

TABLE XXX
AVERAGES OF HOURLY VALUES OF TEMPERATURE, 1871–1915

	0 h.	2 h.	4 h.	6 h.	8 h.	10 h.	12 h.	14 h.	16 h.	18 h.	20 h.	22 h.	Range of Hourly Means
	° F.	° F.	° F.	° F.	° F.	° F.	° F.	° F.	° F.	° F.	° F.	° F.	° F.
ABERDEEN													
January -	37·7	37·5	37·4	37·3	37·3	38·0	39·4	40·0	39·3	38·5	38·1	37·9	2·7
April -	40·8	40·2	39·7	40·0	42·7	45·0	46·2	46·5	46·0	44·8	42·9	41·8	6·9
July - -	53·4	52·6	52·0	53·9	56·4	58·0	59·0	59·3	58·8	58·0	56·3	54·5	7·3
October -	45·8	45·3	45·0	44·9	45·6	48·1	49·9	50·4	49·5	47·7	46·7	46·0	5·6
Whole year	44·3	43·8	43·4	44·0	45·4	47·2	48·5	49·0	48·3	47·2	45·9	45·0	5·5
KEW													
January -	38·2	37·9	37·8	37·6	37·5	38·8	40·7	41·8	41·0	39·7	39·1	38·6	4·3
April -	43·5	42·4	41·6	41·6	44·9	48·8	51·7	53·2	53·1	51·0	47·4	45·2	12·1
July - -	58·0	56·6	55·5	57·1	60·8	64·2	66·7	68·5	68·7	67·5	63·6	60·3	13·5
October -	47·4	46·8	46·4	46·1	47·2	51·0	53·8	54·9	53·9	51·1	49·2	48·2	8·8
Whole year	46·8	45·9	45·3	45·6	47·6	50·7	53·3	54·5	54·2	52·4	49·9	48·1	9·4
VALENTIA													
January -	44·3	44·2	44·1	44·0	44·0	44·5	45·7	46·2	45·8	44·8	44·5	44·3	2·2
April -	46·3	45·8	45·3	45·1	47·0	49·4	51·0	51·7	51·5	50·2	48·1	47·0	6·7
July - -	56·5	56·0	55·7	56·1	58·2	60·3	61·6	62·1	62·1	61·0	59·0	57·3	6·6
October -	50·5	50·2	50·1	49·9	50·2	52·2	53·7	54·1	53·6	52·0	51·2	50·7	4·3
Whole year	49·4	49·1	48·8	48·8	49·8	51·6	53·1	53·7	53·4	52·1	50·8	49·9	4·9

in ameliorating these conditions, owing to the low noon altitude of the sun and the shortness of the period of daylight.

It is nevertheless a rare event for a place in the south of England to experience a mean temperature below freezing point for a whole calendar month. The following is a complete list of such occurrences at Oxford : 1823, January, 31·9° F. ; 1830, January, 31·7° F. ; 1838, January, 28·7° F. ; 1855, February, 29·0° F. ; 1879, January, 31·0° F. ; 1881, January, 30·3° F. ; 1890, December, 29·2° F. ; 1895, February, 28·5° F. ; 1929, February, 31·7° F. Of these nine very cold months five occurred in January, three in February and one in December. February 1929 provides the only example during the past forty years ;

in that month the mean temperature was as low as 29·9° F. at Hampstead, London.

72. **Diurnal variation.** The method of obtaining data in regard to the regular diurnal variation of temperature, by taking monthly averages of hourly readings, has already been described. Hourly averages covering the period of forty-five years, 1871-1915, are available for the

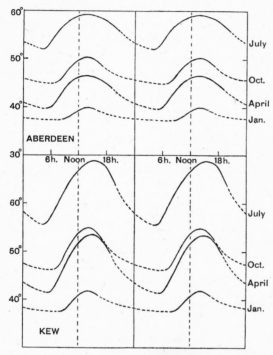

Fig. 54.—Normal diurnal variation of temperature (two repetitions) at Aberdeen and Kew in January, April, July, and October.
(Broken portions of the curves indicate the period between sunset and sunrise.)

principal British observatories. In Table XXX we give the values at the even hours for January, April, July, October, and the whole year, at Aberdeen, Kew and Valentia. The values for the four typical months at Aberdeen and Kew are shown in Fig. 54. In order to bring out certain points of interest two repetitions of the curves are given, and the parts of the curves which represent the hours between sunset and sunrise are shown as broken lines.

Perhaps the most obvious point that strikes the eye in looking at the curves in Fig. 54 is the smallness of the diurnal range in winter as compared with summer. This is also seen from the figures in the last column of Table XXX, where the range of the hourly means—taking into account the odd hours as well as the even hours—is given. At each station the range in July is about three times as great as in January. In the spring month, April, the range is almost as great as in July at Aberdeen and Kew, and is actually greater at Valentia. In October the range has an intermediate value, about equal to the mean range averaged over the whole year. An examination of the original data for all twelve months shows that at Aberdeen the mean diurnal range is practically the same, 7·4° F. or 7·3° F., in each month from May to September; the minimum range, 2·1° F., occurs in December. At Kew the maximum range, 13·8° F., occurs in June, and the minimum, 3·9° F., in December. At Valentia the maximum range, 7·6° F., occurs in May, and the minimum, 2·1° F., in December, as at Kew and Aberdeen. We see in these figures a tendency for the magnitude of the diurnal range to keep in step with the sun's declination, a result we should expect from the fact that the diurnal variation of temperature is a direct effect of solar radiation. The mean intensity of the vertical component of the sun's radiations has its maximum at the summer solstice and its minimum at the winter solstice, consequently the amplitude of the diurnal range of temperature may be expected to exhibit a maximum and minimum at the same epochs. At the coastal stations, and particularly at Aberdeen, the diurnal sea-breeze introduces complications, but at Kew the expectation is realized very exactly.

The general shape of the curves in Fig. 54 is familiar to everyone who has had occasion to look at the records furnished by thermographs. We note that in all cases the trough of the curve coincides almost exactly with the hour of sunrise. After sunrise the temperature rises rapidly at first, but the rate of increase falls off quite markedly as the sun's altitude increases. The maximum is not reached, however, until from two to four hours after noon. The subsequent fall of temperature is at first slow, but becomes very rapid an hour or two before sunset; the falling part of the curve is, on the whole, concave upwards. A curious fact which is illustrated by each of the curves in Fig. 54 is that the downward sweep is entirely unaffected by the setting of the sun. There is no evidence of any discontinuity at this epoch; the rising of the sun is obviously an event of major importance in relation to the diurnal variation of temperature, but the setting of the sun produces no noticeable effect on the shape of the curve.

The entire rise of temperature occurs between sunrise and about 2 p.m. or 3 p.m. In winter this is an interval of only a few hours, consequently the diurnal variation takes the form of a quick rise and a slow fall. Even at midsummer the period occupied by the rise is decidedly less than the time occupied by the fall. Another point of interest is the fact that the fall of temperature between sunset and sunrise, due to terrestrial radiation, is decidedly smaller in winter than at other seasons, in spite of the fact that nights are longest in winter. Actually, the maximum difference of temperature between sunset and sunrise appears to occur in spring and summer.

Lastly, we may draw attention to a peculiarity in the shape of the Aberdeen curves for April and July. It will be noticed that the crests of these two curves are very decidedly flattened as compared with the October and December curves, or with any of the Kew curves. This flattening is a direct effect of the diurnal sea-breeze, which tends to prevent the attainment of high afternoon temperatures in spring and summer. The thermal effects of the sea-breeze will, however, be more fully discussed in the section on coastal climates in Chapter XII.

The form of variation derived from the mean hourly values is to be seen on almost any thermograph record selected at random. The amplitude of the oscillation varies a good deal, however, according to the state of the sky and other factors. In fine weather, particularly in spring, the amplitude may greatly exceed the normal value ; in cloudy weather, on the other hand, more especially with north-east winds in winter, the diurnal variation may be totally suppressed.

73. Daily maximum and minimum temperatures. In the climatic tables in the Appendix, monthly averages of the daily maximum and minimum temperatures are given for a number of stations. It has already been explained that these data are derived from the readings of self-registering thermometers. Climatologically, they are of interest from two points of view. In the first place they give some idea of the average thermal conditions by day and by night ; in the second place they furnish information in regard to the " daily range " of temperature. It is necessary to distinguish carefully between the daily range, obtained by subtracting the mean minimum from the mean maximum, and the " mean diurnal range " or " mean range of hourly values " which we have been discussing in the previous paragraph. They are by no means the same thing, because the mean daily range takes account of the chance fluctuations which are, on the whole,

eliminated by the process of averaging hourly values. Suppose, for
example, there were two occasions during a given month on one of which
the temperature rose steadily from 40° F. to 50° F. between successive
times of setting the maximum and minimum thermometers, while on
the other occasion the temperature fell steadily from 50° F. to 40° F.
during a corresponding interval. Both these occasions would give a
daily range of 10° F., but they would cancel out and therefore contribute nothing at all to the diurnal range deduced from the means of
hourly values. The mean daily range is thus invariably bigger than
the difference between the highest and lowest of the mean hourly
values.

In Chapter I it was explained that there is some difference of practice at various classes of British stations in regard to the hours of setting
the maximum and minimum thermometers. It was also pointed out
that the average " night minimum " is rather higher than the average
" 24-hour minimum ", while the average " day maximum " is rather
lower than the average " 24-hour maximum ". The differences are too
large to be neglected, especially when we are dealing with the mean
daily range. For the purpose of studying the geographical distribution
of the mean daily range, or of the mean maximum or mean minimum, it
is therefore necessary to make a choice between the two alternatives.
In view of the arguments set out in Chapter I there can be no doubt
that the difference between day maximum and night minimum gives
the better estimate of the mean daily range. The chart reproduced
as Fig. 55 shows the distribution calculated on this basis. The distribution of the mean daily range derived from 24-hour maxima and
minima would be similar, but the actual values would be increased
everywhere by about 1° F.

74. **Mean daily range.** Broadly speaking, the chart shows that the
mean daily range is largest at the most inland places, decreasing to
low values along the coast. In addition, there is a tendency for an
increase from west to east; thus we find the 8° F. line skirting the
west coasts while the 10° F. line skirts the east coasts. Inland we have
values exceeding 14° F. over a considerable area in eastern and southern
England, and in small patches over Devonshire and the Grampians in
Scotland.

No very high degree of accuracy can be claimed for Fig. 55 because
it is based on only fifteen years of observations; also, on account of
the paucity of stations which observe day maximum and night minimum,
it was necessary, in order to complete the chart, to utilize 24-hour

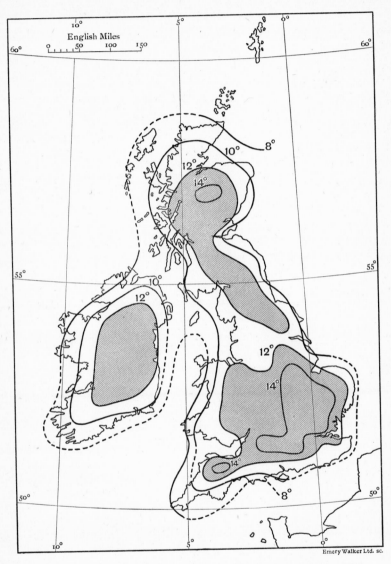

English Miles

Emery Walker Ltd. sc.

FIG. 55.—Mean daily range of temperature (day maximum minus night minimum); whole year (1921-1935).
(Areas with mean daily range above 12° F. are shaded.)

extremes for other stations, applying an estimated correction. Using 24-hour extremes for the period 1906 to 1935 we obtain mean daily ranges, averaged over the whole year, of about 16° F. at a number of inland stations including Cambridge (15·9° F.), Chelmsford (15·9° F.), Halstead, Essex (16·0° F.), Worksop (16·1° F.) and Shrewsbury (15·9° F.). Lower values are found in London, e.g. 14·6° F. at Camden Square, 14·4° F. at East Ham, 14·2° F. at Kew.

In individual months the mean daily range approaches or even exceeds 20° F. during the early summer at certain inland stations. Thus at Cambridge we have 19·6° F. in May and 19·2° F. in June ; at Chelmsford, 20·1° F. in June ; and at Halstead, Essex, 20·1° F. in May. At the Royal Observatory, Greenwich, the mean range is 20·6° F. in May, 20·6° F. in June and 20·3° F. in July, but the thermometers there are not exposed in the conventional manner and tend to record high maxima. Low values of the mean range occur at all stations in winter months. The "day maximum—night minimum" values in December varies from about 5° F. at the outlying islands to about 8° F. in southeast England.

75. Mean maximum and mean minimum. The mean daily maximum, averaged over the entire year, is highest in areas where a high annual mean temperature occurs in combination with a large mean daily range. Having regard to the fact that the mean annual temperature is highest in the extreme south, while the mean daily range is largest in the inland districts of southern England, we should expect the mean daily maximum to show an approximation to uniformity over southern England. This is actually the case, practically all stations having values round about 56° F. or 57° F. Rather higher values are found in London, where 58·5° F. is the mean maximum at Camden Square. In the extreme north we have the opposite combination—a low mean annual temperature and a small daily range. Consequently the lowest mean daily maximum, slightly below 50° F., is found in the Shetlands and Orkneys.

In regard to the mean daily minimum, averaged over the year, we must look for the highest values in regions where a high mean annual temperature occurs in combination with a small daily range. This combination is found in the Scilly Isles, the Channel Islands and coastal areas on the south-western seaboard. Thus we have a mean value as high as 48·4° F. at Scilly and Guernsey, 47·7° F. at Penzance and 46·3° F. at Valentia. In the extreme north the mean annual temperature is low but the daily range is small. Thus the Orkneys and Shetlands are not remarkable for cold nights; the mean night minimum at Lerwick, 41·8° F., differs by only two degrees from the mean night minimum at Croydon, 43·9° F. The lowest mean minima are actually found at high-level stations in Scotland, where we have the combination of a low mean annual temperature, a moderately large daily range and high altitude. At Braemar (1,111 feet) and Balmoral (927 feet) the mean minimum is 36° F. Locally the mean minimum may be considerably affected by the topography; a station in a valley may experience lower minima on " radiation nights " than a neighbouring station at a higher level. The relation between mean minimum temperature and altitude is therefore not a simple and direct one.

76. The annual variation of mean maximum and mean minimum. From the monthly means of daily maximum and minimum temperatures we obtain a rough idea of the variation during the year of the day temperature and the night temperature. The values for Kew Observatory are shown by the curves marked EE and FF in Fig. 56, and the corresponding figures are given in the lines similarly marked in Table XXXI. For the purpose of this particular illustration, means for the period 1881-1915 were used, because they afford the best available basis of comparison with the results derived from hourly means, which refer to the period 1871-1915. It will be seen that in all months the mean daily maximum is from one to two degrees higher than the maximum of hourly values, while the mean daily minimum is from one to three degrees lower than the minimum of hourly values, the largest differences occurring in winter in the latter case. The curves are all very similar in shape, and there is agreement also in respect to the seasons of greatest range.

From the fact that the daily range is much greater in summer than in winter, it follows that the annual variation of mean maximum is decidedly greater than the annual variation of mean minimum. Thus the mean maximum is 28° F. higher in July than in January, but the mean minimum is only 20° F. higher. The fact that the mean daily range is large in spring, and relatively small in autumn, is also an important point. We noted in paragraph 68 that the mean temperature was distinctly lower in spring months than in autumn months similarly spaced with respect to the winter minimum. We may now observe that the differences are relatively small when we consider the mean maximum, but are large when we consider the mean minimum. Thus at Kew the mean November maximum is only 0·4° F. higher than the March maximum, but the November minimum is nearly 3° F. higher

TABLE XXXI

Variations of Temperature at Kew Observatory (Surrey)

	Jan.	Feb.	Mar.	Apr.	May	June	July	Aug.	Sep.	Oct.	Nov.	Dec.
	° F.	° F.	° F.	° F.	° F.	° F.	° F.	° F.	° F.	° F.	° F.	° F.
BB Monthly mean (1871–1915) -	39·1	40·2	42·3	47·1	52·9	58·9	**62·5**	61·4	56·8	49·7	43·9	40·3
GG Highest monthly mean (1871–1935)	45·8	45·9	46·7	51·7	57·5	63·2	**68·3**	68·0	61·3	56·2	48·4	46·3
Year	1916	1872	1912	1893	1919	1917	1921	1911	1895	1921	1881	1918
HH Lowest monthly mean (1871–1935)	31·7	*29·2*	36·5	42·8	48·9	54·8	58·3	57·7	52·9	45·2	38·9	29·4
Year	1881	1895	1883	1917	1879	1916	1919	1920	1877	1887	1871	1890
CC Maximum of hourly means (1871–1915) - -	41·8	43·8	47·6	53·5	59·6	65·6	**69·1**	68·1	63·5	54·9	47·4	42·8
DD Minimum of hourly means (1871–1915) - -	*37·5*	37·8	38·2	41·4	46·1	51·9	55·6	55·2	51·4	46·1	41·8	38·9
Mean diurnal range	4·3	6·0	9·4	12·1	13·5	**13·7**	13·5	12·9	12·1	8·8	5·6	3·9
EE Mean daily max. (1881–1915) -	43·1	45·0	48·7	55·0	61·7	67·6	**71·0**	69·7	64·9	56·2	49·1	44·7
FF Mean daily min. (1881–1915) -	*34·6*	35·1	36·0	39·5	45·0	50·8	54·3	53·5	49·3	43·5	38·8	35·9
Mean daily range -	8·5	9·9	12·7	15·5	16·7	**16·8**	16·7	16·2	15·5	12·7	10·3	8·8
Highest mean max. (1871–1935) - -	50·4	50·7	55·2	62·4	68·0	72·5	**78·8**	77·9	71·8	66·4	54·0	50·9
Year	'16 '22	1872	1893	1893	1922	1917	1921	1911	1898	1921	1881	1934
Lowest mean min. (1871–1935) - -	27·3	*23·8*	30·1	35·8	41·1	47·8	51·3	50·2	46·2	37·0	33·1	25·3
Year	1881	1895	1883	1917	1879	1916	1919	1920	1925	1919	1910	1890
II Mean monthly max. (1881–1915) - -	53	54	60	67	75	80	**82**	81	75	65	58	54
JJ Mean monthly min. (1881–1915) - -	*22*	24	26	31	35	42	47	45	38	32	28	25
Mean range - -	31	30	34	36	**40**	38	35	36	37	33	30	29
KK Highest maximum (1871–1935) - -	57	62	68	80	87	88	90	**94**	92	83	63	59
Year	1922	1899	1918	1893	1922	1917	'81 '23	1911	1906	1921	1876	1931
LL Lowest minimum (1871–1935) - -	*9*	11	17	26	30	37	43	41	31	25	20	11
Year	1881	1895	1909	1922	1877	1880	1884	1890	1919	1895	1871	1890
Extreme range -	48	51	51	54	57	51	47	53	**61**	58	43	48

The letters in column 1 correspond with the curves in Fig. 56.

than the March minimum. Similarly, the October maximum is about 1° F. higher than the April maximum, but the minima differ by 4° F. Spring is a season of cold nights as compared with autumn; the

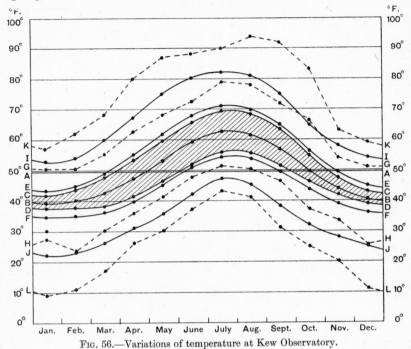

FIG. 56.—Variations of temperature at Kew Observatory.

AA Mean annual temperature, 1871-1915.
BB Mean monthly temperature, 1871-1915.
CC Mean maximum of hourly values, 1871-1915.
DD Mean minimum of hourly values, 1871-1915.
EE Mean daily maximum, 1881-1915.
FF Mean daily minimum, 1881-1915.
GG Highest monthly mean, 1871-1935.
HH Lowest monthly mean, 1871-1935.
II Average monthly maximum, 1871-1921.
JJ Average monthly minimum, 1871-1921.
KK Highest on record, 1871-1935.
LL Lowest on record, 1871-1935.

" trough " of the curve representing the annual variation of mean minimum is very flat, with the result that the mean minimum shows very little change from December to March.

These remarks are based on the results for Kew Observatory, but they may be regarded as of general application.

The mean maximum exceeds 70° F. in July and August at most inland stations in east and south-east England; the highest values are reached in London, where the average for Camden Square (1906-1935) is 73·7° F. in July and 72·7° F. in August. On the coast the values for these summer months are in general about 2° F. or 3° F. lower than at neighbouring stations a few miles inland. The mean maximum in summer decreases towards north and towards west; at Deerness (Orkney) the value is as low as 58·3° F. in July and 58·0° F. in August. At Valentia, in south-west Ireland, the mean maximum in July, 63·7° F., is about 10° F. lower than the value observed in the middle of London; the mean minima in that month are, however, about the same (Camden Square 55·1° F., Valentia 54·3° F.). Except at high-level stations, there is in fact little variation in the mean minimum in July over the British Isles. The values range from slightly under 50° F. in the extreme north to about 55° F. in the south of England.

There is a corresponding tendency to uniformity in the mean maximum in January and February; the values range from about 43° F. in the extreme north to 48° F. or 49° F. in the mildest parts of the south-west coasts. The geographical variation of the mean minimum in winter months is not much greater. At most stations the lowest mean minimum tends to occur in February rather than January; in this month we find a range from about 33° F. at inland stations near sea level in the north to 41·1° F. at Penzance, 40·4° F. at Valentia and 42·5° F. at Scilly. There is relatively little variation from north to south at coastal stations; the following are some typical February mean minima: Deerness (Orkney), 36·4° F.; Inverness, 34·4° F.; Aberdeen, 35·2° F.; Dundee, 33·6° F.; Edinburgh, 34·7° F.; Hull, 35·0° F.; Lowestoft, 35·0° F.; Folkestone, 35·9° F.; Bognor Regis, 36·7° F. Thus in winter the average night temperature is about the same along the south coast of England as in the Orkneys and Shetlands. It is natural that we should find the lowest mean minima in winter months at high-level stations in Scotland. At Braemar the mean minimum is below freezing point in each month from November to March, the lowest mean being 29·0° F. in February.

77. Monthly and yearly extremes. If note is taken of the highest daily maximum and the lowest daily minimum in each month and these extremes are averaged over a period of years, we are provided with a set of data which give a very good idea of the variability of the climate of the station. These data are accordingly included in the climatic tables in the Appendix. In Table XXXI a fairly complete summary of the temperature data for Kew Observatory is given, and the values of the average highest and lowest temperatures in each month are given in lines *II* and *JJ* ; they are also shown graphically in Fig. 56. At this station we see that the average maximum in July and August slightly exceeds 80° F., while the average minimum is 32° F. or below from October to April. The range of the average monthly extremes varies from about 30° F. in winter months to 40° F. in May, with slightly lower values in the summer months. It is of interest to compare these figures with those for Deerness (Orkney). At Deerness the mean of the highest values in July is no more than 66° F. ; the extreme minima average 26° F. in February and 27° F. in January ; the range varies from 21° F. in December to 26° F. in May ; the highest temperature for the year averages only 68° F. as compared with 85° F. at Kew. The average of the lowest temperature each year is 19° F. at Kew, 24° F. at Deerness ; thus Kew has an average annual range of 66° F. as compared with 44° F. at Deerness.

Values of the average annual extremes and the absolute extremes for a number of representative stations are given in Table XXXII. In regard to the average maximum for the year, and the extreme maximum, the values for Greenwich are outstanding, and this may be attributed, at least in part, to the abnormal exposure of the thermometers. With this exception Cambridge shows the highest mean annual maximum, 87° F., and also the highest extreme, 96° F. At that station the average annual range is 72° F. and the extreme range 96° F. Buxton, at 1,000 feet in Derbyshire, is the only station in the list which shows an extreme minimum below zero Fahrenheit, notwithstanding the fact that Ben Nevis is included. In contrast with the great variability of temperature at these inland stations, we may note that the average annual range is only 40° F. at Scilly. In the Scilly Isles frost is of rare occurrence and subtropical vegetation flourishes in the open. We see also that the south-west coasts of England, represented by Falmouth, and of Ireland, represented by Valentia, enjoy a marked immunity from extremes of heat or cold.

The absolute extremes in each month for Kew Observatory are indicated by lines *KK* and *LL* in Table XXXI and Fig. 56. The graphs so lettered in Fig. 56 may be regarded as the upper and lower boundaries of the field of variation of temperature at this station. The shaded area on the diagram shows how much of this field of variation is accounted for by the regular annual and diurnal oscillations ; it is a small fraction of the whole, particularly in winter months. The temperature has been as high as 57° F. in January and as low as 43° F. in July ; temperatures between 43° F. and 57° F. have thus occurred in all months of the year.

TABLE XXXII

Average Annual Extremes and Absolute Extreme Temperatures

Station	Average annual extremes		Highest on record	Lowest on record
	Highest	Lowest		
	° F.	° F.	° F.	° F.
Scotland				
Deerness (*Orkney*) - -	68	24	76	8
Stornoway (*Hebrides*) - -	72	21	78	11
Ben Nevis (*Inverness*) - -	62	7	66	1
Fort William (*Inverness*) -	78	16	86	5
Aberdeen (*Aberdeen*) - -	76	15	86	4
Rothesay (*Bute*) - - -	79	21	85	11
Glasgow (*Lanark*) - -	78	19	85	7
England and Wales				
Douglas (*Isle of Man*) - -	75	23	81	11
Tynemouth (*North.*) - -	78	20	88	6
Yarmouth (*Norfolk*) - -	78	21	89	10
Cambridge (*Cambs.*) - -	87	15	96	0
Buxton (*Derby*) - - -	80	9	89	−11
Oxford (*Oxon.*) - - -	84	17	·95	6
Greenwich (*London*) - -	89	19	100	4
Kew Observatory (*Surrey*) -	85	19	94	9
Dungeness (*Kent*) - -	77	19	83	9
Southampton (*Hants.*) -	85	21	92	11
Southport (*Lancs.*) - -	80	18	89	2
Stonyhurst (*Lancs.*) - -	79	17	88	5
Holyhead (*Anglesey*) - -	76	27	86	17
Falmouth (*Cornwall*) - -	75	29	85	20
Jersey (*Channel Is.*) - -	83	25	96	12
Scilly (St. Mary's) - -	71	31	82	25
Ireland				
Dublin (*Dublin*) - - -	76	23	87	13
Armagh (*Armagh*) - -	78	17	85	5
Valentia (*Kerry*) - - -	76	26	81	20

78. The highest and lowest temperatures on record. The highest recorded temperature in the British Isles is 100·5° F. at Tonbridge, Kent, on 22nd July, 1868. A value of 100° F. has been registered on only one other occasion, namely at the Royal Observatory, Greenwich, on 9th August, 1911. Readings exceeding 90° F. are infrequent, even in warm summers, and values above 95° F. are decidedly rare. The most recent occurrence was in August 1932, when on the 19th the thermometer reached 99° F. at Greenwich, 97° F. at Halstead and various London stations, and 96° F. at Jersey (St. Heliers), Norwich, Cambridge and other stations in East Anglia. The famous warm summer of 1921 was remarkable for drought and persistent warmth rather than for exceptionally high readings on individual days ; the extreme maximum for Greenwich was only 94° F. In 1933 also, the extreme readings were not very striking, though 96° F. was reached at Greenwich on 6th August. On the whole it appears that one may put the upper limit of temperature for the British Isles at about 100° F. with some confidence. Readings of the order 95° F.-100° F. are likely to be confined to the inland regions of east and south-east England and the southern and eastern parts of the midland counties. In Scotland and Ireland the upper limit may be put at about 90° F.

The lowest temperature on record is − 23° F. at Blackadder, East Berwickshire, on 4th December, 1879. This reading was obtained with an uncertified thermometer in a wall-screen and there must therefore be some doubt about its accuracy. The weather of December 1879 was certainly exceptionally cold, and a reading of − 16° F. was recorded at Kelso on 3rd, with a verified thermometer in a Stevenson screen. If we set aside the Blackadder reading, the record is held by Braemar, Aberdeenshire, where − 17° F. was registered on 11th February, 1895. During the severe frost of January and February 1895 readings below zero occurred on numerous occasions at stations in Scotland, northern and eastern England and the Midlands. On 11th February − 11° F. was recorded at Buxton, and this is the extreme minimum for the British Isles outside of Scotland. Since 1895 there have been very few occurrences of temperatures below zero ; the following is believed to be a complete list [1] :

1917.	Feb.	6.	Benson (*Oxfordshire*)	−4° F.
		6.	Wellington (*Shropshire*)	−3° F.
	Mar.	9.	Braemar (*Aberdeen*)	−3° F.
1919.	Nov.	14, 15.	Kingussie (*Inverness*)	−5° F.
		14.	Balmoral (*Aberdeen*)	−6° F.
		14.	Braemar (*Aberdeen*)	−10° F.
		14.	Logie Coldstone (*Aberdeen*)	−4° F.
		14.	Kettins (*Angus*)	−3° F.
		14.	Perth (*Perth*)	−7° F.
		14.	West Linton (*Peebles*)	−6° F.
1929.	Feb.	14.	Ross-on-Wye (*Hereford*)	−1° F.
		14.	Usk (*Monmouth*)	−1° F.
		17.	Houghall (*Durham*)	−1° F.

[1] The list does not include " unofficial " readings.

The most remarkable entries in this list are those referring to 14th November, 1919 ; having regard to the normal conditions it is far more extraordinary for temperatures below zero to occur in November than in January or February.

BIBLIOGRAPHY

(33) *Averages of Temperature for Periods ending* 1935 (M.O. 407).   (H.M.S.O.)

(34) A. Buchan, " Interruptions in the regular rise and fall of temperature in the course of the year," *Jour. Scot. Meteor. Soc.*, **2**, 1869, p. 4.

(35) C. E. P. Brooks and S. T. A. Mirrlees, " Irregularities in the annual variation of the temperature of London," *Q.J.R. Meteor. Soc.*, **56**, 1930, p. 375.

CHAPTER VIII

SUNSHINE AND CLOUD

79. Sunshine records. The registration of the duration of bright sunshine has received far more attention in the British Isles than in other countries. We may attribute this fact mainly to the introduction, in 1881, of the Campbell-Stokes sunshine recorder, a remarkably simple and efficient instrument for the purpose. Some remarks about the instrument will be found in Chapter I; we have now to examine the data which have been accumulated as a result of its use. In doing so we may have two different objects in mind : first to consider the data on their own merits as facts relating to a meteorological element which is obviously important for the health and pleasure of the community ; second, to regard the data as measurements from which it is possible to derive information in regard to the incidence of cloud and fog. In pursuit of either of these aims, and particularly the latter, we have to take account of the variation during the year of the number of hours per day during which the sun is above the horizon in a given latitude. Also, we shall do well to take note of the variation, with latitude and with the time of the year, of the sun's altitude or angular elevation above the horizon. It will be found convenient therefore to recapitulate briefly the more important facts in regard to the sun's behaviour as a heavenly body before examining the data furnished by the Campbell-Stokes recorder.

80. The sun's annual and diurnal movements. Every one is familiar with the fact that the rotation of the earth causes the sun to pursue an apparent daily path from east through south to west across the heavens, the journey being accompanied by an increase in altitude from zero at sunrise up to a maximum at noon, decreasing again to zero at sunset. Other familiar facts are (*a*) that the interval between sunrise and sunset is a maximum at midsummer and a minimum at midwinter ; (*b*) that the altitude of the sun at noon is also a maximum at midsummer and a minimum at midwinter. These seasonal variations arise from the fact that the sun's declination, or angular distance from the celestial equator, goes through an annual cycle. Twice a year, namely at the vernal equinox (21st March) and the autumnal equinox (23rd September), the sun is actually on the equator. At all places on the earth's surface the celestial equator intersects the horizon at points due east and west of the point of observation ; consequently the sun rises due east and sets due west, everywhere, at either equinox. Half its apparent path is above the horizon and the length of the day is equal to the length of

TABLE XXXIII

MEAN VALUES OF THE DURATION OF DAYLIGHT IN EACH MONTH, AND THE YEAR, WITH THE VALUES AT THE SOLSTICES

	Latitude (North)					
	50°	52°	54°	56°	58°	60°
	hrs.	hrs.	hrs.	hrs	hrs.	hrs.
January - - -	8·55	8·26	7·95	7·60	7·18	6·70
February - - -	10·00	9·85	9·67	9·48	9·26	9·02
March - - -	11·81	11·79	11·77	11·75	11·73	11·70
April - - - -	13·69	13·82	13·96	14·11	14·28	14·47
May - - - -	15·33	15·60	15·89	16·21	16·60	17·03
June - - - -	16·22	16·57	16·96	17·41	17·94	18·59
July - - - -	15·83	16·13	16·48	16·88	17·34	17·88
August - - -	14·40	14·59	14·79	15·01	15·26	15·55
September - - -	12·60	12·64	12·69	12·74	12·80	12·86
October - - -	10·73	10·63	10·52	10·40	10·26	10·12
November - - -	9·03	8·80	8·53	8·24	7·90	7·51
December - - -	8·09	7·77	7·40	6·98	6·49	5·93
Year - - -	12·20	12·21	12·23	12·25	12·27	12·30
Summer Solstice - (21st June)	16·30	16·67	17·07	17·53	18·08	18·75
Winter Solstice - (21st December)	8·00	7·67	7·28	6·85	6·33	5·75

[From *Averages of Bright Sunshine* (M.O. 408)]

the night in all latitudes (actually the length of the day slightly exceeds the length of the night, owing to the effect of the refraction of the sun's rays by the atmosphere).

It is important, however, to observe that although the length of the day is the same everywhere at either equinox, the apparent path of the sun varies with the latitude. At a point on the earth's equator the sun would be observed to rise vertically above the eastern horizon, pass through the zenith at noon, and set vertically in the west. At either pole, the sun would just appear with half its disc above the horizon and pass right round the horizon without noticeable change of altitude during the twenty-four hours ; there would be no distinction between day and night. In middle latitudes the sun would reach an altitude at noon equal to the co-latitude, or ninety degrees minus the latitude. In general, if γ is the latitude of the place, and δ is the sun's declination (north, positive ; south, negative) the sun's altitude at noon is equal to $90° - \gamma + \delta$. The declination δ has the value $0°$ at either equinox, $+23\frac{1}{2}°$ (approximately) at the summer solstice (22nd June), and $-23\frac{1}{2}°$ (approximately) at the winter solstice (22nd December). Thus for any

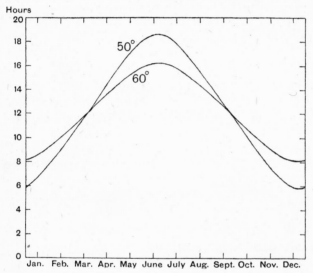

Fig. 57.—Annual variation of the mean daily duration of daylight in latitude 50° N. and 60° N.

place outside the tropics the noon altitude of the sun varies over a range of 47° during the year. In latitude 60° N., which is about the latitude of the Shetlands, the maximum noon value of the sun's altitude is $53\frac{1}{2}°$ and the minimum noon value is $6\frac{1}{2}°$. For latitude 50° N., corresponding to the extreme south-west of England, the values are $63\frac{1}{2}°$ and $16\frac{1}{2}°$.

The duration of daylight, that is to say the interval between sunrise and sunset, can be calculated from the sun's declination, and the latitude by means of an equation which will be found in text-books of mathematical astronomy, but which need not be given here. On account of the incidence of leap year the values are not quite the same on the same date in successive years. Average values are, however, near enough for our purpose, and we give in Table XXXIII the values of the mean length of the day in each calendar month, for intervals of 2° of latitude. These values include a correction for refraction of the sun's rays by the earth's atmosphere. The values at the solstices, giving the maximum and minimum for the whole year, are appended. It will be observed that the longest day in latitude 60° N. exceeds the longest day in latitude 50° N. by 2½ hours. There is a slightly smaller difference between the lengths of the shortest days, but in the opposite sense. Another point of interest is that the mean daily duration of daylight for the whole year is 0·1 hour (six minutes) longer in latitude 60° than in latitude 50° ; the difference arises from the effect of the correction for refraction.

The annual variation of the daily duration of daylight in latitudes 50° N. and 60° N. is shown graphically in Fig. 57. An interesting feature of these curves is the straightness of the ascending and descending branches. From about the middle of January to the end of May the length of the day increases at a steady and nearly uniform rate ; for the next six weeks, in the middle of which the summer solstice occurs, there is little change. Then from the middle of July to the end of November the days shorten at the same rate that they increased during the earlier months ; for the next six weeks there is little variation during the passage through the winter solstice, and then the cycle is repeated again. Since the passage into law of the " Summer Time " Act the uniformity of this annual march of the sun has been rendered less noticeable by the abrupt change in our habits which accompanies the putting forward and backward of the hands of the clock.

The diurnal variation of the sun's altitude and azimuth at the solstices and equinoxes is illustrated in Fig. 58 for latitudes 50° N. and 60° N. It is necessary to draw attention to the fact that in this diagram the scale of altitudes is double the scale of azimuths ; the curves are therefore very distorted representations of the sun's apparent path. Nevertheless they enable us to form a fairly clear idea of the course of events at the northern and southern extremities of the British Isles. From the autumnal equinox through the winter solstice to the vernal equinox the sun's altitude is higher at all hours of the day in latitude 50° N. than in latitude 60° N. During the summer half-year the sun rises earlier in the more northern latitude, but climbs more slowly, with the result that at some time in the morning and again at some time in the evening the altitude is about the same at all places in the British Isles. At the

summer solstice this equality occurs at about 7 h. and 17 h., when the
altitude is approximately 28°. When sunrise occurs in latitude 50° N.
the sun has already been up for more than an hour in latitude 60° N.,
but it is only five degrees above the horizon. Thus we may regard the
additional hours of daylight in high northern latitudes as a mere prolongation of the early morning and late evening hours, during which
the sun is at a low altitude. We shall see later that the recorded duration of bright sunshine increases rapidly with the altitude of the sun ;
consequently the greater length of the summer day in high northern
latitudes does not in practice confer much advantage on those regions
in regard to the recording of sunshine. In winter, on the other hand,

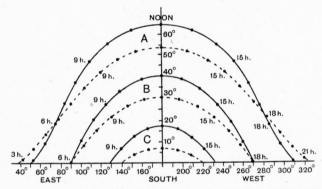

FIG. 58.—Diurnal variation of sun's altitude and azimuth in latitude 50° N.
(full lines) and 60° N. (broken lines).
A—summer solstice, B—equinoxes, C—winter solstice.

the south has the double advantage of longer days and a higher altitude
of the sun at all hours. A noticeable feature of the curves in Fig. 58
is the flattened form of their upper portions ; there is little variation in
the sun's altitude for about two hours on either side of noon. It should
be noted that the hours marked on this diagram refer to local apparent
time, that is to say, the time indicated by a sundial or by the sunshine-
recorder itself.

81. The mean daily duration of sunshine. The daily duration of
bright sunshine, averaged over the entire year, varies from less than
three hours in the Shetlands and over parts of the mainland of Great
Britain to rather more than five hours in the Channel Isles and at one
or two points on the south-east coast of England. The geographical
distribution, based on records covering the period 1906 to 1935, is shown

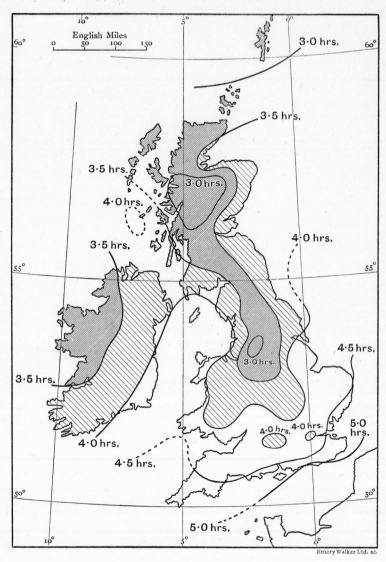

Emery Walker Ltd. sc.

FIG. 59.—Mean daily duration of sunshine, whole year (1906-1935).
(Areas with less than 4·0 hours per day are shaded ; darker shading denotes
areas with less than 3·5 hours per day.)

in Fig. 59. An area of low duration (less than 3·5 hours per day) covers most of Scotland and extends in the form of an elongated trough down the Pennines to the Peak District. There is another area with less than 3·5 hours per day over western Ireland. Between these two areas a " ridge " in which the daily average exceeds four hours extends over the south-east coast of Ireland, the Isle of Man and the west coast of England and Wales. An " outlier ", the conjectural character of which is indicated by broken lines, is seen over the southern portion of the Hebrides. The evidence for this relatively sunny patch in the north-west is furnished by the records from an instrument installed at Tiree in 1926 which indicate an annual average of the order of four hours. Over Great Britain we may recognize three distinct influences: (a) a general increase of sunshine from north to south ; (b) a decrease of sunshine from the coast inland ; (c) a decrease of sunshine with altitude. The records from individual stations also show the effects of a fourth influence, namely town smoke. It will be noticed that in Fig. 59 London is indicated by a small closed curve, within which the average annual duration is under four hours. The actual values for London stations are as follows : Hampstead 4·06, Kew 4·02, Enfield 4·00, Greenwich 3·97, Tottenham 3·87, Westminster 3·68, Regent's Park 3·59, City (Bunhill Row) 3·36. In the country around London we have Croydon 4·17, Wisley 4·15. Here we see a very definite decrease in sunshine from the outskirts towards the centre of the city, due to the obscuration of the sun's rays by smoke.[1] We should expect to find the lowest sunshine records in England in the industrial areas of the north and Midlands, which suffer from a heavily polluted atmosphere. Actually the lowest annual averages are found at Manchester, Oldham Road (2·65 hours), Bolton (2·82 hours) and Burnley (3·04 hours), all in Lancashire. The records for the West Riding of Yorkshire are distinctly better, e.g. Bradford (3·31 hours), Sheffield (3·59 hours). No figures are available for the " Black Country " of Staffordshire.

Over the mountainous area of Scotland there is a large region with an annual average of under three hours. There are not many sunshine records for this area, and its limits cannot be regarded as accurately defined. On the higher peaks the value is certainly much less than three hours. Records obtained at Ben Nevis Observatory during the period 1891 to 1902 gave a daily average of 2·13 hours. It seems probable also that the value may be under three hours on the summits of the mountains in other areas, particularly in western Ireland.

[1] See also Chapter XII, p. 304.

The highest daily mean values on the mainland are found at East-bourne (5·02 hours), Worthing (5·02 hours) and Bognor Regis (4·99 hours) on the Sussex coast; several other stations on the south-east coast, and the Isle of Wight, have values approaching five hours. These records are exceeded in the Channel Islands where the daily average is 5·16 hours at Guernsey and 5·10 hours at Jersey.

82. Percentage of possible sunshine. As the mean daily duration of daylight throughout the year is very nearly the same all over the British Isles, namely about $12\frac{1}{4}$ hours, the distribution of mean daily sunshine for the whole year, expressed as a percentage of the possible amount, is obtained from Fig. 59 by attaching different numbers to the lines, viz. 3 hours = 24 per cent., 3·5 hours = 29 per cent., 4 hours = 33 per cent., 4·5 hours = 37 per cent., 5 hours = 41 per cent. Thus in the sunniest areas the duration of bright sunshine slightly exceeds forty per cent. of the total time. For London the value is about thirty-three per cent.; it falls somewhat below twenty-five per cent. in the dullest areas and is as low as seventeen per cent. at the summit of Ben Nevis.

83. Cloudiness and its relation to sunshine. One of the items in the observational routine at meteorological stations is to estimate the number of tenths of the area of the sky covered by clouds of all types. An entirely clear sky would be represented by figure 0 and an entirely overcast sky by figure 10. The value obtained in this way is known as the "amount of cloud" or the "cloudiness". Averages of cloudiness for a number of stations will be found in the climatic tables in the Appendix, and it is natural to regard these averages as data having a definite relationship to the recorded amount of sunshine. On examination, however, it is found that the relationship between cloud and sunshine is not so simple and direct as might be supposed. The cloudiness data for a number of typical stations are given in Table XXXIV. The first four columns contain the means for the four equinoctial and solstitial months, March, June, September and December; in the next column we have the means for the whole year. By multiplying these figures by ten we get the mean percentage area of the sky covered with cloud. If now we subtract the percentage values from 100 we get the mean percentage area of the sky free from cloud. These values are given in the last column but one and we should expect them to agree fairly closely with the mean percentage of possible sunshine given in the last column. For many of the stations this expectation is realized, but other stations, for example Inverness, Dover and Scilly, show large discrepancies.

TABLE XXXIV

MEAN CLOUDINESS (TENTHS OF SKY COVERED)

Station	March	June	Sept.	Dec.	Whole Year		
					Cloudi-ness	Per cent. of sky free from cloud	Sunshine as per-centage of possible
SCOTLAND							
Lerwick (*Shetland*) - -	7·7	7·5	7·4	7·4	7·5	25	24
Deerness (*Orkney*) - -	7·5	7·6	7·7	7·4	7·5	25	25
Stornoway (*Hebrides*) -	7·2	7·6	7·5	7·4	7·5	25	27
Tiree (*Hebrides*) - -	6·9	6·4	7·4	7·5	7·0	30	33
Aberdeen (*Aberdeen*) -	6·5	6·5	6·4	6·1	6·5	35	30
Inverness (*Inverness*) -	5·7	5·6	6·0	5·5	5·8	42	28
Leith (*Midlothian*) - -	7·0	6·7	6·5	6·7	6·9	31	32
ENGLAND AND WALES							
Douglas (*Isle of Man*) -	6·6	6·5	6·3	7·3	6·8	32	35
Yarmouth (*Norfolk*) -	6·6	6·7	6·4	6·9	6·8	32	36
Spurn Head (*Yorks.*) -	7·3	6·8	6·8	7·2	7·1	29	34
Oxford (*Oxon.*) - -	6·7	6·4	6·0	7·2	6·6	34	34
Greenwich (*London*) -	6·8	6·8	6·0	7·4	6·9	31	33
Dover (*Kent*) - - -	6·7	6·4	6·3	7·2	6·8	32	39
Holyhead (*Anglesey*) -	6·8	6·2	6·1	7·2	6·6	34	35
St. Ann's Head (*Pembroke*)	6·4	5·8	6·0	7·0	6·4	36	35
Scilly (*St. Mary's*) - -	7·2	6·6	6·5	7·4	6·9	31	38
IRELAND							
Markree Castle (*Sligo*) -	7·0	7·3	7·2	7·6	7·3	27	28
Malin Head (*Donegal*) -	6·8	6·7	7·0	7·2	6·9	31	30
Dublin (*Dublin*) - -	5·9	6·2	5·8	6·3	6·2	38	32
Valentia (*Kerry*) - -	7·1	7·3	6·9	7·7	7·2	28	31

To understand these differences we must consider the factors which may give rise to them ; they are as follows :

(*a*) The sunshine data are derived from continuous records, but the cloud data depend upon estimates made at fixed hours ; the latter may not give an accurate mean of the state of the sky between sunrise and sunset.

(*b*) Sunshine is intercepted by smoke-haze, mist and fog, as well as by cloud.

(*c*) Even on clear days the sunshine recorder is insensitive to weak sunshine such as occurs shortly after sunrise and shortly before sunset ; on the other hand intermittent sunshine is over-recorded.

(d) All cloud does not intercept sunshine completely, a continuous record may be produced when the sky is overcast with thin cirrus cloud.

Interception of sunshine by fog or haze would tend to make the percentage of sunshine lower than the percentage of sky free from cloud ; the over-registration of sunshine during intermittent cloud, and the transparency of thin cloud would have the opposite effect. An examination of the last two columns in Table XXXIV shows that in most cases the percentage of sunshine tends to be higher than the percentage of clear sky. On the whole, therefore, it would appear that loss due to smoke and fog is of less importance in reducing the record

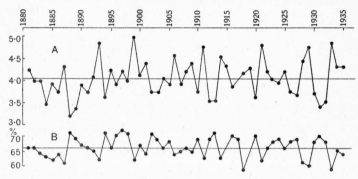

Fig. 60.—Oxford (Radcliffe Observatory) ; fluctuations of mean daily duration of sunshine (A), and percentage of cloud (B) (1881-1935).

of sunshine than might be supposed—at any rate in coastal and rural situations. In large towns evidence of the great loss due to smoke is afforded at once by the sunshine records as compared with those from neighbouring rural areas.

Illustrations of the seasonal variations of the above factors will be forthcoming later. Readers who desire further information on the relationship between cloud and sunshine should consult a paper by Dr. C. E. P. Brooks quoted under reference (36) in the bibliography.

84. Fluctuations of mean annual sunshine and cloudiness. In Fig. 60 we have diagrams showing the sequence of mean annual values of daily sunshine and cloud percentage at the Radcliffe Observatory, Oxford, from 1881 to 1935. At this station the mean daily sunshine (1881 to 1930) is 4·06 hours ; in individual years the value has varied from 3·17 hours (twenty-two per cent. below the mean) in 1888, to 4·95

hours (twenty-two per cent. above the mean) in 1899. The mean percentage of cloud is sixty-six, and there have been variations from fifty-nine in 1918 and 1933 to seventy-two in 1897. On reference to Fig. 60 it will be seen that sunshine was slightly *above* normal in the year of maximum cloudiness, a circumstance which serves to illustrate the lack of close relationship between sunshine and cloudiness. On the whole, however, we may say that there is a fair degree of inverse correlation between graphs A and B of Fig. 60. In most cases, a rise in graph A coincides with a fall in graph B, and *vice versa*.

85. The annual variation. Graphs of the mean daily sunshine averaged for each calendar month are given for eight typical stations in Fig. 61. The curves for all stations show a conspicuous maximum about the time of the summer solstice and a minimum in December, as was to be expected from the annual variation in the sun's declination described at the beginning of this chapter. In addition to this seasonal change the curves show one or two peculiarities. Thus, at the beginning of the year we have a steady rise from January to April; from May to August the curves are distinctly less regular; then from September we have a steady descent to the winter minimum. At every station the minimum occurs in December and no exception to this rule is to be found among the large number of averages given in the official publication, *Averages of Bright Sunshine for periods ended* 1935, from which our data are taken. On the other hand, there is a certain amount of variation in the month of occurrence of the maximum; in the Orkneys and Shetlands, western and northern Ireland, Norfolk, Suffolk and east Kent it occurs in May, in all other districts in June. The districts which furnish the exception to the general rule are very widely separated and it is difficult to see what there is in common between, *e.g.* Kirkwall in the Orkneys, Norwich and Valentia Observatory, to account for the observed result.

In many of the remaining districts the mean value for June exceeds that for May or July by only a small margin; thus for Eastbourne we have May 7·70 hours, June 7·92 hours, July 7·62 hours. On the other hand, the June maximum is very conspicuous in certain areas, especially in Scotland, Wales and western England. Thus we have for Edinburgh (Blackford Hill), May 5·26 hours, June 6·44 hours, July 5·33 hours; and for Haverfordwest (Pembroke), May 6·53 hours, June 7·66 hours, July 6·70 hours. These variations are perhaps due, to some extent, to the fact that thirty years is hardly long enough to give a smooth set of monthly averages. Some of the averages for stations in east and south-east England indicate a tendency for July to be the sunniest month : this appears to occur, however, only at stations where the averages are based on substantially fewer than thirty years of observation, and there is no reason to suppose that it is a permanent climatological feature.

The range of the annual variation is decidedly greater in the sunny

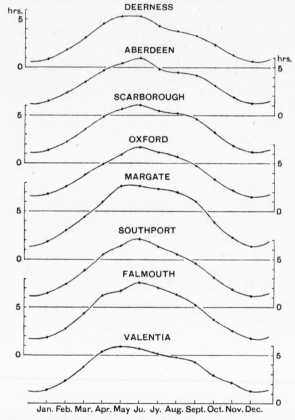

Fig. 61.—Annual variation of mean daily duration of sunshine at typical stations (1906-1935).

districts on the south coast of England than at places, whether in the far north or on the mainland, where the mean daily duration is low. Thus at Deerness, Orkney, the range is from 0·63 hour per day in December to 5·28 in May and June, and at Manchester (Oldham Road) from 0·23 in December to 5·18 in June. At Eastbourne we have a range from 1·72 in December to 7·92 in June, and at Guernsey, from 1·61 to

8·33. These differences in range arise mainly from the large excess of midsummer sunshine in the south as compared with the north ; at midwinter the differences are not so great.

86. Distribution of sunshine in June. Fig. 62 shows the geographical distribution of mean daily sunshine in June. Broadly speaking, the chart resembles the annual chart, Fig. 59, but it is distinctly more complicated. The areas of low sunshine, under 5·5 hours in this month, occupy similar positions, namely in the extreme north, over western Ireland, the central mountainous area of Scotland and the industrial area of south Lancashire. At the other extreme we have slightly more than 8 hours per day locally in the Isle of Wight (Sandown, 8·09 hours) and the Channel Islands (Guernsey, 8·33 hours). On the mainland Eastbourne (7·92 hours) claims the highest value. In the London area it is of interest to note that the mean for the City (Bunhill Row), 6·37 hours, is not far behind the value for Kew Observatory, 6·76 hours ; at Hampstead the mean value for the twenty-five years 1911 to 1935 is as high as 7·06 hours. In the south-west there is an interesting intrusion of a sunny area up the Bristol Channel. Thus at Cardiff we have a June average as high as 7·45 hours, and it is a remarkable circumstance that an industrial city should register in this month an amount of sunshine which compares favourably with that of many south coast health resorts. At Weston-super-Mare which faces Cardiff on the other side of the Bristol Channel, the average is no higher than 6·74 hours.

Even more remarkable is the record of Tiree where during the nine years 1927 to 1935 the daily sunshine has averaged 8·1 hours in May and 7·5 hours in June. If this average is maintained we shall have to recognize the fact that in May the sunniest region in the British Isles is to be found in the southern portion of the Inner Hebrides, instead of on the south-east coast of England as had always been previously supposed. Even if the Tiree records revert to values which seem more appropriate to that region, meteorologists will not find it easy to explain why for a period of nine years Tiree has recorded more sunshine in May than any other place in the British Isles.

87. Distribution of sunshine in December. The sunshine chart for December, the dullest month in the year, Fig. 63, is very much simpler than the chart for June. The total range of variation is from under half an hour per day in the Shetlands, the Highlands of Scotland and the industrial area of Lancashire to about 1·9 hours at one or two points on the south coast of England (Bournemouth 1·93, Torquay 1·91). Areas with less than 1·0 hour cover most of Scotland, parts of

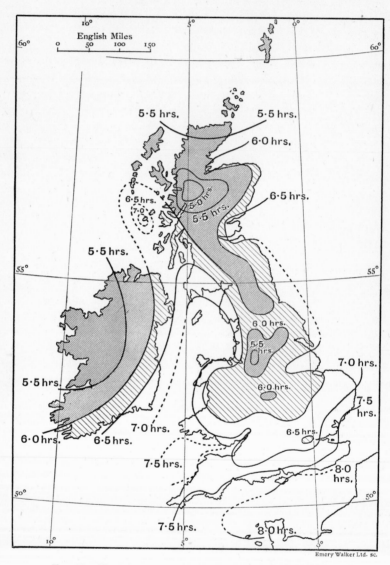

FIG. 62.—Mean daily duration of sunshine in June (1906-1935).
(Areas with less than 6·5 hours per day are shaded ; darker shading denotes
areas with less than 6·0 hours per day.)

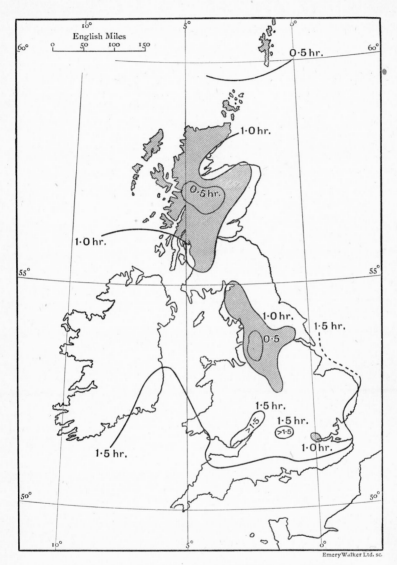

FIG. 63.—Mean daily duration of sunshine in December (1906-1935).
(Areas with less than 1·0 hour per day are shaded.)

north-west England and the Midlands, and the London area. Apart from Ben Nevis, the lowest values are found at Baltasound (Shetland) 0·35 hour, Fort Augustus (Inverness) 0·41 hour, London (Bunhill Row) 0·34 hour, Manchester (Oldham Road) 0·23 hour and Burnley 0·42 hour. The region with more than 1·5 hours includes the English counties south of a line from Hartland Point to the North Foreland, south-east Ireland and the south-west corner of Wales. Detached areas with more than 1·5 hours are also found in the form of a patch over Oxfordshire, a strip extending from Cardiff north-eastward to Malvern, and a coastal patch in Suffolk and Essex.

88. **Percentage of sunshine and cloudiness—annual variation.** Graphs of the annual variation of percentage of possible sunshine at Deerness, Aberdeen, Oxford and Scilly are shown by full lines in Fig. 64. It will be seen that in each case the percentage is lowest in December, the value in that month ranging from ten at Deerness to twenty-one at Scilly. The results for other stations show that in December the percentage is as low as six at Baltasound (Shetlands), six at Fort Augustus, four at Bunhill Row (London), and, in Lancashire, three at Manchester (Oldham Road), six at Bolton and six at Burnley. At the other end of the scale the December percentage exceeds twenty at many stations on the south coast of England and is as high as twenty-four at Bournemouth and Torquay. In the four examples illustrated in the diagram there is considerable variation in the form of the percentage curve from spring to autumn. At Deerness the value reaches a maximum (thirty-two per cent.) in April and then falls slowly to twenty-six in October, after which it decreases rapidly. At Aberdeen the values are nearly the same (thirty-three or thirty-four per cent.) in April, May, June and September, with decidedly lower values in July and August. Oxford shows a maximum (forty per cent.) in June, but there is not much variation from April to September. A similar statement applies to Scilly except that the values in April and June are the same (forty-six per cent.). The general tendency is for the curve to divide itself into three portions, (a) a rapid rise in the early months of the year, (b) a flat portion representing nearly constant percentages from April to September, (c) a rapid descent in the late months of the year to the December minimum.

Among the records for stations on the south coast of England and the Channel Islands we find values approximating to fifty per cent. between April and September. Thus at Guernsey the percentages for these months are 48, 49, 52, 51, 53 and 48 respectively. Sandown (Isle of Wight) has a percentage of fifty in June, and Eastbourne fifty per cent. in May. In the London area the maximum is round about forty-one per cent., varying slightly at different stations.

In Fig. 64 we have added graphs, in broken lines, showing the percentage of sky free from cloud, for comparison with the sunshine figures. It will be seen that the two graphs show very little resemblance at any

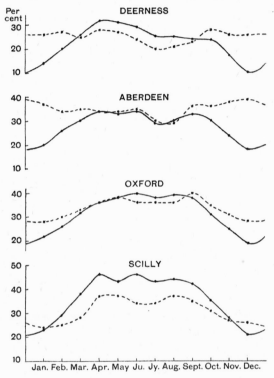

FIG. 64.—Annual variation of percentage of possible sunshine (full lines),
and percentage of sky free from cloud (broken lines).

of the stations. At Scilly the clear sky percentage is nearly equal to the sunshine percentage in November and January and is somewhat greater in December. In all other months the sunshine percentage exceeds the clear sky percentage by a large margin. At Aberdeen and Oxford there is a fair measure of agreement between the two curves during the summer half-year, but in the winter half-year the clear sky percentage is much greater than the sunshine percentage. At Deerness, also, the latter part of this statement is true, but Deerness resembles Scilly in that the

N

sunshine percentage exceeds the clear sky percentage during the summer half-year by a considerable margin.

At Oxford and Scilly the graphs of clear sky percentage show a form of seasonal variation similar to that of sunshine percentage ; that is not the case, however, at Deerness and Aberdeen, where the clear sky percentage is actually lower in July and August than in the winter months.

If the data for individual stations are examined it will be found that there are much smaller seasonal and geographical variations in the cloudiness than in the duration of sunshine or the percentage of possible sunshine. We can explain most of the observed facts in the following way : at any time of the year sunshine may be intercepted by cloud or it may be scattered by haze to such an extent that the transmitted intensity falls below the limit of registration by a sunshine recorder. In either case the cut-off will diminish as the angle of incidence decreases. A thin uniform horizontal cloud sheet may transmit sufficient sunshine to affect the recorder when it is traversed by rays inclined at say 45° to the vertical, but the extra thickness to be traversed when the angle of incidence is increased to say 75° may entirely prevent registration. Also, in a " lumpy " cloud layer, in which the individual clouds are separated by spaces of clear sky, the sun's rays are more likely to find their way through the interspaces when the rays are inclined to the surface at a large angle than when they are nearly parallel to the surface. In regard to haze, the loss by scattering increases very rapidly with increase in the length of the path. Even if there were no seasonal variation in the amount of cloud and in the concentration of atmospheric suspensoids we should expect, therefore, to record a higher percentage of sunshine when the sun's altitude is high than when it is low : that is to say we should expect higher percentages in summer than in winter, in low latitudes than in high latitudes, and at midday than near sunrise or sunset. To round off this explanation we may also add that when an observer estimates cloudiness he looks at the whole sky, including the zenith. He can often see clear patches of blue sky above his head, which are invisible when he looks towards the point where the sun is because the view is blocked by the upper portions of the clouds. Thus no sunshine may be recorded when the sun is low in a sky which the observer judges to be only about half or three-fourths covered with cloud. In urban areas interception or scattering of sunshine by smoke is much greater in winter than in summer because convectional circulation of the atmosphere, which has the effect of distributing the pollution through a great vertical thickness of the atmosphere, is much less active in winter than in summer. Also the portion of the total smoke emanating from domestic chimneys is very much greater in winter than in summer.

89. Fluctuations of monthly sunshine. Table XXXV shows the highest and lowest daily means of sunshine recorded at the Radcliffe Observatory, Oxford, during the fifty-five years 1881 to 1935. In each case the extreme values are expressed as percentages of normal, and we shall probably not stray far from the truth if we assume that the percentage values are fairly representative of the variations for other parts of the British Isles. It will be seen that in the sunniest month on record,

TABLE XXXV

SUNSHINE AT OXFORD : HIGHEST AND LOWEST MEANS, 1881–1935

	Jan.	Feb.	Mar.	Apr.	May	June	July	Aug.	Sept.	Oct.	Nov.	Dec.	Year
Normal 1881-1930	hr. 1·66	hr. 2·37	hr. 3·28	hr. 5·00	hr. 6·23	hr. **6·51**	hr. 6·16	hr. 5·65	hr. 4·71	hr. 3·26	hr. 2·05	hr. 1·41	hr. 4·06
Highest on record	2·64	3·76	6·40	8·43	9·50	8·91	**10·00**	8·08	7·42	5·15	3·60	2·41	4·95
Year - -	1905	1899	1893	1893	1909	1925	1911	1899	1911	1921	1923	1917	1899
Per cent. of normal - -	159	158	**179**	169	152	137	163	143	157	158	175	171	122
Lowest on record	0·48	1·07	2·00	2·81	3·63	3·65	3·18	3·15	1·94	1·60	0·99	*0·16*	3·17
Year - -	1885	1897	1916	1889	1932	1909	1913	1912	1896	1894	1888	1890	1888
Per cent. of normal - -	29	45	56	56	58	56	52	56	62	49	48	*11*	78

July 1911, the mean value, 10·00 hours, exceeded the normal by sixty-three per cent. As regards the percentage of normal, the records for March 1893 (179 per cent.) and November 1923 (175 per cent.) were, however, more remarkable. The value for March 1893 was, in fact, nearly equal to the normal value for June. In all months except June and August the extreme value exceeded the normal by more than fifty per cent. The greatest percentage variations above normal occurred in the spring months March and April, and in November and December.

The dullest month on record was December 1890 when the mean daily duration was no more than 0·16 hour (ten minutes) and the total for the month was only five hours. The percentage of normal (eleven) was much lower in that month than in any month of different name which gave the lowest record. It will be noticed that months giving less than half the normal have all occurred during the period October to

February, but the value was not much above half the normal in July 1913.

The extremes for Oxford have, of course, been surpassed in both directions at other stations. Thus, for example, in July 1911 the daily mean was as high as 12·3 hours at Bournemouth and Brighton. In December 1890 the aggregate duration for the whole month at Bun-

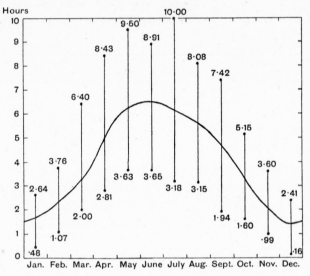

FIG. 65.—Mean daily duration of sunshine at Oxford (Radcliffe Observatory), 1881-1930, with highest and lowest monthly means recorded during the period 1881-1935.

hill Row (London) was only 0·1 hour, and every day except one was sunless.

The sunniest week on record at Oxford, 4th-10th July, 1934, gave a total of 100·1 hours, or an average of 14·3 hours per day. During the first ten days of July 1934 sunshine was practically uninterrupted over southern England, and the daily average for this period was 13·1 hours at Kew Observatory.

90. Fluctuations of sunshine and cloudiness in June at Oxford. In Fig. 66 we give graphs of the mean daily sunshine, and of the percentage of sky free from cloud, in each June from 1881 to 1935. As cloud rather than haze is likely to be the controlling factor in respect to sunshine at an inland station in the south of England during a summer month, we should expect the two graphs to show a fair degree of correlation. On the whole this expectation is borne out by the graphs, the peaks and troughs being coincident in practically every case. In particular we may note that the year 1909 which gave the minimum duration of sunshine in June also gave the minimum percentage of clear sky. The sunshine in the June with the highest clear sky percentage, 1887, was, however, slightly exceeded in 1899, 1908 and 1925. The range of variation of sunshine was from twenty-two per cent. to fifty-four per cent. of the possible amount and the range of variation of the clear sky percentage was from seventeen to sixty-one.

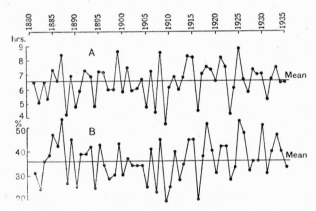

FIG. 66.—Oxford (Radcliffe Observatory) ; fluctuations of mean daily duration of sunshine (A), and percentage of sky free from cloud (B), in June.

91. Frequency-distribution of sunshine duration. The Meteorological Office has published a table giving the average and percentage number of days with bright sunshine between stated limits for various stations. These data have been discussed by E. G. Bilham and Miss L. F. Lewis (37), and charts based upon them have been drawn by J. Glasspoole and D. A. Hancock (38). By way of illustration, the data for four stations, Aberdeen, Kew, Falmouth and Valentia are given in Table XXXVI. We have added values of the percentage frequency of days with more than half the possible sunshine, computed by Bilham and Miss Lewis, who took that criterion as defining a " sunny day ".

The figures show that sunless days number about one in five, on the average for the year, at Aberdeen, Kew and Valentia, and about one in six at Falmouth. The percentage of sunless days is as high as twenty-five (one day in four) at Deerness (Orkney) and also at Renfrew and Eskdalemuir, both in Scotland. The frequency of sunless days shows a

THE CLIMATE OF THE BRITISH ISLES

very pronounced annual variation from a maximum in the winter to a minimum in the summer. At Kew such days approximate to fifty per cent. in December and January, and that value is exceeded in December

TABLE XXXVI

PERCENTAGE FREQUENCIES OF DAYS WITH BRIGHT SUNSHINE BETWEEN STATED LIMITS (TWENTY YEARS, 1913–1932)

Sunshine	Jan.	Feb.	Mar.	Apr.	May	June	July	Aug.	Sept.	Oct.	Nov.	Dec.	Year
ABERDEEN (Aber.)													
Nil - - -	40	31	19	12	11	7	9	11	14	19	31	39	20
0·1 to 3·0 hrs. -	39	37	35	26	23	24	31	33	31	33	36	44	33
3·1 to 6·0 hrs. -	19	20	22	27	23	21	26	24	24	28	28	17	23
6·1 to 9·0 hrs. -	2	12	18	21	22	19	18	20	21	18	5	0	15
Over 9·0 hrs. -	0	0	6	14	21	29	16	12	10	2	0	0	9
More than half poss. - -	17	20	25	26	26	30	18	20	28	26	22	14	23
KEW (Surrey)													
Nil - - -	46	32	20	11	7	5	5	4	10	16	37	47	20
0·1 to 3·0 hrs. -	33	40	33	31	22	20	28	26	28	37	36	34	30
3·1 to 6·0 hrs. -	18	20	24	23	19	20	20	25	22	29	20	18	22
6·1 to 9·0 hrs. -	3	8	19	21	20	22	22	23	25	17	7	1	16
Over 9·0 hrs. -	0	0	4	14	22	33	25	22	15	1	0	0	12
More than half poss. - -	12	14	24	28	41	39	32	34	37	24	16	11	26
FALMOUTH (Corn.)													
Nil - - -	34	25	14	9	10	6	6	6	12	15	25	30	16
0·1 to 3·0 hrs. -	38	36	28	21	19	17	21	24	25	33	38	43	29
3·1 to 6·0 hrs. -	21	22	23	19	19	12	17	18	19	24	23	22	20
6·1 to 9·0 hrs. -	7	16	24	20	18	20	21	23	23	23	14	5	18
Over 9·0 hrs. -	0	1	11	31	34	45	35	29	21	5	0	0	17
More than half poss. - -	17	23	36	45	42	50	43	43	41	33	24	17	35
VALENTIA (Kerry)													
Nil - - -	38	29	17	10	11	11	12	13	18	23	31	38	21
0·1 to 3·0 hrs. -	43	38	30	24	23	29	35	29	31	36	40	47	34
3·1 to 6·0 hrs. -	16	20	25	21	19	15	18	20	20	23	19	13	19
6·1 to 9·0 hrs. -	3	12	18	23	19	16	15	18	19	15	10	2	14
Over 9·0 hrs. -	0	1	10	22	28	29	20	20	12	3	0	0	12
More than half poss. - -	12	18	29	37	35	32	24	29	29	23	19	11	25

[From *Averages of Bright Sunshine* (M.O. 408) and *Professional Notes*, No. 69]

at Deerness, Renfrew and Eskdalemuir. On the other hand, sunless days are relatively rare from June to August at Kew, Falmouth and other stations in the south.

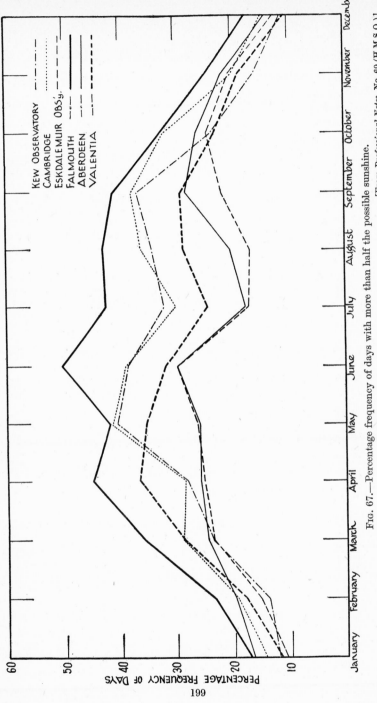

KEW OBSERVATORY ─ ·─ ·─
CAMBRIDGE ············
ESKDALEMUIR OBSy. ─ · · ─
FALMOUTH ──────
ABERDEEN ─ ── ─
VALENTIA ─ ·· ─

FIG. 67.—Percentage frequency of days with more than half the possible sunshine.

[From *Professional Notes*, No. 69 (H.M.S.O.)]

Days with more than nine hours of sunshine naturally occur mainly in the summer months. At Falmouth their frequency is as high as forty-five per cent. in June, and at Kew they occur as often as one day in three in that month.

The data in regard to the frequency of occurrence of days with more than half the possible sunshine are of special interest, because they are based on a criterion which takes account of the variation of the length of the day with latitude and time of year. Graphs of the values for the four stations in Table XXXVI and also for Cambridge and Eskdalemuir are given in Fig. 67. The maximum frequency occurs in April, May or June at all the stations. Then follows a sharp drop in July followed by a recovery to a secondary maximum in September (August at Falmouth). The values are particularly low at the two Scottish stations in July and August; at Eskdalemuir there are only seventeen per cent. of sunny days in these two months as compared with thirty per cent. in June.

It will be noticed that the graphs for Cambridge and Kew Observatory agree closely from April to September, but from October to March Cambridge enjoys a much higher frequency of sunny days than Kew: a result which we may attribute to the interception of sunshine at Kew by London smoke.

For the whole year the frequency of sunny days is about one in four at Aberdeen, Kew and Valentia, and rather more than one in three at Falmouth.

92. Diurnal variation. Averages of hourly values of sunshine at Aberdeen, Kew, Falmouth and Valentia for the equinoctial and solstitial months are given in Table XXXVII. The values for other months are given in the volumes of *Hourly Values from Autographic Records*, published by the Meteorological Office during the years 1915, 1916 and 1917.

The average altitude of the sun is a maximum for the noon hour 11.30-12.30 in June and we might therefore expect the hourly average to attain its maximum value at that epoch. We see, however, that the maximum is attained at an early afternoon hour in June at Aberdeen, Falmouth and Valentia. The complete set of averages shows that the highest hourly values for the year are as follows :

> *Aberdeen*—0·48 at 12 h. and 13 h. in May.
> *Kew*—0·54 at 11 h. in May, 10 h. and 11 h. in August.
> *Falmouth*—0·61 at 15 h. in May.
> *Valentia*—0·53 at 13 h. in May.

In general there is little change in the hourly values for some hours on either side of noon in the brighter months of the year. The hourly values increase rapidly for about four hours after sunrise and decrease rapidly during the four hours before sunset ; in the intervening period, varying in length with the time of year, there is very little change. We may also remark that there is very little change in the maximum hourly values from April to September. Thus for Kew we have :

		Maximum hourly value
March	- - - - - -	0·40
April	- - - - - -	0·50
May -	- - - - - -	0·54
June -	- - - - - -	0·52
July -	- - - - - -	0·52
August	- - - - - -	0·54
September	- - - - -	0·52
October	- - - - - -	0·39

It appears therefore that sunshine only tends to increase with the altitude of the sun up to a certain point. Perhaps a more accurate way of putting it would be to say that the factors, other than cloud amount, which tend to limit the duration of sunshine, become ineffective when the sun's altitude has reached a certain value. If that be a correct deduction it will also be true to say that the average amount of cloud tends to be nearly constant during the brighter daylight hours from April to September.

93. Morning and afternoon sunshine. The values for Falmouth given in Table XXXVII for the month of June show a very definite tendency for sunshine to be more abundant in the afternoon hours than in the morning. If we split the noon value equally between morning and afternoon we find that the mean daily value of 7·28 hours is made up of 3·35 hours (forty-six per cent.) in the forenoon and 3·93 hours (fifty-four per cent.) in the afternoon. Corresponding percentages for each of the four stations in each month are given in Table XXXVIII. It will be observed that although the afternoon sunshine exceeds the morning sunshine in most months at all four stations, there are nevertheless some exceptions. At Kew the percentage difference is largest in winter months, but retains the same sign throughout the year. At Falmouth morning sunshine exceeds afternoon sunshine in winter months. At Valentia the maximum difference in favour of afternoon sunshine also occurs in summer months. At Aberdeen the seasonal variation is similar to that at Kew, but the forenoon and afternoon values reach equality from July to September.

TABLE XXXVII

HOURLY MEANS (LOCAL APPARENT TIME) OF SUNSHINE, 1881–1915

Month	4 h.	5 h.	6 h.	7 h.	8 h.	9 h.	10 h.	11 h.	12 h.	13 h.	14 h.	15 h.	16 h.	17 h.	18 h.	19 h.	20 h.	Day
	hr.	hr.	hr.	hr.	hr.	hr.	hr.	hr.	hr.	hr.	hr.	hr.	hr.	hr.	hr.	hr.	hr.	hr.
						ABERDEEN (*Aberdeen*)												
March -	—	—	0·01	0·11	0·29	0·38	0·42	**0·43**	0·42	0·40	0·39	0·35	0·29	0·14	0·01	—	—	3·63
June -	0·07	0·23	0·31	0·35	0·38	0·41	0·43	0·45	0·45	0·45	**0·46**	0·44	0·41	0·39	0·36	0·27	0·08	5·95
Sept. -	—	—	0·04	0·20	0·33	0·39	**0·42**	0·41	**0·42**	0·41	0·40	0·38	0·34	0·23	0·03	—	—	4·00
Dec. -	—	—	—	—	—	0·01	0·14	0·24	**0·27**	0·25	0·17	0·03	0·00	—	—	—	—	1·10
Year -	0·01	0·06	0·11	0·17	0·23	0·30	0·36	0·38	**0·39**	**0·39**	0·37	0·31	0·24	0·18	0·11	0·06	0·01	3·67
						KEW (*Surrey*)												
March -	—	—	0·00	0·09	0·23	0·33	0·37	**0·40**	**0·40**	**0·40**	0·37	0·35	0·28	0·13	0·01	—	—	3·36
June -	—	0·16	0·34	0·41	0·44	0·48	0·50	0·50	**0·52**	0·51	0·51	0·50	0·48	0·45	0·42	0·28	0·01	6·46
Sept. -	—	—	0·02	0·18	0·33	0·43	0·50	**0·52**	**0·52**	**0·52**	0·51	0·51	0·44	0·31	0·05	—	—	4·84
Dec. -	—	—	—	—	—	0·05	0·17	0·21	0·22	**0·23**	0·20	0·09	—	—	—	—	—	1·17
Year -	—	0·04	0·12	0·19	0·25	0·32	0·37	**0·40**	**0·40**	**0·40**	0·39	0·35	0·28	0·22	0·15	0·07	0·01	3·96
						FALMOUTH (*Cornwall*)												
March -	—	—	0·01	0·16	0·37	0·43	0·46	**0·49**	0·48	0·48	0·47	0·44	0·39	0·21	0·01	—	—	4·40
June -	0·01	0·23	0·38	0·40	0·44	0·47	0·49	0·53	0·53	0·54	0·57	**0·58**	**0·58**	0·55	0·49	0·30	0·01	7·28
Sept. -	—	—	0·06	0·27	0·43	0·49	0·52	0·54	0·55	**0·56**	0·54	0·53	0·49	0·36	0·07	—	—	5·41
Dec. -	—	—	—	—	0·01	0·14	0·27	0·31	**0·32**	0·29	0·25	0·13	0·01	—	—	—	—	1·73
Year -	—	0·05	0·14	0·22	0·32	0·40	0·45	**0·48**	0·47	0·47	0·46	0·43	0·35	0·27	0·19	0·07	—	4·77
						VALENTIA (*Kerry*)												
March -	—	—	—	0·13	0·32	0·39	0·42	**0·45**	0·43	0·42	0·39	0·34	0·19	0·02	—	—	—	3·95
June -	0·02	0·20	0·32	0·39	0·42	0·44	0·46	0·46	0·48	**0·50**	**0·50**	0·49	0·47	0·43	0·37	0·27	0·04	6·26
Sept. -	—	—	0·02	0·18	0·33	0·40	0·45	0·46	**0·47**	**0·47**	**0·47**	0·45	0·40	0·27	0·06	—	—	4·43
Dec. -	—	—	—	—	—	0·06	0·20	**0·26**	**0·26**	0·24	0·19	0·10	0·00	—	—	—	—	1·31
Year -	—	0·04	0·11	0·17	0·24	0·32	0·38	0·40	**0·41**	**0·41**	0·40	0·36	0·29	0·22	0·14	0·06	0·01	3·96

The values refer to periods of sixty minutes centred at exact hours of Local Apparent Time.

(From *Hourly Values from Autographic Records*, 1915 ; the values for Aberdeen have been amended

Some information in regard to the diurnal variation of cloudiness is given in Table **XXXIX** where we have 30-year averages of the number of tenths of sky covered at 9 h., 15 h. and 21 h. at Aberdeen, Kew and Valentia. For comparison with the sunshine records the values at 9 h. and 15 h. are of most interest. We see that the cloudiness tends to be less in the morning than in the afternoon at Aberdeen from September to May, the reverse being true in June, July and August. At Valentia morning cloudiness exceeds afternoon cloudiness in all months except February and December, but it will be noticed that the amount of cloud increases again at 21 h. in the summer months. At Kew afternoon

TABLE XXXVIII

PERCENTAGE AMOUNTS OF SUNSHINE IN THE MORNING AND AFTERNOON

Month	ABERDEEN		KEW		FALMOUTH		VALENTIA	
	Foren'n	Aftern'n	Foren'n	Aftern'n	Foren'n	Aftern'n	Foren'n	Aftern'n
	%	%	%	%	%	%	%	%
January -	48	52	46	54	52	48	48	52
February -	48	52	46	54	50	50	48	52
March -	51	49	48	52	49	51	49	51
April - -	49	51	49	51	48	52	49	51
May - -	49	51	49	51	48	52	48	52
June - -	48	52	47	53	46	54	47	53
July - -	50	50	48	52	47	53	45	55
August -	50	50	49	51	47	53	46	54
September -	50	50	48	52	48	52	47	53
October -	49	51	48	52	50	50	48	52
November -	48	52	44	56	51	49	49	51
December -	48	52	46	54	51	49	50	50
Year -	49	51	48	52	48	52	47	53

TABLE XXXIX

MEAN CLOUD AMOUNT AT 9 H., 15 H. AND 21 H. (1910–1929)

Month	ABERDEEN			KEW			VALENTIA		
	9 h.	15 h.	21 h.	9 h.	15 h.	21 h.	9 h.	15 h.	21 h.
January - -	6·5	6·6	6·1	7·9	7·8	6·9	8·0	7·9	7·4
February - -	6·8	6·8	6·5	7·6	7·7	6·4	7·8	7·9	7·3
March - -	6·4	6·7	6·4	7·3	7·4	5·6	7·3	7·2	6·6
April - -	6·6	6·6	5·9	6·9	7·2	5·4	7·1	6·9	6·5
May - -	6·5	6·6	6·3	6·4	6·6	5·3	7·4	7·0	7·2
June - -	6·8	6·5	6·3	6·7	6·9	5·5	7·6	7·0	7·5
July - -	7·2	6·9	6·9	7·0	7·1	5·8	7·7	7·2	7·5
August - -	7·4	7·1	6·8	7·0	7·4	5·3	7·9	7·2	7·5
September - -	6·4	6·6	5·7	6·4	6·5	4·5	7·5	7·1	6·9
October - -	6·3	6·4	6·1	7·1	6·9	5·5	7·6	7·3	7·0
November - -	6·2	6·4	5·8	7·4	7·3	6·3	7·5	7·4	6·8
December - -	6·1	6·4	5·7	7·7	7·5	6·7	7·9	8·0	7·5
Year - -	6·6	6·6	6·2	7·1	7·2	5·8	7·6	7·3	7·1

cloudiness exceeds morning cloudiness from March to September, and is less than morning cloudiness from October to February.

For Valentia the data of Tables XXXVIII and XXXIX are in good accord, and the same may be said of the results at Kew from October to February and of the Aberdeen results for March and June. The discrepancies which appear in the results for other months are, no doubt, attributable to the effects of haze. Thus at Kew the atmosphere over the densely populated area lying to eastward of the station is in general more polluted than that over the more rural area lying to westward. Also, since the temperature is, on the average, much higher in the hour or two preceding sunset than in the hour or two following sunrise atmospheric turbulence tends to scatter the smoke particles during the pre-sunset period and prevent their concentration becoming sufficient to prevent the registration of sunshine. We may note, in addition, that water-fog is more frequent near sunrise than near sunset. Thus it is found that the recorded amount of sunshine is considerably greater at Kew in the period preceding sunset than in the period following sunrise, at all times of year, and it may be inferred that the gain resulting from these considerations offsets the loss due to additional cloud in the afternoon in the summer months.

BIBLIOGRAPHY

(36) C. E. P. Brooks, " The relation between the duration of bright sunshine registered by a Campbell-Stokes sunshine recorder and the estimated amount of cloud," *Professional Notes*, No. 53. (H.M.S.O.)

(37) E. G. Bilham and Miss L. F. Lewis, " The frequency of days with specified duration of sunshine," *Professional Notes*, No. 69. (H.M.S.O.)

(38) J. Glasspoole and D. A. Hancock, " The distribution over the British Isles of the average duration of bright sunshine," *Q.J.R. Meteor Soc.*, **62**, 1936, p. 247.

See also :

Averages of Bright Sunshine for periods ending 1935 (M.O. 408). (H.M.S.O.)

CHAPTER IX

HUMIDITY OF THE AIR

94. Water-vapour in the atmosphere. It is well known that atmospheric air always contains a certain amount of water-vapour. In the air of temperate latitudes the amount is always small, usually round about one-half to one-and-a-half per cent. by weight, but the quantity is highly variable. Water-vapour is, in fact, the only constituent of the lower atmosphere which shows appreciable variations with time and place, and its meteorological importance is very great. The theory of water-vapour and its part in the physics and dynamics of the atmosphere are discussed in meteorological text-books. From the climatological point of view water-vapour is of importance because the relative dryness or dampness of the air are matters of great concern in respect to human comfort and also in respect to the growth of plants and the prosecution of certain industries. Our climatological statistics contain a considerable amount of information in regard to this element, but it has not, on the whole, been summarized so thoroughly as, for example, the data in regard to temperature or rainfall. Some difficulty is experienced, therefore, when an attempt is made to present an adequate picture of the distribution in time and space over the British Isles as a whole. This difficulty is due in part to the fact that as a physical entity humidity is inherently more complex than the other climatological elements with which we have to deal. In Chapter I it was explained that our data are derived, in the main, from readings of dry- and wet-bulb thermometers at fixed hours. These readings are, however, only "spot-readings" of an entity which exhibits large diurnal and casual variations. To derive really satisfactory information about humidity we need continuous records from dry- and wet-bulb thermographs. It has only been possible to maintain these at a few first order observatories. In the following discussion we shall find it necessary, therefore, to devote most attention to these observatory records. Fortunately, they suffice to give a fair idea of the main features presented by humidity in our area.

95. Modes of expression. There are various ways of giving numerical expression to the quantity of water-vapour present in the air at a given moment. Perhaps the simplest is to state the quantity as weight per unit volume, *i.e.* grams per cubic metre or grains per cubic foot. The figure giving this information is usually referred to as the *moisture-content*; it is a figure of special interest to the air-conditioning engineer because it tells him what weight of water is already present per unit volume of the air which he desires to bring to a predetermined hygrometric state.

Another method is to state the partial pressure of the water-vapour in millibars, or in inches or millimetres of mercury; this figure is called the " vapour-tension ", or more often nowadays the *vapour-pressure*. Sometimes, also, this value is referred to as the " absolute humidity " [1] in contrast to the *relative humidity*, which represents the percentage degree of saturation of the air. If dry air at a given temperature is brought into contact with a plane surface of water at the same temperature, evaporation will take place from the water surface until the moisture-content of the air has risen to a certain definite value, depending upon the temperature. When the air contains this limiting amount of moisture it is said to be saturated and the partial pressure of the water-vapour is the " saturation vapour-pressure " at the temperature of the air. The relative humidity is the quotient of the actual vapour-pressure divided by the saturation vapour-pressure and multiplied by one hundred.

The difference between the vapour-pressure at the time of observation and the saturation vapour-pressure is known as the " saturation deficiency " or *saturation-deficit*. This quantity, which is especially favoured by entomologists and plant physiologists, is sometimes called the " drying power of the air ", apparently for the following reason. If the vapour-pressure is P on one side of a boundary surface and p on the other, water-vapour will pass across the boundary by molecular diffusion at a rate proportional to $P - p$. If the boundary is a water surface over which we have air at the same temperature, t, we may call P the saturation pressure at temperature t, and $P - p$ is the saturation-deficit; thus the saturation-deficit represents the rate of evaporation into still air. These ideal conditions are, however, very difficult to realize in practice and it is questionable whether the saturation-deficit has more claim to consideration as a measure of rate of evaporation than the depression of the wet-bulb: the latter is, at any rate, a definite index of the rate of evaporation from the wet muslin which surrounds the wet-bulb thermometer.

[1] The term " absolute humidity " is more correctly applied to the moisture-content.

Finally, the hygrometric state of the atmosphere may be indicated by stating the *dew-point*, that is to say, the temperature at which the existing vapour-pressure would suffice to saturate the air. The dew-point is, however, of little interest unless the air temperature is stated simultaneously.

The relationships between most of these different modes of expression have been indicated in the course of defining them. It only remains to state that the moisture-content in grams per metre cube is numerically equal to the vapour-pressure multiplied by the fraction $216 \cdot 7/T$, where T is the absolute temperature. If t is the temperature in degrees Fahrenheit, T is equal to $\frac{5}{9}(t-32)+273$. For a temperature $60°$ F. the value of the multiplier is $0 \cdot 75$ and its value differs but slightly from this figure for temperatures ranging ten degrees or so on either side of $60°$ F.: thus a rough idea of the moisture-content may be formed by taking three-fourths of the vapour-pressure expressed in millibars.

All the modes of expression we have enumerated are in common use, but relative humidity is the most popular with meteorologists. The reason for this preference is that the relative humidity shows at once how near the air is to saturation, a piece of information of great value for numerous purposes. It may be said, indeed, that relative humidity is the only one of the various modes of expression which conveys a simple and direct idea of " degree of moistness " without pre-supposing a knowledge of the temperature also. Relative humidity is, moreover, of great importance in the economy of nature. Certain animal and vegetable structures contract and expand in response to variations of relative humidity ; among such structures is human hair, and advantage is taken of this fact in the construction of direct-reading hygrometers and hygrographs. Readers will also be familiar with the popular " weather-house ", in which the twisting and untwisting of a piece of catgut in response to variations of relative humidity causes one or other of two figures to emerge from doorways.

96. Vapour-pressure and moisture-content of saturated air. For purposes of reference we give in Fig. 68 graphs showing the vapour-pressure in millibars and the moisture-content in grams per cubic metre of air saturated with water-vapour at temperatures from $10°$ F. to $100°$ F. Both the quantities increase rapidly with temperature ; thus the saturation vapour-pressure is approximately $2 \cdot 5$ millibars at $10°$ F., 5 millibars at $27°$ F., 10 millibars at $45°$ F., 20 millibars at $64°$ F. and 40 millibars at $84°$ F., the value being doubled by a rise of temperature of from $17°$ F. to $20°$ F. The moisture-content increases at about the same rate.

We may visualize the quantities we have to deal with in hygrometry in the following manner.   The vapour-pressure and temperature of any sample of unsaturated air may be represented by a point lying to the right of, and below, graph A.   Let *a* be such a point.   Through *a* draw a vertical line intersecting graph A at *b* and the base line at *c* : then *ac*

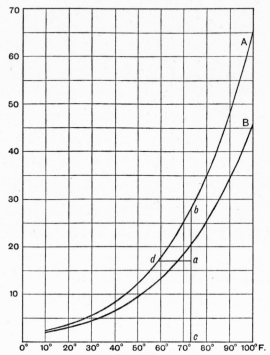

Fɪɢ. 68.—A—Saturation vapour-pressure in millibars.   B—Moisture-content of saturated vapour.
(Conditions of equilibrium over a plane surface of water.)

represents the vapour-pressure, *ab* represents the saturation-deficit and the length of *ac* expressed as a percentage of the length of *bc* represents the relative humidity.   Through *a* draw a horizontal line intersecting graph A at *d* : then the abscissa of the point *d* represents the dew-point.

If air represented by the point *a* is heated at constant pressure without adding or removing water, its vapour-pressure and dew-point will remain the same and its relative humidity will obviously decrease without limit. If a similar mass of air is cooled its relative humidity will increase till it reaches 100 per cent. By that time the state of the air will be represented by the point d and it will be saturated at the dew-point temperature. Further cooling will result in the condensation of moisture and the vapour-pressure will fall, being equal at all stages to the saturation pressure at the temperature of the air.

During these processes of heating and cooling, the moisture-content does not remain the same. Air expands if heated at constant pressure, consequently the moisture-content decreases when unsaturated air is heated and increases when it is cooled. When the dew-point is reached the moisture-content is represented by the point on graph B corresponding to the dew-point temperature. From graph B the amount of liquid water set free by further cooling can be determined approximately; thus the cooling of saturated air from 50° F. to 40° F. sets free about four grams of water from each cubic metre of air.

97. Diurnal variation of relative humidity. In Table XL we give data regarding the diurnal variation of humidity at Kew Observatory in January, April, July and October. The values of relative humidity are taken from published averages (39) referring to the period 1886-1915. The other data were computed by slide-rule from the averages of relative humidity and temperature. The results are probably not quite the same as would have been obtained if individual hourly evaluations had been available for summarization, but the differences are not likely to be serious.

Considering first the data in regard to relative humidity we see that in all months the values are high in the night and early morning hours, decreasing to a minimum about 14 h. The diurnal range is small in January, decidedly greater in October, larger still in April and a maximum in July. The daily mean value is nearly the same in October and January and is decidedly lower in April and July.

Graphs are given in Fig. 69, and it will be observed that the curves bear a strong resemblance to inverted representations of the temperature graphs in Fig. 54. In Fig. 70 graph A shows the mean diurnal variation of relative humidity averaged over the whole year; graph B shows the diurnal variation of temperature, also averaged over the whole year, plotted upside down, and it will be seen that the resemblance between the two graphs is very close indeed.

Further examination of Table XL shows, however, that the diurnal and annual variations of relative humidity differ from those of temperature in certain respects. Thus we find that the highest mean hourly

o

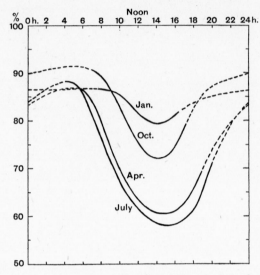

FIG. 69.—Kew Observatory ; diurnal variation of relative humidity
in January, April, July and October.

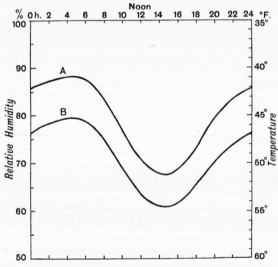

FIG. 70.—Kew Observatory ; diurnal variation of relative humidity (A),
and temperature (B), whole year.
(The temperature curve is inverted.)

values of relative humidity occur during the early morning in October, not in January, as we should expect if there were a perfect inverse correlation between temperature and relative humidity.

TABLE XL

HUMIDITY—DIURNAL VARIATIONS AT KEW OBSERVATORY

	0 h.	2 h.	4 h.	6 h.	8 h.	10 h.	12 h.	14 h.	16 h.	18 h.	20 h.	22 h.	Day*
JANUARY													
Relative humidity (per cent.)	86·4	86·6	86·5	86·8	86·7	85·4	81·5	79·4	81·4	88·9	85·1	85·9	84·5
Vapour-pressure (millibars)	6·8	6·7	6·7	6·6	6·6	6·8	7·0	7·2	7·1	7·0	6·9	6·8	6·8
Saturation-deficit (millibars)	1·0	1·0	1·0	1·0	1·0	1·2	1·6	1·8	1·6	1·3	1·2	1·2	1·2
Moisture-content (gm./m.³)	5·3	5·3	5·2	5·2	5·2	5·4	5·5	5·5	5·5	5·4	5·4	5·4	5·3
Dew-point -	34·5	34·2	34·1	34·0	33·9	34·8	35·5	35·9	35·7	35·3	35·0	34·8	34·6
APRIL													
Relative humidity	83·4	85·5	86·9	86·7	79·9	70·2	63·5	60·8	61·0	65·6	74·0	79·5	74·7
Vapour-pressure	8·0	7·9	7·8	7·8	8·1	8·3	8·3	8·4	8·4	8·4	8·2	8·2	8·3
Saturation-deficit	1·6	1·3	1·2	1·2	2·1	3·5	4·8	5·4	5·4	4·4	3·0	2·1	2·8
Moisture-content	6·2	6·1	6·0	6·0	6·3	6·4	6·3	6·4	6·4	6·4	6·3	6·3	6·4
Dew-point -	38·8	38·4	38·0	38·0	39·1	39·6	39·7	40·0	40·0	39·9	39·5	39·4	39·5
JULY													
Relative humidity	83·8	86·5	88·2	85·5	76·1	67·3	61·7	58·6	58·3	61·5	71·0	79·2	73·0
Vapour-pressure	13·8	13·6	13·3	13·6	13·8	13·8	13·8	14·0	14·0	14·2	14·3	14·2	14·2
Saturation-deficit	2·7	2·1	1·7	2·4	4·4	6·7	8·6	9·8	10·0	8·8	5·8	3·6	5·3
Moisture-content	10·4	10·3	10·1	10·3	10·4	10·3	10·3	10·5	10·6	10·6	10·6	10·6	10·6
Dew-point -	53·1	52·6	52·1	52·9	53·2	53·2	53·1	53·5	53·6	53·8	54·0	53·9	53·6
OCTOBER													
Relative humidity	90·0	90·7	91·3	91·3	89·4	82·6	75·2	72·0	74·8	82·9	87·2	88·7	84·6
Vapour-pressure	10·0	9·9	9·8	9·7	9·9	10·5	10·6	10·6	10·6	10·6	10·4	10·2	10·4
Saturation-deficit	1·1	1·0	0·9	0·9	1·2	2·2	3·5	4·1	3·6	2·2	1·6	1·3	1·8
Moisture-content	7·7	7·6	7·6	7·5	7·6	8·1	8·1	8·0	8·0	8·1	8·0	7·9	7·9
Dew-point -	44·6	44·3	44·0	43·7	44·4	45·8	46·1	46·0	46·0	46·1	45·6	45·0	45·4
WHOLE YEAR													
Relative humidity	85·9	87·3	88·1	87·4	83·1	76·5	70·7	67·9	68·9	73·4	79·4	83·4	79·2
Vapour-pressure	9·4	9·2	9·1	9·1	9·4	9·6	9·8	9·9	9·9	9·9	9·7	9·6	9·9
Saturation-deficit	1·5	1·4	1·2	1·3	1·9	3·0	4·1	4·6	4·5	3·5	2·6	1·9	2·8
Moisture-content	7·2	7·1	7·0	7·1	7·2	7·3	7·5	7·5	7·5	7·5	7·4	7·3	7·4
Dew-point -	42·8	42·3	42·0	42·1	42·8	43·5	44·0	44·1	44·2	44·1	43·8	43·4	43·5

* The " day " values are computed from daily means of temperature and relative humidity.

98. Diurnal and annual variations at six stations. For the purpose of a more general study of the seasonal and diurnal variations of relative humidity, data for the six observatories from which averages of hourly values are available, are given in Table XLI. To avoid circumlocution we may refer to the values given in line (*a*) in each case as the " early morning " values, and to the values given in line (*c*) as the " afternoon " values. We see that the early morning values are highest in late summer or autumn at all stations ; the actual values are round about ninety or

TABLE XLI

Relative Humidity : Monthly Means and Diurnal Ranges

Observatory		Jan.	Feb.	Mar.	Apr.	May	June	July	Aug.	Sep.	Oct.	Nov.	Dec.	Year
		%	%	%	%	%	%	%	%	%	%	%	%	%
Aberdeen	*a*	*81·8*	*81·6*	*83·0*	*84·4*	*86·1*	*86·4*	*86·4*	*87·1*	*86·3*	*86·0*	*83·8*	*83·4*	*84·6*
(*Aberdeen*)	*b*	80·7	79·6	78·7	78·0	78·5	78·1	78·5	79·5	80·3	**82·4**	82·1	82·3	79·9
	c	*78·0*	*75·4*	*72·1*	*70·5*	*71·8*	*71·2*	*71·3*	*70·9*	*71·9*	*75·2*	*78·5*	*80·0*	*74·0*
Diurnal range	-	3·8	6·2	10·9	13·9	14·3	15·2	15·1	16·2	14·4	10·8	5·3	3·4	10·6
Glasgow	*a*	*86·4*	*85·9*	*84·8*	*84·7*	*85·1*	*86·5*	*87·5*	*88·5*	*88·7*	*87·4*	*86·7*	*86·5*	*86·4*
(*Lanark*)	*b*	84·9	83·2	79·8	75·8	74·4	75·5	77·7	79·8	81·7	83·2	84·6	**85·5**	80·5
	c	*82·2*	*78·1*	*71·7*	*64·9*	*62·9*	*63·9*	*66·5*	*68·8*	*71·1*	*75·0*	*80·6*	*83·2*	*72·5*
Diurnal range	-	4·2	7·8	13·1	19·8	22·2	22·6	21·0	19·7	17·6	12·4	6·1	3·3	13·9
Eskdalemuir	*a*	*89·1*	*88·1*	*87·4*	*87·8*	*88·9*	*88·4*	*90·8*	*91·0*	*89·5*	*89·4*	*88·3*	*89·1*	*88·7*
(*Dumfries*)	*b*	87·8	86·4	82·9	79·9	79·6	78·1	82·0	84·0	84·0	85·6	86·5	**88·4**	83·8
	c	*85·9*	*82·7*	*74·8*	*68·5*	*68·4*	*67·4*	*71·8*	*74·2*	*74·3*	*76·9*	*81·8*	*86·0*	*76·2*
Diurnal range	-	3·2	5·4	12·6	19·3	20·5	21·0	19·0	16·8	15·2	12·5	6·5	3·1	12·5
Kew (*Surrey*)	*a*	*86·8*	*85·8*	*87·2*	*86·9*	*87·5*	*86·4*	*88·2*	*89·4*	*90·5*	*91·3*	*89·3*	*88·0*	*88·1*
	b	84·5	81·6	79·3	74·7	73·4	72·8	73·0	75·8	79·2	84·6	**85·9**	**85·9**	79·2
	c	*79·4*	*73·7*	*67·7*	*60·7*	*59·4*	*58·5*	*58·0*	*60·1*	*63·4*	*72·0*	*78·3*	*81·0*	*67·9*
Diurnal range	-	7·4	12·1	19·5	26·2	28·1	27·9	30·2	29·3	27·1	19·3	11·0	7·0	20·2
Falmouth	*a*	*85·4*	*84·0*	*85·6*	*85·6*	*88·1*	*89·9*	*90·2*	*90·7*	*90·0*	*91·3*	*85·9*	*85·2*	*87·6*
(*Cornwall*)	*b*	83·8	81·7	81·3	79·6	80·2	81·4	81·6	82·9	84·2	**85·2**	83·8	84·1	82·5
	c	*80·3*	*76·7*	*74·7*	*72·1*	*71·9*	*72·9*	*72·2*	*73·4*	*75·8*	*73·9*	*79·2*	*81·1*	*75·4*
Diurnal range	-	5·1	7·3	10·9	13·5	16·2	17·0	18·0	17·3	14·2	17·4	6·7	4·1	12·2
Valentia	*a*	*87·2*	*87·7*	*87·3*	*87·0*	*87·9*	*88·2*	*89·6*	*89·6*	*88·3*	*87·2*	*87·7*	*88·0*	*87·8*
(*Kerry*)	*b*	86·2	85·5	83·7	82·1	81·2	81·7	83·7	84·7	84·2	84·4	85·8	**87·2**	84·2
	c	*84·0*	*81·3*	*78·1*	*75·5*	*74·3*	*74·7*	*77·0*	*78·2*	*77·6*	*79·0*	*82·0*	*85·3*	*79·0*
Diurnal range	-	3·2	6·4	9·2	11·5	13·6	13·5	12·6	11·4	10·7	8·2	5·7	2·7	8·8

a—highest mean hourly value (early morning)
b—daily mean
c—lowest mean hourly value (afternoon)

ninety-one per cent. at Eskdalemuir, Kew, Falmouth and Valentia, but are distinctly lower at Glasgow and Aberdeen. The lowest afternoon values occur in spring or early summer and vary considerably from station to station. The lowest values occur in June and July at Kew, where the mean is as low as 58·0 per cent. in July. At the other extreme we have Valentia, where the lowest mean hourly value throughout the year is 74·3 per cent. at 14 h. in May.

The mean diurnal range is smallest in December, averaging from under three per cent. at Valentia to seven per cent. at Kew. The largest value of the mean diurnal range occurs in May at Valentia, in June at Glasgow and Eskdalemuir, in July at Kew and Falmouth and in August at Aberdeen. In all months the mean diurnal range at Kew greatly exceeds the value at any of the other stations.

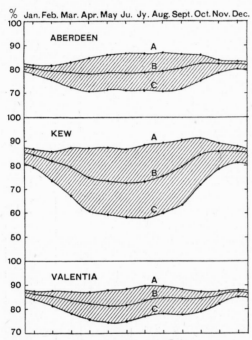

Fig. 71.—Seasonal variation of relative humidity.
A—Early morning (maximum of hourly means).
B—Mean for the whole day.
C—Afternoon (minimum of hourly means).

The mean relative humidity averaged over the whole year does not vary very greatly from station to station. Thus the mean values at Aberdeen, Glasgow and Kew are all near eighty per cent. Falmouth shows a mean annual value of 82·5 per cent. and the values for Eskdalemuir and Valentia are both about eighty-four per cent.

In the winter months from October to February the mean relative humidity is markedly lower at Aberdeen than at any other station. On account of its larger diurnal range Kew is, however, slightly drier than Aberdeen in the afternoon in October and February. Kew has the highest early morning humidity in the autumn months September to November. The early morning humidity is decidedly lower at Aberdeen than at other stations in most months, though Glasgow has a slightly lower value in May.

Graphs of the variations at Aberdeen, Kew and Valentia are given in Fig. 71. In each case A shows the annual variation of early morning humidity, B the mean for the day and C the afternoon humidity.

TABLE XLII
VAPOUR-PRESSURE AND SATURATION-DEFICIT : MONTHLY MEANS
(MILLIBARS)

Observatory	Jan.	Feb.	Mar.	Apr.	May	June	July	Aug.	Sep.	Oct.	Nov.	Dec.	Year
	mb.	mb.	mb.	mb.	mb.	mb.	mb.	mb.	mb.	mb.	mb.	mb.	mb.
ABERDEEN													
Vapour-pressure	6·3	6·3	6·5	7·4	8·9	10·7	12·1	12·1	10·8	9·1	7·5	6·6	8·7
Saturation-deficit	1·5	1·6	1·8	2·1	2·4	3·0	3·3	3·2	2·7	1·9	1·7	1·4	2·2
GLASGOW													
Vapour-pressure	6·9	6·8	6·9	7·7	9·0	11·2	12·5	12·5	11·3	9·2	7·8	7·1	8·9
Saturation-deficit	1·2	1·4	1·7	2·4	3·1	3·6	3·7	3·2	2·5	1·9	1·5	1·2	2·3
ESKDALEMUIR													
Vapour-pressure	6·3	6·2	6·3	7·0	8·9	10·2	12·2	12·1	10·3	8·7	6·9	6·5	8·5
Saturation-deficit	0·9	0·9	1·3	1·8	2·2	2·9	2·6	2·3	1·9	1·4	1·3	0·9	1·7
KEW													
Vapour-pressure	6·8	6·9	7·3	8·3	10·2	12·5	14·2	14·2	12·6	10·4	8·4	7·3	9·9
Saturation-deficit	1·2	1·6	1·9	2·8	3·7	4·7	5·3	4·6	3·4	1·8	1·4	1·2	2·8
FALMOUTH													
Vapour-pressure	8·0	7·8	8·1	9·0	10·8	13·1	14·7	14·8	13·6	11·3	9·5	8·7	10·8
Saturation-deficit	1·6	1·8	1·8	2·3	2·6	3·0	3·3	3·0	2·5	1·9	1·8	1·6	2·4
VALENTIA													
Vapour-pressure	8·6	8·5	8·5	9·4	10·9	12·8	14·2	14·4	13·2	11·0	9·6	9·1	10·9
Saturation-deficit	1·3	1·4	1·7	2·0	2·4	2·9	2·7	2·6	2·5	2·0	1·6	1·3	2·0

The graphs show interesting features at all three stations. Thus at Aberdeen the mean relative humidity is nearly the same throughout the year, and the annual variation is not much greater at Valentia. The latter station is peculiar in having a nearly constant early morning relative humidity, though reference to Table XLI shows that the seasonal variation of the early morning value is small at all stations. The diagram also shows very clearly how much greater are the seasonal variations of mean relative humidity, and of the afternoon minimum, at Kew than at other stations.

99. Vapour-pressure and moisture-content at Kew. Reference to Table XL shows that the diurnal variation of vapour-pressure is very small at Kew in each of the four typical months ; the diurnal range varies from 0·6 millibar in January and April to 1·0 millibar in July. The minimum value occurs in the early morning hours, about the time of sunrise, but the hour of incidence of the maximum value varies from the early afternoon in January to the late evening in July. The daily mean value varies from 6·8 millibars in January to 14·2 millibars in July.

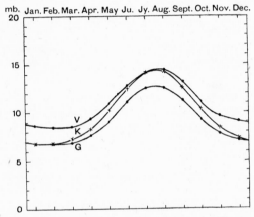

Fig. 72.—Vapour-pressure ; seasonal variation at Glasgow (G),
Kew (K) and Valentia (V).

It will be seen from Table XL that the diurnal variation of moisture-content is even smaller than that of vapour-pressure, the diurnal range being no more than 0·3 gm./m.³ in January, 0·4 in April, 0·5 in July and 0·6 in October. The daily mean value varies from 5·3 gm./m.³ in January to 10·6 in July.

100. Seasonal variation of vapour-pressure. Monthly and annual mean values of the vapour-pressure at the six observatories are given in Table XLII along with values of saturation-deficit which will be referred to later. The three Scottish stations, Aberdeen, Glasgow and Eskdalemuir, show very similar values in all months ; in particular, the values for Aberdeen and Eskdalemuir are nearly identical. There is also a similarity in the vapour-pressure for Kew, Falmouth and Valentia in summer months, but Kew shows more resemblance to Glasgow in the winter months. To illustrate this rather curious feature in the data the values for Glasgow, Kew and Valentia are graphed in Fig. 72.

On the whole it would appear from Table XLII that the geographical variation of vapour-pressure within the British Isles is not very great. Eskdalemuir, where the values are lowest in most months, has an annual average of 8·5 millibars, as compared with 10·9 at Valentia and 10·8 at Falmouth ; the differences are of about the same order of magnitude in each month.

The form of the annual variation of vapour-pressure resembles that of temperature (Fig. 47) very closely, the minimum occurring in January or February, and the maximum in July or August. There is also a resemblance in the fact that the curve tends to rise more slowly in spring than it descends in autumn, with the result that the spring months are not only relatively cold, but relatively dry (in respect to atmospheric moisture), as compared with the autumn months.

TABLE XLIII

MOISTURE-CONTENT : MONTHLY MEAN VALUES (IN GRAMS PER CUBIC METRE)

Observatory	Jan.	Feb.	Mar.	Apr.	May	June	July	Aug.	Sep.	Oct.	Nov.	Dec.	Year
Aberdeen - -	4·9	5·0	5·1	5·8	6·8	8·1	9·1	9·2	8·2	7·0	5·8	5·2	6·7
Glasgow - -	5·3	5·3	5·3	5·9	6·9	8·5	9·5	9·5	8·6	7·1	6·1	5·5	7·0
Eskdalemuir -	5·0	4·9	4·9	5·4	6·8	7·8	9·2	9·2	7·8	6·7	5·4	5·1	6·5
Kew - - -	5·3	5·4	5·7	6·4	7·7	9·4	10·6	10·6	9·5	7·9	6·5	5·7	7·4
Falmouth - -	6·2	6·1	6·2	6·9	8·2	9·9	11·0	11·1	10·3	8·6	7·3	6·7	8·2
Valentia - -	6·6	6·5	6·6	7·2	8·2	9·7	10·7	10·8	10·0	8·4	7·4	7·0	8·3

101. Seasonal variation of moisture-content. Monthly and annual averages of moisture-content for the six observatories are given in Table XLIII. In view of the fact that moisture-content in grams per cubic metre is equal to vapour-pressure in millibars multiplied by a factor which does not vary much from three-quarters, there is a considerable degree of similarity between the seasonal and geographical variations of moisture-content and those of vapour-pressure. We have a summer maximum varying from 9·2 gm./m.[3] at Aberdeen and Eskdalemuir to 11·1 at Falmouth, and a winter minimum varying from 4·9 at Aberdeen to 6·5 at Valentia. The variations in a given month from station to station are thus relatively small. The average value for the whole year varies from 6·5 at Eskdalemuir to 8·3 at Valentia.

102. Saturation-deficit. Since the saturation-deficit represents the amount in millibars by which the vapour-pressure falls short of saturation it gives a direct measure of the " dryness " of the air. It is readily seen that the saturation-deficit is equal to

$$\frac{100 - \text{R.H.}}{100} \times p$$

where R.H. is the relative humidity and p is the saturation vapour-pressure. The saturation vapour-pressure is a quantity which depends

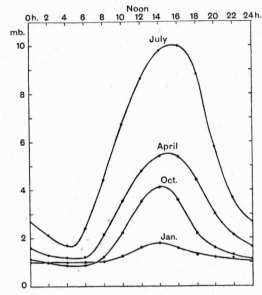

FIG. 73.—Kew Observatory; diurnal variation of saturation-deficit in January, April, July and October.

simply on the air temperature; consequently saturation-deficit is a quantity involving both relative humidity and temperature.

If on two occasions the vapour-pressure is the same but the temperature is different, the saturation-deficit will be higher on the occasion with the higher temperature. We have already seen that the diurnal variation of vapour-pressure is very small; consequently the diurnal variation of saturation-deficit is similar to that of temperature. The data for Kew are given in Table XL and graphs in Fig. 73. In January the diurnal range is from 1·0 millibar in the early morning to 1·8 millibar at 14 h.; in April the range is from 1·2 millibar to 5·4 millibars; in

July from 1·7 millibar to 10·0 millibars, and in October from 0·9 millibar to 4·1 millibars. Thus the early morning value tends to remain about the same throughout the year, while the afternoon value is very much greater in summer than in winter, a result which agrees with our ordinary experience in regard to the " drying-power " of the air.

Monthly averages of the daily mean values for the six observatories are included in Table XLII. In all cases the minimum occurs in December or January and the maximum in June or July. The phase of the

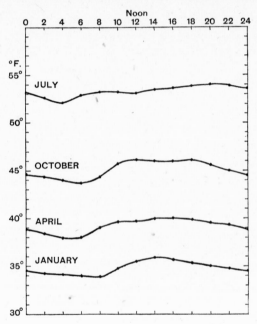

Fig. 74.—Kew Observatory ; diurnal variation of dew-point in January, April, July and October.

annual variation is thus a little in advance of the phase of the annual variation of temperature. The mean for the whole year is lowest (1·7 millibar) at Eskdalemuir, and highest (2·8 millibars) at Kew. For Kew this result is mainly due to high values in summer months from April to September. During winter months the results are very similar for all the stations except Eskdalemuir, where the values are conspicuously low in all months.

103. The dew-point. Data are given in Table XL from which it will be seen that the dew-point exhibits a small but quite definite diurnal variation at all seasons. From these figures or from the graphs in Fig. 74 we observe that at Kew Observatory the minimum value of the dew-point occurs at about the hour of sunrise. In January a fairly rapid rise then occurs to a maximum value about 2° F. higher at 14 h. In other months the changes during the daytime are not so simple. In April and October the value rises quickly at first, and then remains fairly constant until about 18 h. after which it falls steadily to the early morning minimum. In July there is an irregular rise to a maximum in the late evening. In each month the range of the diurnal variation is about 2° F. The values of air temperature and dew-point at the time of occurrence of the minimum are as follows :

	January	April	July	October
Air temperature	37·5° F.	41·6° F.	55·5° F.	46·1° F.
Dew-point -	33·9° F.	38·0° F.	52·1° F.	43·7° F.

Thus, at the hour of incidence of the minimum dew-point the air temperature is, on the average, from $2\frac{1}{2}$° F. to $3\frac{1}{2}$° F. above the dew-point.

TABLE XLIV
DEW-POINT : MONTHLY MEAN VALUES

Observatory	Jan.	Feb.	Mar.	Apr.	May	June	July	Aug.	Sep.	Oct.	Nov.	Dec.	Year
	°F.	°F.	°F.	°F.	°F.	°F.	°F.	°F.	°F.	°F.	°F.	°F.	°F.
Aberdeen - -	32·7	32·8	33·6	36·9	41·4	46·1	49·5	49·6	46·5	42·1	37·2	34·0	40·2
Glasgow - -	34·8	34·6	34·9	37·6	41·6	47·5	50·6	50·5	47·6	42·5	38·1	35·7	41·3
Eskdalemuir -	32·8	32·3	32·7	35·5	41·3	45·0	49·6	49·5	45·2	40·9	34·9	33·7	39·4
Kew - - -	34·6	35·0	36·4	39·6	45·0	50·5	54·0	53·6	50·7	45·4	40·0	36·4	43·5
Falmouth - -	38·8	38·1	39·0	41·9	46·5	51·7	54·9	55·1	52·6	47·7	43·1	40·8	45·9
Valentia - -	40·5	40·1	40·4	42·8	46·6	51·1	53·9	54·3	52·0	47·0	43·5	42·0	46·2

The mean for the day varies from 34·6° F. in January to 54·0° F. in July. Monthly means for other observatories are given in Table XLIV. Since the dew-point is determined directly by the vapour-pressure, we naturally find differences between stations, and a form of annual variation, similar to those noted under the head of vapour-pressure. The order of magnitude of the dew-point at different stations in different months is therefore the main point of interest. We note that the value exceeds 55° F. at Falmouth in July. At Eskdalemuir it approaches freezing-point from January to March, but it does not fall below 40° F. at Valentia in any month.

The annual variation of dew-point is very similar to that of mean daily minimum temperature, as will be seen, for example, if the values for Kew in Table XLIV are compared with the means of daily minimum temperature in Table XXXI. It will be found, indeed, that the figures are nearly identical in most months. This agreement, though striking, cannot be said to have any special significance. We have already noticed that the mean daily minimum temperature is decidedly lower than the mean minimum of hourly values, owing to the effect of non-periodic changes. We have no data in regard to the mean daily minimum dew-point, but if we had we should certainly find that it was lower than the minimum of the hourly values of dew-point, and therefore distinctly lower than the mean daily minimum temperature. That must, indeed, be so, because we know from experience that the air is not saturated with water-vapour every night.

104. General remarks on the data. During our brief survey of the results obtained at the observatories we have paused only to take note of the diurnal and annual variations which they reveal, and of the more conspicuous differences between stations. We may now look a little more closely at the collected data, having regard to the different types of geographical situation represented by the several observatories.

Two of the quantities dealt with, namely relative humidity and saturation-deficit, show conspicuous diurnal variations which have obvious relationships with the diurnal variation of temperature. From Table XLI we see that the diurnal variation of relative humidity is large in places where the diurnal variation of temperature is large, and the same parallelism is seen if we compare the variations in the diurnal range of humidity at different seasons with those of temperature. It is clear, therefore, that the diurnal variation of relative humidity, or of saturation-deficit, is a direct consequence of the diurnal variation of temperature. The seasonal variation of relative humidity is related to that of temperature in a much less definite manner. At Kew there is an approach to an inverse correlation, but that appears to be a secondary effect arising from the diurnal variation. We do, however, find a close parallelism between the seasonal variation of temperature and that of any of the quantities, vapour-pressure, moisture-content or dew-point, which measure the absolute humidity.

We noted a general tendency for low values of relative humidity at Aberdeen, particularly in the winter. This would appear to be due to a " Föhn effect "—that is to say dynamic warming and drying of air brought down to the surface from high levels by eddies—due to the presence of the Grampians to westward of the station, and the prevailing westerly winds. The two coastal stations in the south-west, Valentia and Falmouth, show consistently high values of the absolute humidity at all seasons ; they also show a general high level of relative humidity. One of the stations, Eskdalemuir, is an inland station at a moderately high level (794 feet). This situation confers upon it a climate rather similar, in respect to relative humidity, to that of the Atlantic coast stations ; the absolute humidity is very markedly higher at the latter stations than at Eskdalemuir, or at the other two northern stations, in all months.

105. Geographical distribution of relative humidity. From the observatory data we have been able to form some general impressions of the distribution of humidity, but it is clearly desirable to obtain, if possible, a more detailed picture. Unfortunately we do not at present possess averages of relative humidity, or of other hygrometric elements, for a sufficient number of stations to permit of the construction of average charts. We may hope, however, to obtain some useful information by examining charts for individual months. The months selected for this purpose are January, April, July and October 1935. The following are brief notes on the general weather conditions in the selected months, based on information given in the *Monthly Weather Report*.

January 1935. Westerly to northerly winds predominated, but temperature was slightly above normal in most districts, the excess being greatest in Scotland east (+1·8° F.) and Scotland north (+1·6° F.). Rainfall exceeded the normal in England east and England north-east but was considerably below normal in other districts, especially in the Midlands, England south-west, Ireland south and the Channel Islands, where the percentages of the normal were respectively 45, 38, 31 and 35. At the observatories the mean relative humidity at 13 h. differed from the normal by the following amounts : Aberdeen, −1 per cent. ; Eskdalemuir, −3 per cent. ; Kew, −3 per cent. ; Valentia, −5 per cent.

April 1935. A dull wet month, with rainfall about double the normal in the eastern districts of Great Britain and in south-west England ; the excess was smaller in Ireland and in other parts of Great Britain. Temperature was slightly below normal in the north and east of Scotland, but was slightly above normal elsewhere. At the observatories the mean relative humidity at 13 h. differed from the normal by the following

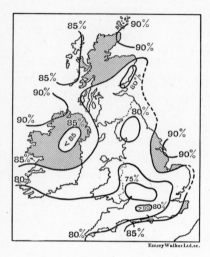

FIG. 75.—January 1935, 13 h.
(Areas above 85 per cent. shaded.)

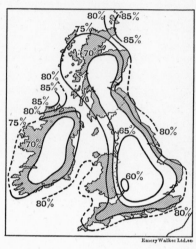

FIG. 76.—April 1935, 13 h.
(Areas above 70 per cent. shaded.)

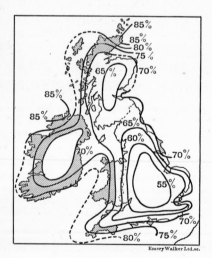

FIG. 77.—July 1935, 13 h.
(Areas above 70 per cent. shaded.)

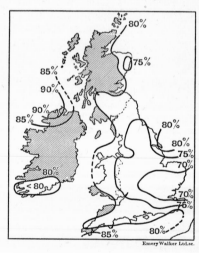

FIG. 78.—October 1935, 13 h.
(Areas above 80 per cent. shaded.)

Distribution of mean relative humidity at mid-day in certain months of 1935.

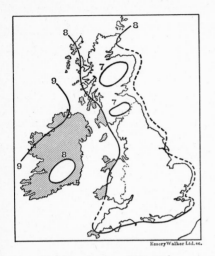

FIG. 79.—January 1935, 13 h.
(Areas above 8 mb. shaded.)

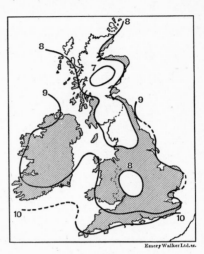

FIG. 80.—April 1935, 13 h.
(Areas above 8 mb. shaded.)

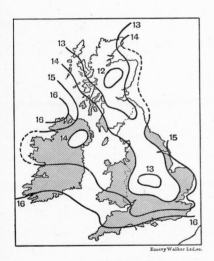

FIG. 81.—July 1935, 13 h.
(Areas above 14 mb. shaded.)

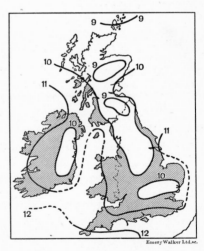

FIG. 82.—October 1935, 13 h.
(Areas above 10 mb. shaded.)

Distribution of mean vapour-pressure in millibars at mid-day in certain
months of 1935.

amounts : Aberdeen, +6 per cent. ; Eskdalemuir, 0 ; Kew, +2 per cent. ; Valentia, −5 per cent.

July 1935. A fine, warm and sunny month in all districts, with sunshine twenty to forty per cent. above normal. Rainfall was very much below normal, especially in the Midland counties and England north-east, which received respectively only fourteen per cent. and sixteen per cent. of the normal amount. At many stations it was the driest July for at least fifty years. Temperature was well above normal in all districts, the excess amounting to about 3° F. in the eastern districts of Great Britain. At the observatories the mean relative humidity at 13 h. differed from the normal by the following amounts : Aberdeen, −2 per cent. ; Eskdalemuir, −4 per cent. ; Kew, −8 per cent. ; Valentia, −1 per cent.

October 1935. A dull wet month with frequent gales. Rainfall exceeded twice the normal in the north and west of Scotland, but was slightly below normal in England east and Ireland south. Temperature was slightly below normal in all districts. At the observatories the mean relative humidity at 13 h. differed from the normal by the following amounts : Aberdeen, −1 per cent. ; Eskdalemuir, +3 per cent. ; Kew, −4 per cent. ; Valentia, +1 per cent.

Charts of the mean relative humidity at 13 h. for each of these months are given in Figs. 75 to 78. They were constructed from the readings at forty-six synoptic stations. This number of stations does not suffice to reveal the finer details of the distribution and the charts must therefore be regarded merely as representations of the broader features.

In the January chart we have an area with relative humidity below eighty per cent. extending eastward from the south coast of Ireland, over south-west England and the south coast of Wales, into the Midland counties. Within this area there is a patch with relative humidity slightly below seventy-five per cent. covering the Severn estuary and the upper Thames valley. Northward of the main area of low humidity we have further areas below eighty per cent. over northern England and eastern Scotland. At the other end of the scale we find a mean relative humidity slightly exceeding ninety per cent. in the neighbourhood of Malin Head (Donegal), Wick (Caithness) and Spurn Head (Yorks.).

The April chart shows a distinctly different form of distribution. Here there is a very definite decrease of mean relative humidity from high values on the coast to low values inland. Over most of the inland districts of Great Britain and Ireland the value is below seventy per cent., and it is below sixty-five per cent. over the central area of England ;

the lowest reading, sixty per cent., occurs at Ross-on-Wye. At most points on the coast the value is between seventy and eighty per cent., but the mean reading at Malin Head and Wick slightly exceeds eighty-five per cent.

The July chart shows similar features to the April chart. The distribution is essentially similar, and the only important point of difference is the fact that over Great Britain the inland values are five to ten per cent. lower. This difference is no doubt due in part to the unusually warm and dry character of July 1935.

The October chart shows a large area with relative humidity below seventy-five per cent. covering the whole of central and eastern England. Within this area we have values below seventy per cent. over East Anglia, the eastern Midlands and the lower Thames valley. There is a patch with relative humidity below eighty per cent. over southern Ireland. In the neighbourhood of Malin Head a mean value slightly exceeding ninety per cent. is found.

From our previous study of the observatory records we should expect that in all months the average charts of relative humidity at 13 h. would show a decrease from high values on the coast to low values inland, with the lowest values in regions subject to a large diurnal variation of temperature. The charts for April and July 1935 show a close approach to this expected form of distribution. In the charts for January and October 1935 we can also discern a tendency in the same direction, but the distribution is obviously complicated by the special meteorological features of those particular months. It is probably correct to say that the chart for any individual month during the summer half-year would deviate but little from the pattern of Figs. 76 and 77. During the winter half-year the control by diurnal solar heating is relatively feebler, and the distribution at 13 h. would thus be more liable to disturbance in individual months by effects due to changes in the prevailing wind.

106. Geographical distribution of vapour-pressure. Charts of the distribution of vapour-pressure at 13 h. in January, April, July and October 1935 are given in Figs. 79 to 82.

In the January chart the 8-millibar line passes round the coast line of Great Britain, enclosing an area in which the vapour-pressure is below eight millibars. Within this area the value is below seven millibars in two patches, one over central Scotland, the other over the southern uplands of Scotland. In Ireland the vapour-pressure exceeds nine millibars on the north-west coasts and is below eight millibars in a patch in the south-east.

P

In the charts for April, July and October the general pattern of the distribution is very similar, though the actual values of vapour-pressure are of course different. In each case we see a combination of two effects, namely an increase of vapour-pressure from north to south combined with a tendency for low values to occur inland, especially over the high land. Thus on each chart we find a tongue of low vapour-pressure projecting southward over Great Britain, with the lowest values in a patch over the Grampians.

We saw in paragraph 103 that there is a considerable degree of parallelism between the mean values of dew-point and minimum temperature; this implies a parallelism also between the mean values of vapour-pressure and minimum temperature. It appears therefore that the distribution of mean vapour-pressure, or of the vapour-pressure at any fixed hour—since the diurnal variation is everywhere small—is very similar to that of mean minimum temperature; low values of mean vapour-pressure will occur in areas where the average minimum temperature is low, and *vice versa*.

107. Extremes of relative humidity. Our attention has been mainly devoted in this chapter to average values derived from observations extending over periods of years. Like every other meteorological element, however, humidity is subject in the British Isles to relatively large casual variations. The average values do not therefore give a complete picture. The range of the diurnal variation of relative humidity depends a good deal, like that of temperature, on the conditions in respect to wind and cloud. In clear calm weather the relative humidity at inland stations during the summer half-year often varies from an early morning maximum of ninety-five or even 100 per cent. to an afternoon minimum of forty per cent. or lower. Values of 100 per cent. are not uncommon at all times of the year; in spring, summer and early autumn they are confined, except at high levels, to the night and early morning hours, but in late autumn and winter they may also occur during the daytime, usually in association with wet fog. Values below fifty per cent. are uncommon in winter and values below thirty per cent. are practically confined to the spring and summer months at inland stations subject to a large diurnal variation of temperature.

So far as can be ascertained the relative humidity has never fallen below fifteen per cent. at a British station. This value occurred at Cardington (Bedfordshire), on 1st April, 1931, and at South Farnborough (Hants.), on 10th July, 1934. Both these occasions produced low relative humidities over a wide area; the latter case was of exceptional interest, and we give in Fig. 83 graphs of the variations of temperature, relative humidity and dew-point at Kew Observatory during the twenty-four hours. These curves are constructed from the hourly readings and naturally do not show the smaller fluctuations. The temperature curve is of a normal type for a warm summer day, with a minimum hourly value of 57·4° F. at 4 h. and a maximum of 80·1° F. at 16 h. The relative humidity was rather low, even in the early morning hours, the maximum value being seventy-three per cent. at 4 h. and 5 h. At 5 h. the value of the vapour-pressure was 12·1 millibars, but it increased to 14·4 millibars with dew-point 54·2° F. at 8 h., values which differ little

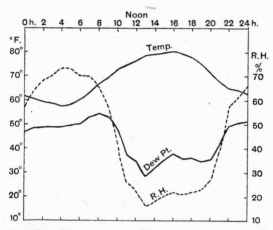

FIG. 83.—Kew Observatory ; variations of temperature, dew-point and relative humidity, 10th July, 1934.

from the normal for July (see Table XL). As is common in fine summer weather the relative humidity decreased rapidly after 7 h., but it descended to the very low value of sixteen per cent. at 13 h. ; subsequently it rose a little but the value was no higher than twenty-seven per cent. at 20 h. A rapid rise then occurred, the value at midnight being sixty-six per cent. Meanwhile very remarkable changes occurred in the absolute humidity. There was no evidence of a change in the source of the air supply, but nevertheless the vapour-pressure fell from 14·4 millibars at 8 h. to 5·3 millibars at 13 h. This corresponds to a dew-point of 28·5° F., a value substantially below the normal for *January*! Subsequently there was a recovery to a vapour-pressure of 12·6 millibars (dew-point 51·1° F.) by midnight.

In this case a very low relative humidity was caused by an altogether abnormal variation of absolute humidity, superposed on the normal diurnal change of relative humidity due to temperature. This very remarkable result appears to have been due to the descent of a dry stratum of air from higher levels to the surface, but the case, of which some further details will be found in the *Meteorological Magazine*, September 1934, has not been investigated as fully as it deserves. The dry air affected a considerable area in the Midlands and southern England.

Occurrences of relative humidity below twenty per cent. are decidedly rare. At Kew Observatory only two other cases have been recorded, namely seventeen per cent. at 12 h. on 1st April, 1931, and nineteen per cent. at 14 h. on 11th July, 1921. We have already referred to the occasion on 1st April, 1931, as having produced a relative humidity of fifteen per cent. at Cardington. At Kew the vapour-pressure at 12 h. was no higher than 1·8 millibar, corresponding to a dew-point of 4·0° F.

108. Extremes of absolute humidity. Since the saturation vapour-pressure increases rapidly with temperature we naturally expect to find the highest recorded values of the absolute humidity on occasions of high temperature. F. H. Dight (40) has prepared a table of all occasions from 1900 to 1933 when temperature exceeded 85° F. at Kew Observatory, with the associated humidity data. From his table we have extracted the occasions which showed a notably high value of the absolute humidity and have set them out in Table XLV. They may be regarded as the most outstanding periods of damp heat which have occurred during the present century. The highest values of vapour-pressure (23·9 millibars) both occurred in August 1930, the next highest value (23·8 millibars) in July 1900. On these three occasions the moisture-content was about seventeen grams per cubic metre, and the dew-point approximately 68·5° F. At Enfield on 20th August, 1932, at 15 h. the dry-bulb read 85·0° F. and the wet-bulb 75·0° F., giving a relative humidity of sixty-one per cent., vapour-pressure 25·2 millibars, dew-point 70° F. and moisture-content 18·1 grams per cubic metre. It is difficult to be sure of the accuracy of these extreme readings ; if the supply of water to the wet-bulb was inadequate the wet-bulb thermometer would read too high and the calculated values of vapour-pressure, dew-point and moisture-content would also be too high. At Kew Observatory special precautions are taken to avoid this source of error, but the improved methods used at Kew have not yet come into general use.

Very low values of the absolute humidity would naturally be associated with very low readings of temperature, such as the −17° F. registered at Braemar in February 1895. Assuming the air to be saturated on that occasion the vapour-pressure would be 0·7 millibar. The same vapour-pressure would occur with air fifty per cent. saturated at 1° F. or twenty-five per cent. saturated at 15° F. Thus we are probably justified in saying that the vapour-pressure has fallen below one millibar on a number of occasions. Exact information is almost impossible to obtain, because the wet-bulb thermometer is not often

TABLE XLV

KEW OBSERVATORY : OCCASIONS OF HIGH ABSOLUTE HUMIDITY,
1900–1933

Date			Maximum	Wet-bulb	Relative Humidity	Vapour-Pressure	Moisture-Content
			° F.	° F.	%	mb.	gm./m.³
1900	16th July	-	89·4	73·0	44	20·4	14·5
	20th July	-	89·4	75·4	51	23·8	16·9
	24th July	-	86·0	71·8	48	20·3	14·4
1923	11th July	-	88·5	73·4	47	21·4	15·1
	12th July	-	90·1	73·2	42	20·4	14·5
1929	20th July	-	85·6	71·4	48	19·9	14·3
1930	27th August	-	88·0	75·0	52	23·9	17·0
	28th August	-	88·0	73·4	48	21·6	15·3
	29th August	-	89·1	75·7	52	23·9	17·1
1932	18th August	-	88·3	73·2	47	21·2	15·1
	19th August	-	91·6	75·4	45	22·8	16·1
	20th August	-	86·4	74·1	54	23·3	16·7

reliable at readings below freezing-point, and few stations are equipped with hair hygrographs. In the previous section we noted a case, 1st April, 1931, in which the vapour-pressure was as low as 1·8 millibar at Kew Observatory. The temperature on that occasion was 45·9° F., but the air was very dry. During the famous cold spell of February 1929 the relative humidity was only forty-six per cent. at 16 h. on 14th at Kew Observatory, with a temperature of 26·2° F., giving a vapour-pressure of 2·2 millibars. In the London area the vapour-pressure has probably not fallen below two millibars very often.

When the air is very dry and the temperature is low the problem of producing a healthy atmosphere by artificial heating becomes acute. Thus if we take air with a vapour-pressure of two millibars and heat it to the comfortable temperature of 65° F. without adding moisture, the relative humidity would be under ten per cent. In practice, of course, the moisture-content, and therefore the relative humidity, would tend to be raised by the evaporation or expiration of moisture from objects within the building, including the human occupants. So dry an atmosphere would naturally be very deleterious not only to human health, but also to furniture and other woodwork. To take a more ordinary case, the relative humidity would be only twenty-nine per cent. in air initially saturated at 32° F., " dry-heated " to 65° F. It is generally agreed that a relative humidity of the order of sixty or seventy per cent. should be aimed at in association with the temperature mentioned. Considerations of this kind have given rise to the modern science of air-conditioning, but it is probably true to say that the harmful effects arising from the application of dry heat are still far from being realized by the ordinary citizen.

BIBLIOGRAPHY

(39) " Hourly Values, 1915 " (*British Meteorological and Magnetic Year Book*). (H.M.S.O.)

(40) F. H. Dight, " An analysis of warm spells in London from 1900-1933, with special reference to the prevailing conditions of humidity," *Meteorological Magazine*, **69**, 1934, p. 109. (H.M.S.O.)

See also :

The Book of Normals (Section VI, Relative Humidity). (H.M.S.O.)

W. F. Stacey, " Distribution of relative humidity in England and Wales," *Q.J.R. Meteor. Soc.*, **41**, 1915, p. 45.

Hygrometric Tables. (M.O. 265.) (H.M.S.O.)

CHAPTER X

GROUND FROST, SNOW, HAIL AND THUNDER

WE now have to consider a group of data which usually appear in meteorological publications under the heading of "miscellaneous phenomena". In summaries, the data available are mainly in the form of frequencies—the number of days of occurrence per month or per year. They are of considerable climatological importance not only as facts which are interesting on their own merits, but on account of their interrelationships with other elements of climate. Thus the frequency of ground frost has affinities not only with temperature, but also with wind and cloudiness ; snow is related both to temperature and precipitation, while hail is linked up with temperature, precipitation and thunder. In this book we are concerned with the facts rather than with the interrelationships, but the latter necessarily call for some attention. We shall find it convenient to consider the phenomena in the order indicated by the title of this chapter.

GROUND FROST

109. The " grass-minimum " temperature. Data in regard to ground frost are derived from readings of a minimum thermometer freely exposed in contact with the tips of the grass-blades on a lawn or similar expanse of turf. The instructions to observers state that the thermometer should be set out in the evening and read the following morning ; in other words, the aim is to obtain a " night-minimum " rather than a " 24-hour minimum " temperature. It is known, however, that the summarized readings have not been obtained entirely in this manner. The point is of some importance because the recorded frequency of ground frosts is likely to be greatly increased if the observer makes a practice of setting his thermometer after reading it at 9 h. A ground frost is said to occur when the reading, rounded off to the nearest whole degree, is 30° F. or lower. When readings are made to one-tenth of a degree Fahrenheit, the limit implied by this definition is 30·4° F.

The temperature registered by a grass-minimum thermometer on a given occasion represents the resultant effect of several factors. During the night the supply of heat from the sun is cut off and the temperature of the earth's surface tends to fall continuously owing to the radiation of heat from the earth into space. The rate at which the heat is radiated depends simply on the surface temperature, but the net loss is considerably reduced by the presence of a cloud layer, which reflects back some of the terrestrial radiation and also radiates heat itself towards the earth. Also, the temperature at the surface tends to be maintained by the upward conduction of heat from the earth ; the gravitational run-off of the chilled air and its replacement by warmer surrounding air tends in the same direction. Lastly, when the temperature falls to the dew-point the latent heat set free by condensation of water tends to check a further fall in temperature. The conditions affecting a grass-minimum thermometer are thus very complex, and the relationship between its readings and those of a screened minimum thermometer is also complex. In general a grass-minimum thermometer reads lower than the screened minimum. The difference is small on occasions when the sky is clouded and a wind current prevails all night, because radiation is checked and air chilled at the surface is mixed rapidly with the overlying air by wind-eddies. The difference is large on clear calm nights, especially if the air is dry, because radiation from the earth can then build up a steep inversion of temperature.

The reading of a grass-minimum thermometer may be regarded as a measure of the temperature conditions on the grass surface upon which it is exposed. It would be incorrect to suppose that it represents, with any degree of precision, the temperature of anything else exposed to the night sky. The latter must necessarily depend upon the height of the object above the ground and upon the thermal conductivity and emissivity of the material. Upon the ground itself we should naturally expect there to be differences between various materials of differing conductivity, such as grass, asphalt, gravel and wood. These differences are rendered very evident to the eye, on a morning of " white frost ", by the varying density of the deposit of hoar frost. The reading of a grass-minimum thermometer does not therefore possess the sort of " absolute " character possessed by the reading of a thermometer in a screen ; it is more properly to be regarded as an index of the night conditions in respect to temperature and radiation, obtained by a method which happens to be convenient. Similarly, the definition of a ground frost by reference to the readings of the grass-minimum thermometer, is purely a convention, and that is a point which has to be borne in mind when the data are put to practical use.

110. Results for Oxford and Glasgow. Data in regard to screen-minimum and grass-minimum temperatures based on long series of observations are given for Oxford (Radcliffe Observatory) in Table XLVI and for Glasgow Observatory in Table XLVII. From Table XLVI we see that the mean difference varies at Oxford from 4° F. in January to 5° F. in October, and that the mean grass-minimum temperature is

TABLE XLVI

OXFORD, RADCLIFFE OBSERVATORY: SCREEN-MINIMUM AND GRASS-MINIMUM TEMPERATURES (1881–1930)

Month	Mean minimum		Mean monthly minimum		Absolute minimum	
	Screen	Grass	Screen	Grass	Screen	Grass
	° F.	° F.	° F.	° F.	° F.	° F.
January - -	34·4	30·4	21·7	16·2	5·9	0·5
February - -	34·4	30·1	22·8	16·3	7·1	−2·4
March - -	35·4	30·9	25·0	18·4	14·5	9·9
April - -	38·6	34·1	28·7	21·9	23·1	16·4
May - -	44·2	40·1	33·5	26·9	29·4	21·2
June - -	49·4	45·7	40·0	34·1	34·4	27·4
July - -	53·1	49·5	44·8	38·9	41·1	33·8
August - -	52·5	48·4	43·7	37·5	38·3	32·7
September -	48·5	43·7	36·9	30·7	30·9	23·9
October - -	43·0	38·0	30·4	24·3	22·9	16·7
November -	38·0	33·2	25·2	19·5	16·2	11·9
December -	35·3	31·1	22·7	17·4	7·9	5·0
Year - -	42·2	37·9	—	—	5·9	−2·4

below freezing-point from December to March. In each of these months the extreme grass-minimum is below 10° F., and a reading below zero Fahrenheit has been recorded in February. We also see from the column of extremes that a ground frost has been recorded in all months except July and August.

At Glasgow Observatory (Table XLVII) the average difference between the grass-minimum and screen-minimum thermometer readings is greater in all months than at Oxford. The difference varies from 4·8° F. in February to 6·8° F. in October. (The fact that the maximum difference occurs in October at both stations is a point of interest, and it is not easy to see why it should be so.) At Glasgow a grass-minimum

TABLE XLVII

GLASGOW OBSERVATORY : SCREEN-MINIMUM (1868–1912) AND GRASS-MINIMUM TEMPERATURES (1868–1917)

Month	Mean Minimum		Absolute Minimum	
	Screen	Grass	Screen	Grass
	° F.	° F.	° F.	° F.
January - - -	34·8	29·7	8·4	−4·0
February - - -	35·0	30·2	6·6	0·4
March - - -	35·6	30·4	19·0	9·8
April - - -	38·7	33·1	22·3	11·6
May - - - -	43·0	37·3	29·0	18·2
June - - -	48·4	42·8	36·0	25·0
July - - -	51·4	46·0	41·2	29·4
August - - -	50·9	45·2	35·0	27·5
September - -	47·5	41·0	30·6	20·1
October - - -	42·1	35·3	24·1	11·0
November - -	37·9	31·5	15·2	8·2*
December - -	35·2	29·4	7·9	4·7
Year - - -	41·7	36·0	6·6	−4·0

* 6·3 in 1919

(From *Geophysical Memoirs*, No. 23)

TABLE XLVIII

GLASGOW : GRASS-MINIMUM TEMPERATURES, 1868–1917

Month	Percentage of days with minimum on grass less than				
	5° F.	10° F.	20° F.	25° F.	32° F.
January - -	0·5	1·4	12·5	24·5	60·2
February - -	0·4	0·8	8·4	22·2	57·2
March - -	—	0·1	6·0	21·3	57·9
April - -	—	—	2·0	10·9	42·1
May - -	—	—	0·1	3·0	21·0
June - -	—	—	—	—	0·5
July - -	—	—	—	—	0·5
August - -	—	—	—	—	1·5
September -	—	—	—	0·7	11·9
October - -	—	—	3·2	10·6	35·2
November -	—	0·2	9·2	21·1	51·7
December -	0·1	1·4	13·7	28·3	60·9
Year - -	0·1	0·3	4·6	11·8	33·6

(From *Geophysical Memoirs*, No. 23)

temperature as low as 29·4° F. has been recorded in July and ground frosts have thus occurred in every month.

For Glasgow we give in Table XLVIII a table showing the percentage frequency of occurrence, in each month, of grass-minimum temperatures below 5° F., 10° F., 20° F., 25° F. and 32° F. From the figures in the last column we see that the frequency of readings below 32° F. decreases very suddenly after May and increases again very suddenly after August. No reading below 25° F. has occurred in June, July and August.

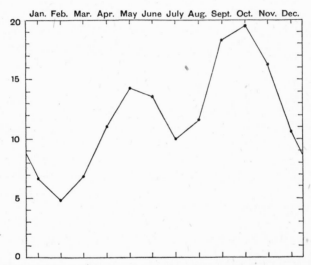

FIG. 84.—Glasgow Observatory; percentage frequency of nights on which the screened-minimum temperature exceeded the grass-minimum by more than 10° F.

It is of interest to note that readings below 20° F. have been rather more frequent in November than in February. The table does not give specific information in regard to the frequency of ground frosts, as conventionally defined, but we may judge that these have been rather more frequent at Glasgow in December than in any other month.

In Fig. 84 we give a graph showing the percentage frequency of occurrence, at Glasgow, of a grass-minimum temperature more than 10° F. below the screen-minimum. This curve is of great interest. It shows a major maximum (19·5 per cent.) in October and a major minimum (4·9 per cent.) in February, with a minor maximum in May and a minor minimum in July. It appears that conditions are on the whole more favourable at Glasgow for vigorous night radiation in the autumn and in the late spring, than in winter or in summer. That the conditions here represented should occur four times as often in October as in February is very remarkable.

111. Frequency of ground frosts. From a table published by the Meteorological Office (41) we reproduce the data given in Table XLIX. We see that the mean annual frequency of ground frosts varies from twenty-seven at Guernsey to over 150 at Balmoral. The figure is in the neighbourhood of 100 at places as widely separated as London, Glasgow (Springburn Park), Cockle Park in Northumberland, Belvoir Castle in Leicestershire, Birmingham, Dublin (Phoenix Park) and Birr Castle in the centre of Ireland. In general, the coastal stations show relatively low frequencies, while high frequencies occur at inland places like Rounton, Cambridge and Berkhamsted. There are some remarkable discrepancies between the results for neighbouring stations, for example Dublin (City) and Dublin (Phoenix Park). They seem too large to represent real climatological differences and we may presume that the results have been affected by faulty exposure of the thermometer at the City station (Fitzwilliam Square), or by differences in observational procedure.

We noted from the data in Table XLVIII that ground frosts seemed to be more numerous at Glasgow Observatory in December than in any other month. Only one other station in Table XLIX shows this peculiarity; in general, ground frosts are most frequent in January, but quite a number of stations show a maximum frequency in March.

The best set of monthly averages we possess for an individual station are those for Belvoir Castle (Leicestershire), which will serve to give a fair idea of the seasonal variation :

BELVOIR CASTLE : MONTHLY AVERAGE NUMBER OF GROUND FROSTS, 1896–1930

January	-	- 16·3	July	-	-	0
February	-	- 15·7	August -	-	-	0
March -	-	- 14·5	September	-	- 1·2
April	-	- 11·5	October	-	- 7·0
May	-	- 4·1	November	-	- 13·9
June	-	- 0·9	December	-	- 14·4

Year   -   - 99·5

It will be seen that the frequency shows little change from November to March, and that there is only a slight reduction in April. In May ground frosts occur four times per year on the average at this station, and the results are similar for other stations having an annual frequency in the neighbourhood of 100.   The liability of our climate to late frosts

TABLE XLIX

AVERAGE ANNUAL FREQUENCY OF GROUND FROSTS, AND THE MONTH
OF GREATEST FREQUENCY

Station	Height	Annual Frequency	Maximum Frequency	
	feet	days	days	
SCOTLAND				
Balmoral (*Aberdeen*) - - - -	930	151	January	23
Rothesay (*Bute*) - - - -	200	77	January	15
Glasgow Observatory (*Lanark*) - -	180	79	December	12
Glasgow (Springburn Park) - -	351	101	March	18
ENGLAND				
Douglas (*Isle of Man*) - - -	277	44	March	10
Cockle Park (*North.*) - - -	324	105	January	19
Rounton (*Yorks.*) - - - -	249	132	January	23
Cambridge (*Cambs.*) - - -	41	112	January	19
Berkhamsted (*Herts.*) - - -	450	126	January	20
Clacton (*Essex*) - - - -	54	61	February	13
Sheffield (*Yorks.*) - - - -	429	69	February	13
Buxton (*Derby*) - - - -	987	111	March	18
Belvoir Castle (*Leics.*) - - -	259	99	January	16
Birmingham (*Warwick*) - - -	535	102	January	17
Oxford (*Oxon.*) - - - -	208	91	March	15
Greenwich (*London*) - - - -	149	101	March	16
Kew Observatory (*Surrey*) - -	18	101	Jan., Mar.	15
Portsmouth (*Hants.*) - - -	11	61	January	13
Southport (*Lancs.*) - - -	37	83	March	13
Stonyhurst (*Lancs.*) - - - -	375	83	January	15
Liverpool (Bidston) (*Cheshire*) - -	188	79	March	18
Falmouth (*Cornwall*) - - -	167	48	March	10
Guernsey (*Channel Is.*) - - -	295	27	Jan., Feb.	6
IRELAND				
Armagh (*Armagh*) - - - -	204	75	March	13
Dublin (City) - - - -	47	35	December	7
Dublin (Phoenix Park) - - -	155	97	March	17
Birr Castle (*Offaly*) - - -	175	102	March	19
Limerick (*Limerick*) - - -	55	90	January	17

(From *The Book of Normals*, Section IVB)

is of course well known to gardeners.   In these figures we see the combined effects of cold winds, clear air and the persistence of low soil temperature in the spring months.

SNOW

112. Days with snow. Although snow is by no means rare except on the coast in the extreme south and south-west of the British Isles, falls of sufficient intensity to produce a covering deep enough to impede traffic in low-lying districts are uncommon. Also, after a fall of snow, the temperature does not often remain continuously below freezing-point for very long. Thus the fallen snow generally disappears fairly quickly ; in many cases when snow is falling the temperature of the air and earth remain above freezing-point, with the result that the snow never " lies " at all. In recent years heavy snow has been so uncommon that we are perhaps tending to form incorrect ideas in regard to the potentialities of the British winter. Occasionally, as at Christmas 1927, we have received a sharp reminder that snow may sometimes occur in unpleasant abundance, even in the south of England. Speaking generally, however, the younger generation of to-day may be excused for wondering why snow should be associated so closely in British folk-lore and tradition with winter, and particularly with Christmas. There can be no doubt that we have here a survival of recollections of days when our winter climate was definitely more severe ; when it was natural for a King Wenceslas or an outcast heroine to face snow instead of rain or fog.

Our meteorological statistics include records of the number of " days with snow ". The observer is instructed to take note of all occasions of snow or sleet, however slight, occurring between midnight and midnight. It is obvious that the number of such occasions recorded must depend a good deal upon the vigilance of the observer, and upon the possibility of a continuous watch being maintained at the station. Some uncertainty must therefore attach to the statistics. The snow which falls into the rain-gauge is simply melted and included in the ordinary records of precipitation as " rain ". We are not therefore in a position to quote figures in regard to the average " snow-fall " of different places. We may, however, say with confidence that except in cold elevated regions like the Highlands of Scotland, snow contributes only a small proportion of the annual total precipitation.

We give in Table L averages of the monthly and annual number of days with snow at various stations, based on data published by the Meteorological Office (42). For most stations the averages are based on thirty-five years of observations. The table includes averages for the Ben Nevis Observatory, where during the period of its existence from 1884 to 1903 snow was abundant in all months from October to May,

TABLE L

AVERAGE NUMBER OF DAYS WITH SNOW

Station	Jan.	Feb.	Mar.	Apr.	May	June to September	Oct.	Nov.	Dec.	Year
SCOTLAND										
Sumburgh Head (*Shetlands*) - -	4	4	6	3	0·8	0	0·8	2	4	25
Deerness (*Orkney*) -	6	6	6	4	1	0·1	0·9	3	4	31
Stornoway (*Hebrides*)	5	5	5	3	0·8	0	0·9	2	4	25
Wick (*Caithness*) -	4	5	5	3	0·8	0·1	1	2	4	25
Ben Nevis (*Inverness*)	22	19	21	18	15	19	16	17	22	170
Aberdeen (*Aberdeen*)	7	7	7	3	0·8	0·1	1	3	5	34
Balmoral (*Aberdeen*)	9	8	10	5	1	1	2	5	8	50
Braemar (*Aberdeen*)	8	7	9	6	2	0·5	2	4	7	47
Leith (*Midlothian*) -	4	3	5	1	0·4	0	0·2	0·9	3	17
Rothesay (*Bute*) -	3	3	3	1	0·5	0	0·3	0·7	2	14
Glasgow (*Lanark*) -	4	3	4	0·7	0·1	0	0·2	1	3	16
ENGLAND, WALES										
Douglas (*Isle of Man*)	4	3	4	1	0·1	0	0·3	1	2	17
N. Shields (*Northd.*) -	5	5	5	2	0·3	0	0·4	1	3	23
Sunderland (*Durham*)	6	6	7	2	0·3	0	0·6	2	4	28
York (*Yorks.*) - -	3	3	3	0·8	0·1	0	0·1	1	3	14
Yarmouth (*Norfolk*)	4	3	4	1	0·4	0	0·1	0·7	2	17
Sheffield (*Yorks.*) -	6	6	6	2	0·3	0	0·4	1	4	26
Buxton (*Derby*) -	8	8	8	3	1	0	0·9	3	6	38
Oxford (*Oxon.*) -	4	4	4	0·9	0·1	0	0·1	1	3	17
Kew Observatory (*Surrey*) - -	3	3	3	1	0·1	0	0	0·6	2	13
Dungeness (*Kent*) -	3	3	3	0·9	0·1	0	0·1	0·4	2	12
Southport (*Lancs.*) -	3	2	3	1	0	0	0	1	2	12
Stonyhurst (*Lancs.*)	6	5	6	2	0·6	0	0·6	1	4	26
Liverpool (*Cheshire*)	3	2	3	0·7	0·1	0	0·1	0·8	2	11
Holyhead (*Anglesey*)	2	1	2	0·4	0	0	0·1	0·4	0·8	7
St. Anne's Head (*Pembroke*) - -	2	1	2	0·3	0	0	0	0·2	0·8	6
Falmouth (*Cornwall*)	1	1	2	0·2	0·1	0	0·1	0·3	0·6	5
Scilly (St. Mary's) -	0·8	0·8	0·9	0·2	0	0	0	0·2	0·2	3
IRELAND										
Malin Head (*Donegal*)	2	2	3	0·6	0·1	0	0·1	0·7	2	11
Donaghadee (*Antrim*)	2	2	2	0·4	0·1	0	0·1	0·5	1	8
Armagh (*Armagh*) -	3	2	2	0·3	0·1	0	0·1	0·6	2	9
Dublin (*Dublin*) -	4	4	5	1	0·3	0	0·2	1	2	18
Birr Castle (*Offaly*) -	3	3	3	0·9	0·1	0	0·2	0·6	2	13
Valentia (*Kerry*) -	1	1	1	0·3	0·1	0	0·1	0·1	0·7	5
Roches Point (*Cork*)	0·8	0·8	0·9	0·2	0	0	0	0·2	0·2	3

For most stations the averages refer to the period 1881-1915

(From *The Book of Normals*, Section IVB)

and was nearly as frequent from June to September as it is during the whole year at most stations outside Scotland. The nineteen days grouped together under the heading " June to September " were made up of five in June, three in July, three in August and seven in September, with an odd one made up of decimals spread over the four months.

The frequency of snow at Ben Nevis is, of course, of an altogether different order of magnitude from that of any other station in the list, as was to be expected on a mountain-top with a very high annual precipitation and a mean annual temperature below freezing-point (actually 31·5° F.). Among the remaining stations, Balmoral heads the list with an annual average of fifty snowy days ; at the other end of the scale we have Scilly and Roche's Point on the south coast of Ireland with no more than three. At Balmoral snow has occurred in all months of the year, but it will be seen from the table that by far the greater part of the annual total at all stations is made up of falls in the six months November to April. An interesting point to notice is that at many stations snow has occurred more frequently in the spring month, March, than in any of the winter months. We also see that snow is rather less rare in May than in October. This very definite tendency for snow to be relatively frequent in spring may be attributed to the frequency of general north-easterly winds during that season, to which attention was drawn in Chapter III.

In regard to geographical distribution, we should expect the frequency of snow to depend partly upon the distribution of temperature and partly upon the frequency of occurrence of days of precipitation, during the winter and spring. In regard to temperature, we saw in Chapter VII that at sea-level in January temperature tended to decrease from west to east ; on these grounds we should expect snow to be more frequent near the east coast than near the west coast. The data of Table L comply with this expectation to some extent, notwithstanding the fact that days of precipitation are more numerous, on the average, in the west than in the east. Thus we find an annual snow-frequency of only seven days at Holyhead as compared with seventeen at Yarmouth and twenty-eight at Sunderland on the east coast of England. Altitude is, however, obviously a very important factor ; thus in the suburbs of London, snow is very much more frequent at Hampstead (500 feet) than at Kew Observatory (18 feet).

113. Mornings with snow lying. Meteorological observers note the occasions when snow is lying over more than half the surrounding country at the morning hour of observation, usually 7 h. or 9 h. Some averages have been published (43), but they refer, unfortunately, to only a short period of years. They indicate, however, that at most low-lying stations the frequency of days with snow exceeds the frequency of mornings with snow lying, as might perhaps be expected in view of the fact that the observation of snow lying is restricted to the morning hour. At Kew Observatory, the average annual frequency during the period 1912-1920 was only four days per annum. On the mild south-west coasts snow lying is a relatively rare phenomenon, for the frequency at Valentia and Falmouth is no more than one day per two years.

In the cold elevated regions of the Highlands of Scotland we have annual averages of eighty-three days at Braemar and sixty-nine at Balmoral. Thus from December to March it is more common than not to see snow lying in the morning at Braemar. The Meteorological Office table provides information in regard to the frequency of snow lying in two other upland regions, namely thirty-one days per annum at Princetown on Dartmoor (1,335 feet) and thirty days per annum at Eskdalemuir, (Dumfries) (794 feet).

114. Depth of snow. The depth of snow lying does not often exceed a few inches on level ground at low altitudes, though drifts several feet deep may be formed by wind action. In our worst storms depths of one foot or more may be deposited over a wide area, as in December 1927. Four to five feet of snow are stated to have fallen in the Isle of Wight and Hampshire in January 1881, and a depth of about the same order on Dartmoor between 9th and 13th March, 1891. According to Rev. H. H. Breton (44) snow fell to a depth of six feet over a small area on the south-eastern fringe of Dartmoor to the west of Holme Chase on 16th February, 1929. On this occasion there was little or no wind, so that drifting was not in question.

When heavy snow occurs in association with strong winds very deep accumulations may be formed in hollows, ravines or railway cuttings. We shall refer to some examples of this in the description of the great snowstorm of Christmas 1927 to be given shortly. In an article on " Snowfall in the British Isles, 1876-1925 ", L. C. W. Bonacina (45) gives a number of remarkable cases of deep drifting. He quotes Rev. Baring Gould as authority for the statement that after the great storm in March 1891 the deep ravine on Dartmoor known as Tavy Cleave was filled with snow to the depth of 300 feet.

115. Permanent snow-beds. The summits of even the highest peaks in the British Isles are well below the permanent snow line, but there are certain hollows and gullies at high levels where snow accumulates in large quantities during the winter, portions of which may remain un-

Q

melted during most summers. These hollows have become known as " permanent snow-beds ". Of these, the best known and the one possessing the best claim to be called permanent is in the great corrie of Allt-a-Mhuillin, north-east of the summit of Ben Nevis. The following description is taken from an article by Rev. R. P. Dansey (46) :

" The summit plateau which rises steeply from the south-west— the Glen Nevis side—terminates, after forming the summit crest, in a magnificent series of precipices, nearly two miles in length, over- looking the north-east face. At the bottom of these precipices runs the small stream of the Allt-a-Mhuillin, whence the corrie takes its name. On the other side of this, rise again the steep scree-covered slopes of Cairn Mor Dearg, 4,012 feet, which at the head of this great corrie joins Ben Nevis on the east by an arête which never falls below 3,478 feet. It will thus be seen that the Allt-a-Mhuillin corrie is enclosed on all sides except the north by very high ground. Indeed under the summit of Ben Nevis the precipices are 2,000 feet in height, and into these grim recesses the summer sun never entirely penetrates. These grand cliffs, however, their two miles of length seamed by buttress, ridge and gulley, not only keep off the sun but they also intercept the warm Atlantic winds which blow over the top and on to the slopes of the opposite mountain, Cairn Mor Dearg, leaving the snow-covered corrie in a cold atmosphere of its own making.

" It will now be seen how favourably situated is this great corrie under the north-east precipices of Ben Nevis for the accumulation and duration of snow.

" And now as regards that accumulation. By far the greater part of the snow that falls on Ben Nevis with all winds from south-by-west to west-north-west—which are the prevailing winds and bring the heaviest snowfalls—is swept off over the precipices where it accumu- lates in the great hollows and gullies underneath, in the Allt-a- Mhuillin corrie. The maximum depth on the summit is generally reached about the end of April or some time in May. The snow usually disappears from the summit about the beginning of July, except in drifts, but the much greater accumulation below still remains. The minimum depth of snow under the precipices is usually found about the beginning of September. . . ."

This snow-bed of Ben Nevis was long thought to be definitely per- manent. It disappeared, however, in 1935 though it survived the warm summer of 1933.

Another snow-bed of rather similar character is found in the great corrie of Braeriach in the Cairngorms, described by Mr. Seton Gordon (47). It melted in September 1933 for the first time, it is believed, in more than fifty years.

Outside Scotland, the " latest snow-spot " is found in a gulley known locally as " Y ffoes ddyfn "—The deep Cut—1,200 yards north-north-east of the summit of Carnedd Llewelyn in the Snowdon range, at an elevation of 3,000 feet. This gulley which is about fifty feet deep becomes filled with snow in winter and remains of it may survive till midsummer. A description of the snow conditions in this area has been given by J. R. Gethin Jones (48).

116. A great snowstorm, 25th-26th December, 1927. Snow is liable to occur at any time in the winter or spring when a current of cold air overruns our area from the north or north-east. Really heavy falls of snow over a wide area appear to occur, however, only in association with a definite depression. In other words there must be an incursion of warmer moist air to supply the material for the heavy precipitation.

We propose to describe here the great snowstorm of 25th-26th December, 1927, as an example of the winter conditions to which the southern districts of England are occasionally liable. The storm was outstanding in regard to the amount of snow which fell and with respect to the interruption of communications by rail and road due to the deep drifts which formed in many districts.

The events preceding the storm were briefly as follows. About 12th December a very large anticyclone came down from the northward between north Greenland and Spitzbergen and eventually covered Iceland and Scandinavia. The result of this was to cause polar air to spread over most of Europe. Following upon snow in central and northern England, Wales and southern Scotland the very cold air reached England on 16th and temperature was very low, day and night, for the next few days. An incursion of moist Atlantic air caused a remarkable " glazed frost " in London and many other parts of England on 21st. On the following day, 22nd December, a very deep depression crossed the British Isles, causing generally heavy rainfall. In the rear of this system, cold north-easterly winds flowed in again from Scandinavia. A "polar front" was nearly stationary over southern England on the 24th and during the following night a deep depression developed over the western part of the English Channel. This depression may be described as the proximate cause of the great blizzard. Snow began to fall in the Midlands on Christmas day, but the precipitation in the south of England

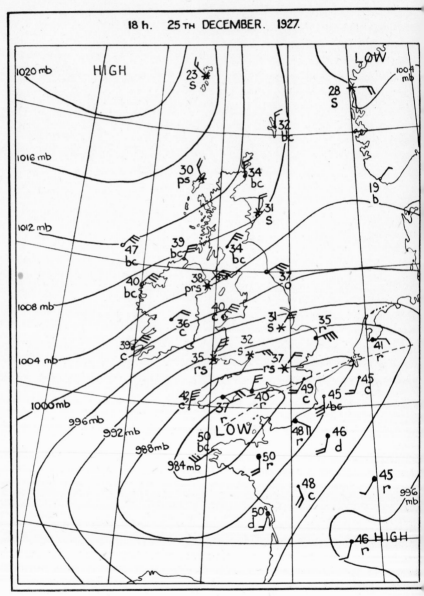

FIG. 85.—The Christmas snowstorm, 1927. Synoptic chart for 18 h., 25th December.

was in the form of heavy rain. This turned to snow in the evening : snow fell heavily throughout the night over nearly the whole of southern England, and throughout Boxing Day and the following night in the south-eastern counties.

We give in Fig. 85 a reproduction of the synoptic chart for 18 h. on Christmas Day. This shows the " polar front " marked as a dotted line running east-north-eastward from the centre of the depression. The front was being pushed slowly south-eastward by the advance of the cold air from the north. The building-up of high pressure over Scotland maintained strong north-easterly winds over southern districts, and it was this strong polar wind which caused the very remarkable snow-drifts which were a feature of the storm.

The total precipitation, expressed as rain, exceeded two inches over a considerable area in south-east England, with over three inches between Ashford and Dover in Kent. Not all of this was in the form of snow, however. In the worst areas the mean depth of snow was of the order of two feet on the hills, about one foot at the low levels, diminishing to half a foot in the London area. The storm appears to have been most severe on Dartmoor, in the Alton-Basingstoke district of Hampshire and along the North Downs. In parts of Cornwall and in the east of Kent no snow fell at all.

The snow drifted to remarkable depths in railway cuttings, lanes and hollows, and in many places transport by railway, road or on foot was brought to a standstill. Many striking photographs were published at the time in the newspapers and periodicals ; a good collection referring to Dartmoor is to be found in a pamphlet published by Rev. H. H. Breton (49), from which the following details are taken. On Dartmoor many villages were snowed up for days, the lanes being blocked by drifts up to fifteen feet deep. Hundreds of sheep were buried, but most of them were dug out some days later, still alive, and the losses were comparatively slight. Princetown was unapproachable by road for nearly a week, and railway traffic ceased for four days until snow-ploughs propelled by two powerful engines could cut a way through the drifts. Prisoners had to be employed in digging away snow which was in many cases banked up to the bedroom windows of the warders' houses.

In Hampshire and parts of the home counties conditions were almost as severe and in some cases it became necessary to supply villagers with food by dropping parcels from aeroplanes. Near Petersfield twenty-two motor cars were buried in a single drift. Travellers by road or rail on Christmas night were in many cases brought to a halt by impassable drifts and had to stay where they were. The branch railway line through Alton was closed to traffic for a week. The north-west corner of Kent also suffered severely. The main road from London to Sevenoaks was closed by drifts fifteen feet deep, and bungalows in the neighbourhood of Biggin Hill were half-buried. The frontispiece to *British Rainfall, 1927,* shows some remarkable photographs of conditions in this area.

HAIL

117. Kinds of hail. Two types of hail are recognized for the ordinary purpose of meteorology, namely " ordinary " hail (ice pellets, often consisting of successive layers of clear and cloudy ice, the latter having a softer consistency) and " soft " hail which is small, white, opaque and soft as if formed of compressed snow. On the continent, where solid precipitation is more frequent and has received more study than in England, three varieties are now recognized, namely " soft hail " (Fr. *neige roulée,* G. *Reifgraupeln*), " small hail " (Fr. *grésil,* G. *Frostgraupeln*) and " hail " (Fr. *grêle,* G. *Hagel*). The first type is sometimes referred to as " granular snow ". The process of formation is probably different for the three types and it is a little invidious therefore to lump them all together under the common term "hail" in climatological summaries. That has, however, been the general practice, and it would indeed be difficult to obtain reliable statistics in regard to the frequency of incidence of each of the three types. The ordinary citizen knows the difference between snow and " hail " ; he recognizes the former as something soft, laminar and crystalline, the latter as something round and usually hard and dense enough to fall quickly and to bounce. But even a trained meteorologist might find difficulty in distinguishing between " neige roulée " and " grésil " on all occasions. Hail of the hard icy variety differs from the other two forms in that it may appear in the form of stones of quite remarkable size. Hailstones have been reported as big as golf balls (fairly frequently), tennis balls (occasionally) and even grape-fruit (on one occasion in America). Such hailstones are naturally destructive to glass houses, etc., and this is also true when the stones are of more ordinary dimensions. Statistics in respect to the frequency of hail are therefore of some practical interest. We are not in a position to distinguish between destructive falls of hail and relatively innocuous falls in the summarized data at our disposal, but an account will be given of a recent storm of outstanding violence after the data in respect to the frequency of hail have been briefly examined.

118. Days with hail. Averages of the number of occurrences of hail in each month and the year are given for a number of typical stations in Table LI. They show a very remarkable degree of variation from station to station, and it is not easy to detect any simple form of geographical distribution, even when the data for other stations are examined. Thus, in southern Ireland we have an annual frequency of 5·4 at Roches Point as compared with 22·9 at Valentia. Dublin (City) with twenty-seven days per year tops the list given in the *Book of Normals*, in contrast to Armagh with only three days. Again in the

TABLE LI

Days with Hail : Monthly and Annual Averages for Typical
Stations

Station	Jan.	Feb.	Mar.	Apr.	May	June	July	Aug.	Sep.	Oct.	Nov.	Dec.	Year
Deerness (*Orkney*)	2·8	2·8	**3·2**	2·8	1·3	0·2	0·0	0·0	0·4	1·4	2·3	2·2	19·⌐
Aberdeen (*Aber.*)	1·9	1·1	**3·2**	2·8	2·0	0·4	0·1	0·1	0·2	1·2	1·2	1·7	15·9
Glasgow (*Lanark*)	1·2	1·1	1·3	1·2	0·8	0·3	0·1	0·0	0·1	0·4	0·6	1·0	8·1
Douglas (*I. of M.*)	2·9	2·6	2·8	2·2	1·2	0·1	0·1	0·0	0·4	2·0	2·9	**3·5**	20·7
N. Shields (*North.*)	1·3	1·5	**1·8**	1·4	0·5	0·2	0·1	0·1	0·1	0·6	0·9	1·1	9·6
Kew Observatory (*Surrey*) - -	0·6	0·5	1·2	0·9	0·9	0·4	0·2	0·2	0·1	0·2	0·2	0·3	5·7
Stonyhurst (*Lancs.*) - -	**3·6**	2·7	3·3	2·7	1·6	0·3	0·3	0·4	0·6	1·7	2·4	3·5	23·1
Falmouth (*Corn.*)	2·9	2·5	2·7	0·9	0·7	0·1	0·1	0·0	0·2	1·2	1·9	2·7	15·9
Malin Head (*Donegal*) -	**4·0**	2·9	3·1	1·8	0·8	0·1	0·1	0·1	0·5	2·2	2·5	3·6	21·7
Armagh (*Armagh*)	0·1	0·2	**0·7**	0·7	0·6	0·2	0·1	0·1	0·1	0·1	0·1	0·1	3·1
Valentia (*Kerry*)	**4·1**	3·7	**4·1**	1·8	0·9	0·0	0·0	0·0	0·2	1·7	2·5	3·9	22·9

Mainly for the period 1881-1915

(From *The Book of Normals*, Section IVB)

extreme north we have 3·4 days at Sumburgh Head (Shetlands) as compared with 19·4 days at Deerness (Orkney) and 21·2 at Stornoway (Hebrides). It seems almost certain that much of this variation is due to differences in the vigilance of observers, or possibly to differences in their ideas as to what should be classed as hail.

119. Seasonal variation of hail. The data given in Table LI indicate that hail tends to occur with maximum frequency from December to March and with minimum frequency in the summer months, June to August. Deerness and Aberdeen show a pronounced maximum in March, and this is also seen further south at North Shields and at Kew Observatory. The results for other stations given in the *Book of Normals* indicate that the March maximum occurs over a wide area. It is a matter of common experience that falls of hail are often associated with thunderstorms, and in fact it may be said that the convectional processes which give rise to thunderstorms are also those which give rise, under suitable conditions of temperature, to hail, or at any rate to hail of the icy variety. In the inland districts of the south of England and the Midlands thunder is a phenomenon characteristic of the summer months, and it is a little surprising to find that the months of maximum thunderstorm frequency at Kew, namely July and August, show a very low frequency of hail—only 0·2 day or one day in five years, in each of the two months. It is, however, to be observed that at stations on the western and northern coasts, such as Valentia, St. Ann's Head, Holyhead, Rothesay and Deerness, which have a low frequency of summer thunderstorms, hail is practically unknown during the summer months.

The tendency for a high frequency of hail in the spring months, and particularly in March, fits in well with what we have already learnt about the " wintry " character of that season when considering the data for winds, temperature, ground frost and snow. These unpleasant characteristics of the English spring are, however, offset by the rapid increase in the hours of sunshine, the consequent bursting forth of vegetation, and the diminution in both the frequency and amount of rainfall. So preponderating are these pleasant and stimulating qualities that for many Englishmen spring is the most enjoyable season of the year.

120. A remarkable hailstorm, 22nd September, 1935. Heavy and destructive falls of hail occur occasionally in association with thunderstorms. One of the worst storms of which particulars are available occurred over the River Nene valley in Northamptonshire in the early morning of 22nd September, 1935. The following details are taken from an article in *British Rainfall*, 1935.

" The thunderstorm with which the hail-fall was associated was one of many which were experienced in the Midlands and north of England during the passage of a depression north-eastwards across England. It is interesting to note that the storms were not preceded by great heat and maximum temperatures seldom exceeded 70° F. either on the 20th or 21st.

" The synoptic chart at 7 h. on the 21st showed an anticyclone centred over Germany extending to the British Isles, and a depression centred south of Iceland, while a shallow depression over the Bay of Biscay was moving north-east.

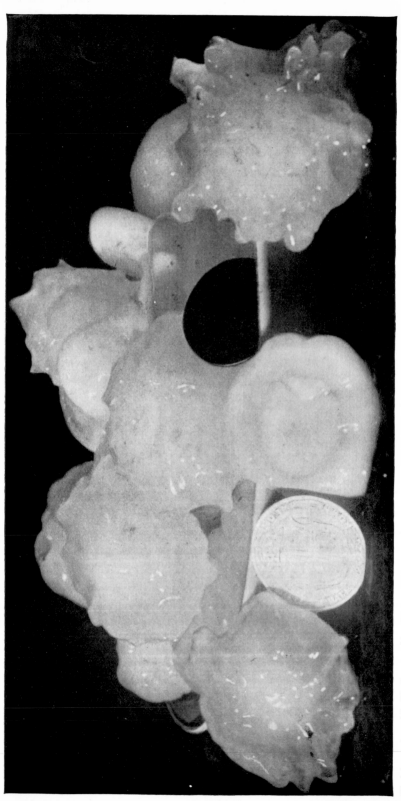

[Photo, A. E. Pollard.

Fig. 86.—Hailstones photographed near Northampton, 22nd September 1935.   (Actual size.)

" The 6 h. aeroplane ascent at Duxford on the 21st showed that above 8,000 feet temperature was above the normal for the season, while the lapse rate was equal to, or exceeded, the saturated adiabatic. The air was relatively moist. Below 8,000 feet there was relatively dry air with a small inversion at about 3,500 feet.

" By 18 h. on the 21st the shallow depression was just south-west of the Scilly Isles, with a ' warm front ' extending across the Midlands just south of a line Holyhead to Cranwell and a ' cold front ' extending from the Scilly Isles across north-west France to south-west France. Behind the ' warm front ' warm damp air had spread across England from the south (vapour pressure in the southern half of England had risen to about seventeen millibars). Surface temperatures and vapour pressures over France were high and pilot balloon ascents in south-east England during the afternoon of the 21st indicated that temperature over England was rising at least in the lowest 6,000-7,000 feet. In addition the air was becoming more moist. Thus conditions very favourable for the development of thunderstorms were present, viz., a lapse rate in excess of the saturated adiabatic from a height of about 6,000 feet to great heights and an adequate supply of moisture in the lower layers. The thunderstorms were started by the ' cold front ', assisted strongly in this case by convergence to the centre of low pressure which deepened considerably as it moved north-eastwards across England.

" At 1 h. on the 22nd the depression was situated over the Bristol Channel with the ' cold front ' extending south-eastwards into north France, and by 7 h. the depression had reached the Humber with the ' cold front ' extending south-eastwards across East Anglia to the Continent. Later the depression deepened very considerably as it moved away north-eastwards, reaching a depth of 980 millibars off southern Norway by 7 h. on the 23rd."

The thunderstorm broke over the neighbourhood of Northampton shortly before 3 h. Shortly after its commencement hail fell for several minutes (up to twenty minutes in places). The stones were of exceptional size, as may be judged from the photograph reproduced in Fig. 86, which shows a number of stones collected by Mr. A. E. Pollard at Weston Favell and photographed by him with coins for comparison. In other places the hailstones appear to have been even larger than those observed at Weston Favell. A stone picked up at Rushden is stated to have been as large as a tennis ball, and some of the glass broken in the storm showed circular holes three inches in diameter. At Great Billing, a village near Northampton, the asbestos cement sheeting forming the roof of a motor garage was pierced in many places. A piece of this roofing, presented to the Meteorological Office by Captain R. P. Elwes, shows two holes, within the larger of which it is possible to draw a circle exceeding four inches in diameter. We thus have evidence that some of the stones which fell in the storm may have exceeded four inches in diameter.

Great damage was done in an area about forty miles long and up to ten miles wide extending north-eastward from Banbury to Irthling-borough. At Northampton the cost of repairing the damage to one building alone, St. Andrews Hospital, exceeded £600. Many thousands of square feet of glass in skylights, window panes and greenhouses were destroyed by an icy bombardment which no brittle material could withstand.

THUNDER

121. Observations of thunder. The data at our disposal in regard to the frequency of thunderstorms refer to occasions of " thunder heard " during the civil day, midnight to midnight. Occasions of lightning without thunder are excluded and no distinction is made in the statistics between overhead storms and occasions when distant thunder only is observed. It has been ascertained that thunder is normally audible at distances up to about ten miles from the observing station. Thus we may say that the statistics relate to occasions when there was a thunder-storm, of greater or less intensity, at or within ten miles of the station. The observation of thunder necessitates the personal attention of the observer, even more than in the case of snow or hail, which may leave traces of their occurrence to be detected at a later hour. Thunder occurring during the night may thus go unrecorded on some occasions, unless a 24-hour watch is kept.

122. Annual frequency of thunder. A chart of the average annual number of days with thunder is given in Fig. 87. This chart is based on data covering, in most cases, a period of thirty-five years, from about seventy stations ; the data were compiled from a table in the *Book of Normals* (50), supplemented by averages from certain additional stations published by W. A. L. Marshall (51) and by others derived from manuscript records in the Meteorological Office. The distribution shown on the chart differs slightly from that indicated on a chart by Marshall, partly because the values for certain stations have been

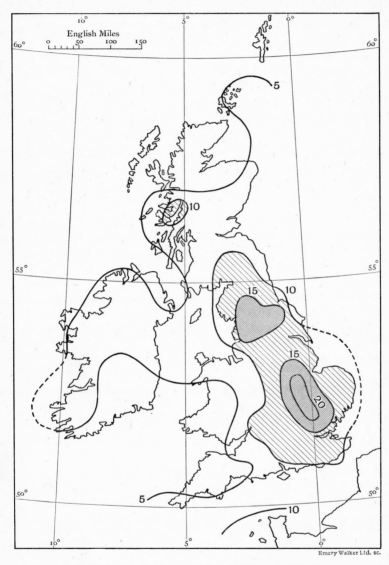

Fig. 87.—Annual average nnmber of days with thunder.
(Areas with more than ten days are shaded ; darker shading denotes areas
with more than fifteen days.)

slightly revised and partly because of the inclusion of data from additional stations.

The most striking feature of the chart is the area covering most of England, in which the frequency of thunder exceeds ten days per year. An additional small area with more than ten days is seen over western Scotland ; this is, however, based on the value for a single station (Strontian, Argyllshire, 11·3). There are two areas, one in the north of England, the other extending from Essex to south Lincolnshire, with more than fifteen days. Within the latter area a small region has an annual frequency exceeding twenty days. Considerable areas in northern Scotland, south Wales and south-west England have fewer than five days per annum with thunder ; the minimum is found in the Shetlands, where the 35-year average derived from observations at Sumburgh Head and Lerwick is only 1·2 days. The average for Deerness, Orkney (7·0 days) is distinctly higher than the value for the Shetlands or for adjacent stations on the mainland.

123. Seasonal variation. The mean frequency of thunder in each month is given for various stations in the Appendix. In Table LII we give seasonal averages for a selection of typical stations. It will be seen that the frequency is a maximum in the summer (June to August) at all the stations in the table, except Stornoway and Valentia, which show a maximum in the winter (December to February). At other stations in the west and north, for example Strontian and Deerness, winter ranks next to summer in regard to thunder frequency, but winter is the season of minimum frequency in the eastern, central and south-eastern districts. These districts also show a relatively high frequency of thunder in the spring, due mainly to occurrences in May. Strontian, on the west coast of Scotland, Falmouth and Valentia show a tendency to uniformity in the seasonal incidence. It is interesting to compare the data for Strontian with those for Leith, the one on the west coast, the other on the east coast of Scotland. Thunder occurs more than twice as often at Strontian as at Leith, but the frequencies for the summer months are the same. The difference in the annual average is due to a much greater frequency at Strontian in spring, autumn and winter.

124. Conditions giving rise to thunderstorms. Thunderstorms occur when a condition of instability exists in a deep stratum of moist air, that is to say there must be a steep lapse rate through a great vertical thickness of the atmosphere at a time when the air is nearly saturated with moisture down to low levels. Thus we should expect thunder during periods of damp heat in the summer when surface heating over the land, due to insolation, provides the stimulus necessary to initiate violent convectional motion. Such storms would occur most frequently over areas with high day temperatures in the summer and it will be seen that the area of high thunderstorm frequency over Great Britain does in fact coincide roughly with the area of high summer temperature.

TABLE LII

SEASONAL FREQUENCY OF THUNDERSTORMS (AVERAGE NUMBER OF DAYS ON WHICH THUNDER IS HEARD IN EACH SEASON, AND THE YEAR)

Station	Spring (March to May)	Summer (June to August)	Autumn (Sept. to November)	Winter (Dec. to February)	Year
SCOTLAND					
Deerness (*Orkney*) - -	0·6	2·9	1·5	2·0	7·0
Stornoway (*Hebrides*) -	0·4	1·1	0·6	1·2	3·3
Aberdeen (*Aberdeen*) -	0·9	4·8	0·6	0·1	6·4
Leith (*Midlothian*) - -	0·8	3·7	0·4	0·3	5·2
Strontian (*Argyll*) - -	2·4	3·7	2·2	3·0	11·3
Glasgow (*Lanark*) - -	1·7	4·1	0·7	0·9	7·4
Eskdalemuir (*Dumfries*) -	2·4	6·1	1·3	0·5	10·3
ENGLAND AND WALES					
Douglas (*Isle of Man*) -	1·8	4·2	2·0	0·6	8·6
N. Shields (*North.*) -	1·2	4·4	0·8	0·3	6·7
York (*Yorks.*) - -	3·2	7·1	1·1	0·1	11·5
Belvoir Castle (*Leics.*) -	5·3	11·8	2·3	0·5	19·9
Kew Observ'y (*Surrey*) -	4·0	8·3	1·8	0·3	14·4
Stonyhurst (*Lancs.*) -	4·2	9·9	3·3	0·8	18·2
Holyhead (*Anglesey*) -	1·3	3·2	1·5	0·4	6·4
Falmouth (*Cornwall*) -	0·9	1·9	1·3	1·0	5·1
IRELAND					
Malin Head (*Donegal*) -	0·9	2·8	0·7	0·6	5·0
Armagh (*Armagh*) - -	1·0	3·7	0·2	0·2	5·1
Dublin (*Dublin*) - -	1·5	5·2	1·1	0·4	8·2
Valentia (*Kerry*) - -	1·4	1·8	1·3	2·0	6·5

Mainly for the period 1881-1915

In winter the necessary conditions of instability may be brought about by the passage of polar air over a long stretch of relatively warm sea. E. V. Newnham (52) showed that on occasions of thunder in winter the air current had in nearly all cases come initially from high latitudes, reaching these islands as a westerly wind current after a long journey over the sea. He also pointed out that orographic action would tend to impart an upward motion when the wind current encountered high land on our western coasts, thus accounting for the relatively high frequency of winter thunderstorms on our western seaboard.

Reference must also be made to thunderstorms of the "frontal" class. These occur in association with the passage of cold or warm fronts. Cold front thunderstorms are usually quite brief and may be associated with line squalls ; they may occur at any time of year. Sometimes, however, in warm weather when the necessary conditions of instability exist up to a great height, the advance of a comparatively feeble cold front may provide the "trigger action" necessary to produce a noteworthy storm. In regard to warm front storms C. K. M. Douglas (53) remarks : "It is only in special conditions that instability up above accompanies warm fronts, but warm front storms of fair severity may occur almost anywhere in the British Isles, and in the south-east they average about one in two years." He points out that the great storm which occurred over south-east England on the night of 9th July, 1923, was associated with a feeble warm front, and he also expresses the view that "surface heating" and "frontal" thunderstorms form overlapping rather than sharply defined categories.

Most of the warm weather thunderstorms of the late spring and summer occur in association with one or other of two types of pressure distribution. These are (a) a feeble and slowly-moving depression over England and (b) a depression over the region of the Bay of Biscay, with surface winds mainly from south-east over southern England. The south-east wind in the latter case is usually overrun by a cool moist south-westerly current.

125. Rainfall in thunderstorms. The characteristic feature of rainfall associated with thunderstorms is its great intensity. When discussing "heavy falls in short periods" in Chapter V we gave a number of examples of intense rains. Details of all falls classed as "noteworthy", "remarkable" or "very rare" are given every year in the annual volume of *British Rainfall* ; with few exceptions they occur during thunderstorms. Not only may the intensity, or rate of fall, be great but the total amount of rain during the storm may also be exceptional. Thus the record daily fall in London, 4·65 inches on 16th June, 1917, occurred during a thunderstorm. The second largest daily fall for the whole of the British Isles (9·40 inches) was caused by a thunderstorm at Cannington, Somerset, on 18th August, 1924. An analysis of the dates of occurrence of the intense falls tabulated in *British Rainfall* shows that about two-thirds of the total number occur in June, July or August. These are the months of maximum thunderstorm frequency except in the western coastal districts of the British Isles. An investigation of the results for Kew Observatory (54) showed that a fall of one inch of rain in five hours or less was registered on twenty-eight occasions during the fifty years 1878 to 1927 ; of these occasions there were two in May, seven in June, six each in July, August and September, one in October and none in any of the months November to April.

We may conclude that rainfall which is both abundant and intense is characteristic of summer thunderstorms. The thunderstorms which occur in winter often produce violent showers of rain or hail but they do not last long enough to precipitate a noteworthy amount.

The heavy rainfall in thunderstorms often causes local flooding, but this effect is mainly confined to towns, the street drainage systems of which are not usually of sufficient capacity to remove water at the rate at which it is deposited in the worst thunderstorms. The worst recorded case of flooding due to thunderstorm rains occurred at Louth, Lincolnshire, on 29th May, 1920. On this occasion heavy rains occurred in many parts of northern England in association with the northward movement of a shallow depression, the centre of which was over Devonshire early on the morning of 29th May and had reached a position in the North Sea off the Firth of Forth twenty-four hours later. West of Louth in Lincolnshire, more than two inches fell over a considerable area of the Wolds district drained by the River Lud which flows through the town of Louth. At Elkington Hall, three miles to the west of the town, the fall for the twenty-four hours ending 9 h. on the 30th May amounted to 4·69 inches, nearly the whole of which fell within three hours, 13 h. to 16 h. In Louth itself the rainfall was no more than 1·42 inch, but the town suffered severely from the flood waters flowing down the River Lud. The river is reported to have risen six feet in ten minutes, and to have reached a level fifteen feet above normal. By 16 h. a torrent 200 yards wide was sweeping through the town. A number of houses were destroyed and twenty-two of the inhabitants were drowned. The damage to property in the town exceeded £100,000, and there was also much damage and loss of livestock in the surrounding country districts.

In the Louth storm the area with more than two inches of rain formed an elongated strip or band about thirty miles long extending southward from the Humber. The tendency for such a strip distribution is characteristic of thunderstorm rains. Sometimes the strip is broken up into patches with intermediate areas of lower rainfall ; also it is not uncommon to find two or more parallel bands, with less rainfall, or even none at all, in the intervening areas. This tendency for the

256   THE CLIMATE OF THE BRITISH ISLES

localization of rain in thunderstorms often gives rise to remarkable variations in the total rainfall at neighbouring stations in individual summer months.

BIBLIOGRAPHY

(41) *The Book of Normals*, Section IV B, Table 15. (H.M.S.O.)

(42) *Ibid.*, Table 13.

(43) *Ibid.*, Table 14.

(44) H. H. Breton, *The Great Winter of* 1928-1929.

(45) L. C. W. Bonacina, *British Rainfall*, 1927, p. 260. (H.M.S.O.)

(46) R. P. Dansey, "The Glacial Snows of Ben Nevis," *Symons' Metl. Mag.*, **40**, 1905, p. 29.

(47) Seton Gordon, *The Cairngorm Hills of Scotland.*

(48) J. R. Gethin Jones, " The spot in England and Wales where snow lies latest," *British Rainfall*, 1909, p. 46.

(49) H. H. Breton, *The Great Blizzard of Christmas* 1927 : *its causes and incidents.*

(50) *The Book of Normals*, Section IV B, Table 12. (H.M.S.O.)

(51) W. A. L. Marshall, " The mean frequency of thunder over the British Isles and surrounding areas," *Q.J.R. Meteor. Soc.*, **60**, 1934, p. 413.

(52) E. V. Newnham, " On the formation of thunderstorms over the British Isles in winter," *Prof. Notes*, No. 29. (H.M.S.O.)

(53) C. K. M. Douglas, " A note on frontal thunderstorms," *Meteor. Mag.*, 1934, p. 205. (H.M.S.O.)

(54) E. G. Bilham and R. F. M. Hay, " The frequency of heavy rains lasting from one to forty-eight hours at Kew Observatory during the period 1878 to 1927," *British Rainfall*, 1934, p. 284. (H.M.S.O.)

CHAPTER XI

ATMOSPHERIC OBSCURITY

126. Observations of visibility. The inclusion of the distance of visibility or "visual range" as an item in the regular routine of meteorological observations is of comparatively recent origin. Before the Great War it was customary to include references to "haze", "mist" and "fog", indicated by Beaufort letters z, m and f, in records of "past weather" and "present weather", and provision was also made for noting occasions of "exceptional visibility" (Beaufort letter v). These terms were not, however, very precisely defined. The needs of aviation during the Great War, and in the years immediately following, led to a reorientation of ideas and it became clear that it was necessary to regard visibility as a continuously variable quality of the atmosphere, like temperature or humidity, and to arrange for data in regard to visibility to be included in weather reports exchanged internationally. Some details of the present system of observations have been given in Chapter I. The entry made by the observer in his register takes the form of a letter indicating the most distant of a series of objects which he can see at the hour of observation. For the purpose of telegraphing the information to headquarters he has to translate the visibility letter into a code figure and since only ten categories are possible with code figures ranging from 0 to 9, the coded information is a little less precise than the original data. Thus letters X and A are combined in code figure 0, B and C in code figure 1, H and I in code figure 6 and K and L in code figure 8. Details of the letter scale and the numerical code are given in Table II (p. 11). The summarized data available for discussion in this chapter are based entirely on the code figures; for convenience of reference they may be expressed in the following way :

Code figure	0	1	2	3	4	5	6	7	8	9
Objects visible at	—	55 yds.	220 yds.	550 yds.	1,100 yds.	1¼ mi.	2½ mi.	6¼ mi.	12½ mi.	31 mi.
But not at	- 55 yds.	220 yds.	550 yds.	1,100 yds.	1¼ mi.	2½ mi.	6¼ mi.	12½ mi.	31 mi.	—

In the actual work of observing visibility, difficulties may arise in various ways. The most frequent cause of difficulty is the absence of a suitable object at, or sufficiently near, the standard distance. In such a case the observer makes the best estimate he can by noting the clearness with which he can see nearer objects. For information in regard to other points of difficulty the reader should refer to the *Observer's Handbook* (1). The determination of visibility during the hours of darkness presents a special problem and it is probably incorrect to assume that the data we shall quote in respect to visibility at 7 h. and 18 h. during the winter months are quite as reliable as the midday observations.

Table II includes a column headed " description " from which it will be seen that the term " fog " is applied to conditions in which the visibility code figure is 3 or less, and the term mist, haze, or very poor visibility to conditions in which the visibility code figure is 4. It is important to note that the observer is not expected to discriminate between occasions when the object at 1,100 yards is rendered invisible by a genuine fog, composed of water droplets, and occasions when that object is obscured by smoke or by heavy precipitation, *e.g.* a snowstorm. The visibility code figure is determined solely by what the observer can or cannot see, and in statistical summaries the frequency of " fog " is deduced solely from the visibility code figures.

In regard to code figure 4, the descriptive terms " mist " and " haze " represent distinctly different modes of obscuration. Mist is regarded as due to the presence of water drops and haze to the presence of solid particles in the atmosphere ; the solid particles may be derived from smoke or they may consist of dust in an extremely fine state of subdivision, with some vegetable additions such as pollen grains. It is usual to distinguish between the two kinds of " suspensoids " by noting the relative humidity, or merely the depression of the wet-bulb ; when the atmosphere is nearly or quite saturated with water-vapour the obscuration is attributed to water droplets and is described as " mist "; in other circumstances it is described as " haze ". There is also an optical means of distinguishing between the two conditions ; in haze the particles are of size comparable with the wavelengths of light and they therefore produce the phenomenon of selective scattering, thus haze appears bluish in colour when seen by reflected light, and sources of light such as the sun, or even street lamps, acquire an orange or reddish tint when seen through a moderate thickness of hazy air. Water particles, on the other hand, are too large to produce selective scattering and a water fog or mist does not give rise to these optical effects. On many occasions the two types of obscuration occur simultaneously, particularly in industrial areas, but we may postpone further consideration of this aspect of the subject until we have examined the data.

127. Visibility at Croydon Aerodrome. In Table LIII we have ten-year averages of the percentage frequency of occurrence of the ten categories of visibility at Croydon Aerodrome ; separate results are given for 7 h., 13 h. and 18 h. This station is situated at a height of 217 feet above sea level on the southern outskirts of London, about ten miles from Charing Cross. Looking first at the results for 7 h. we see that the most frequent range of visibility in all months is that represented by code number 6 (2½ to 6¼ miles). In January, February, April, May and December more than forty per cent. of the observations fall within this range. On the average for the whole year, visibility 7 is next in order of frequency, followed by visibility 5. Very good visibility (code figure 8) shows a very definite seasonal variation with a maximum frequency of twenty per cent. in June and a minimum frequency of only one per cent. in January and December. Code figure 9, representing a visibility exceeding thirty-one miles, occurred on only two occasions at 7 h. in the ten-year period, giving rise to entries of 0·3 per cent. in March and June. The lower visibilities, representing occurrences of fog, mist or haze, also show a fairly definite form of seasonal variation : they are infrequent in the late spring and summer months, May to August ; for other months the values are somewhat irregular but it appears that fogs are rather more numerous in the autumn and early spring than in the winter, at 7 h. Mist or haze (code figure 4) shows a maximum frequency (12·7 per cent.) in September, followed in order of frequency by February, March and April.

The results for 13 h., representing midday conditions, show some points of resemblance and some of difference when compared with the 7 h. values. Visibility 6 remains the most frequent range for the year as a whole, but visibility 8 attains the highest frequency from May to September. In the summer months June, July and August the frequency of visibility 8 exceeds fifty per cent., and in July it exceeds sixty per cent. Thus it is more common than not for visibility to be very good at Croydon at midday in summer. Fogs, however, occur with a fair degree of frequency at this hour from November to February ; thus midday fog is definitely a phenomenon of late autumn and winter. There are no entries of fog at 13 h. from May to August, and none of mist or haze in July and August.

The results for 18 h. show a fairly close resemblance to those for 13 h. ; the higher visibilities are, however, less frequent in nearly all months and the lower visibilities rather more frequent ; in particular we note that fog has occurred on one or two occasions at 18 h. in May

TABLE LIII

Croydon Aerodrome : Visibility Frequencies

Month	Range of visibility									
	Under 55 yds.	55 yds. to 220 yds.	220 yds. to 550 yds.	550 yds. to 1,100 yds.	1,100 yds. to 1¼ mi.	1¼ mi. to 2½ mi.	2½ mi. to 6¼ mi.	6¼ mi. to 12½ mi.	12½ mi. to 31 mi.	over 31 mi.
	0	1	2	3	4	5	6	7	8	9
	%	%	%	%	%	%	%	%	%	%
At 7 h.										
January -	0·3	1·9	2·6	3·9	7·4	18·4	42·9	21·6	1·0	0·0
February -	1·1	4·2	0·7	3·2	11·3	20·6	40·1	15·6	3·2	0·0
March - -	0·3	2·6	3·9	3·6	11·0	15·8	34·8	21·9	5·8	0·3
April - -	0·3	2·4	0·9	2·4	9·1	19·7	42·7	18·2	4·3	0·0
May - -	0·0	0·6	1·5	0·9	4·1	16·1	40·5	24·9	11·4	0·0
June - -	0·0	0·0	0·3	1·2	3·0	8·8	38·2	30·6	17·6	0·3
July - -	0·0	0·3	0·6	0·6	2·3	11·3	35·2	29·7	20·0	0·0
August -	0·0	0·6	0·6	0·6	5·2	9·4	33·6	31·6	18·4	0·0
September -	0·3	2·3	2·3	4·3	12·7	15·7	29·0	26·0	7·4	0·0
October -	1·6	5·5	1·9	3·9	8·1	17·7	31·0	23·9	6·4	0·0
November -	2·0	5·0	2·0	5·3	8·7	19·0	37·3	18·0	2·7	0·0
December -	0·3	3·5	1·3	2·3	8·4	18·7	45·8	18·7	1·0	0·0
Year -	0·5	2·4	1·5	2·7	7·6	15·9	37·6	23·4	8·3	0·1
At 13 h.										
January -	0·6	0·7	0·3	4·8	8·1	18·7	51·9	14·2	0·7	0·0
February -	0·0	0·4	1·1	3·5	9·9	19·1	45·1	19·5	1·4	0·0
March - -	0·0	0·0	0·3	1·3	6·9	13·9	40·5	30·0	7·1	0·0
April - -	0·0	0·0	0·3	0·6	2·4	10·9	37·0	30·0	18·8	0·0
May - -	0·0	0·0	0·0	0·0	0·9	5·3	24·9	31·9	35·8	1·2
June - -	0·0	0·0	0·0	0·0	0·9	1·8	20·0	24·3	51·8	1·2
July - -	0·0	0·0	0·0	0·0	0·0	2·6	14·2	20·0	60·9	2·3
August -	0·0	0·0	0·0	0·0	0·0	2·6	12·9	21·9	58·4	4·2
September -	0·0	0·0	0·0	0·3	2·7	4·3	23·7	31·7	36·3	1·0
October -	0·0	0·0	0·3	1·0	3·5	9·4	38·4	36·1	11·3	0·0
November -	0·7	2·7	3·0	4·7	13·0	15·0	43·0	16·6	1·3	0·0
December -	1·0	1·3	3·5	7·7	13·2	17·1	43·6	12·6	0·0	0·0
Year -	0·2	0·4	0·7	2·0	5·1	10·1	32·9	24·1	23·7	0·8
At 18 h.										
January -	0·7	0·0	1·9	4·8	15·2	23·2	45·5	8·7	0·0	0·0
February -	0·7	0·7	1·4	3·5	19·5	54·3	12·4	7·5	0·0	0·0
March - -	0·0	0·3	1·0	3·5	9·0	21·3	49·4	14·2	1·3	0·0
April - -	0·0	0·0	0·0	1·2	4·8	10·6	48·5	26·7	8·2	0·0
May - -	0·0	0·0	0·0	0·6	1·8	4·7	27·8	28·1	36·4	0·6
June - -	0·0	0·0	0·0	0·3	0·6	1·8	20·3	26·1	49·7	1·2
July - -	0·0	0·0	0·0	0·0	0·0	1·0	16·1	24·5	53·9	4·5
August -	0·0	0·0	0·0	0·0	0·0	2·2	15·5	25·2	52·9	4·2
September -	0·0	0·0	0·0	1·0	2·0	11·0	36·3	32·7	16·0	1·0
October -	0·0	0·0	0·6	2·9	16·5	24·5	44·8	9·7	1·0	0·0
November -	1·7	1·0	3·0	5·3	19·7	26·7	34·0	8·3	0·3	0·0
December -	0·6	1·6	3·6	4·2	18·1	24·2	41·6	5·8	0·3	0·0
Year -	0·3	0·3	1·0	2·3	8·9	17·1	32·7	18·1	18·3	1·0

TABLE LIV

HOLYHEAD : VISIBILITY FREQUENCIES

Month	Under 55 yds. 0	55 yds. to 220 yds. 1	220 yds. to 550 yds. 2	550 yds. to 1,100 yds. 3	1,100 yds. to 1¼ mi. 4	1¼ mi. to 2½ mi. 5	2½ mi. to 6¼ mi. 6	6¼ mi. to 12½ mi. 7	12½ mi. to 31 mi. 8	over 31 mi. 9
	%	%	%	%	%	%	%	%	%	%
AT 7 H.										
January -	0·0	0·0	0·4	0·4	1·1	5·4	27·9	24·0	38·3	2·5
February -	0·0	**0·4**	0·4	0·0	**5·1**	11·0	**28·4**	20·5	29·9	4·3
March - -	0·0	0·0	0·6	1·9	2·3	**12·3**	26·1	23·5	31·0	2·3
April - -	0·0	0·3	1·0	1·3	1·0	7·3	25·7	26·0	34·7	2·7
May - -	0·0	0·0	1·0	**2·6**	1·3	7·1	26·1	24·5	35·1	2·3
June - -	0·0	0·0	0·3	2·0	0·7	3·3	19·3	26·0	44·4	4·0
July - -	0·0	0·0	1·6	1·9	2·9	5·8	26·8	21·6	36·2	3·2
August -	0·0	0·0	**2·3**	1·0	1·0	5·2	19·3	25·1	43·2	2·9
September -	0·0	0·3	1·0	0·7	3·0	6·0	19·3	25·4	41·0	3·3
October -	**0·3**	0·3	0·3	0·0	0·6	4·9	22·3	16·5	**47·7**	**7·1**
November -	0·0	0·0	0·0	0·0	0·6	7·7	21·7	19·3	46·0	4·7
December -	0·0	0·0	0·0	0·4	0·7	4·3	24·7	**26·5**	40·9	2·5
Year -	0·0	0·1	0·7	1·0	1·7	6·7	24·0	23·3	39·0	3·5
AT 13 H.										
January -	0·0	0·0	1·1	0·0	1·4	**5·7**	30·5	**27·6**	30·8	2·9
February -	0·0	0·0	**1·2**	0·4	1·6	4·7	**33·4**	25·2	31·5	2·0
March - -	0·0	0·0	0·0	0·6	1·3	5·5	30·0	23·9	32·9	5·8
April - -	0·0	0·0	0·0	0·0	0·0	4·0	21·7	20·3	43·0	11·0
May - -	0·0	0·0	0·0	0·3	1·0	3·9	25·8	19·7	42·2	7·1
June - -	0·0	0·0	0·0	0·3	1·3	3·3	19·0	22·0	40·7	**13·4**
July - -	0·0	0·0	0·3	0·3	**1·6**	4·9	16·5	20·3	46·1	10·0
August -	0·0	0·0	0·0	**1·0**	1·3	3·2	13·9	17·7	**54·2**	8·7
September -	0·0	0·0	0·3	0·3	1·0	2·3	17·4	21·0	49·0	8·7
October -	0·0	0·0	0·0	0·3	0·3	5·5	14·2	21·3	49·4	9·0
November -	0·0	0·0	0·0	0·0	1·0	3·7	25·3	17·0	47·3	5·7
December -	0·0	0·0	0·0	0·0	0·7	5·4	25·1	26·5	38·7	3·6
Year -	0·0	0·0	0·2	0·3	1·1	4·3	22·7	21·9	42·2	7·3
AT 18 H.										
January -	0·0	0·0	0·4	0·5	1·8	9·0	34·1	26·5	24·5	3·2
February -	0·0	**0·4**	0·8	**1·6**	**2·0**	11·8	33·4	**29·5**	18·5	2·0
March - -	0·0	0·0	0·3	0·3	1·6	9·4	**34·8**	22·3	28·4	2·9
April - -	0·0	0·3	0·7	0·3	0·3	4·0	23·7	20·0	39·4	11·3
May - -	0·0	0·0	0·3	1·0	0·3	5·5	23·6	21·6	37·4	10·3
June - -	0·0	0·0	1·0	0·3	0·3	3·7	18·4	19·0	40·0	**17·3**
July - -	0·0	0·0	**1·3**	0·3	1·6	2·3	19·0	18·7	**43·6**	13·2
August -	0·0	0·3	**1·3**	1·0	0·3	3·9	18·1	21·6	41·3	12·2
September -	0·0	0·0	1·0	0·6	0·6	4·7	18·0	26·7	40·7	7·7
October -	0·0	0·0	0·0	0·0	0·7	7·1	27·4	24·8	35·5	4·5
November -	0·0	0·0	0·0	0·0	0·7	9·3	27·7	27·3	30·7	4·3
December -	0·0	0·0	0·0	0·0	1·1	6·1	33·0	27·6	30·4	1·8
Year -	0·0	0·1	0·6	0·6	0·9	6·4	25·9	23·8	34·2	7·5

and June. Another point of interest is that mist or haze is very decidedly more frequent at 18 h. from October to February, than at either 7 h. or 13 h. A visibility exceeding thirty-one miles is unusual either at 13 h. or 18 h. at Croydon, but it occurs about as often at the latter hour as at the former, and is confined to the months May to September.

128. Visibility at Holyhead. Croydon may be regarded as typical of an inland urban situation in the south-east of England, where although the air is cleaner than that found in the heart of a great city, a fairly high degree of smoke pollution due to the proximity of London may be presumed. By way of contrast it is of interest to examine the visibility data for Holyhead. This station is situated on a small island, which is separated by a larger island, Anglesey, from the north coast of Wales. It is fully exposed to winds from the Irish Sea except on the eastern side, and in that direction it is distant about seventy miles from any large source of atmospheric pollution.

Looking at Table LIV we see that visibility 8 ($12\frac{1}{2}$-31 miles) is the most frequent both at 7 h. and 13 h. in all months ; at 18 h. the same statement applies to the months of April to November, but visibility 6 is the most frequent from December to March. A visibility exceeding thirty-one miles occurs with a fair degree of frequency even at 7 h. in all months. Fogs are very infrequent and are not conspicuously an autumn or winter phenomenon ; in fact they tend to occur with minimum frequency from October to December, and with maximum frequency in the summer. Comparing the results for 7 h., 13 h. and 18 h., we observe that the differences are much less marked than in the case of Croydon. Dense fog, with visibility below 220 yards, is almost unknown, and even mist is infrequent ; on more than ninety per cent. of all occasions visibility exceeds $2\frac{1}{2}$ miles. At 13 h. visibility exceeds $12\frac{1}{2}$ miles on about half the days throughout the year.

129. Visibilities below and above fixed limits. The results given in Tables LIII and LIV refer to single code figures, each defining a certain visual range. For some purposes it is useful to consider the frequencies of visibilities below or above a fixed limit. Thus, to ascertain the frequency of fogs we must know the total number of occurrences of a visibility below 1,100 yards ; this information is obtained from data in the form of Table LIII or LIV by adding up all the entries under code figures 0, 1, 2 and 3. Similarly we can obtain the frequency of visibility less that 2,200 yards by adding up the entries under 0, 1, 2, 3 and 4. Proceeding in this manner we have obtained the results shown graphically in Fig. 88. In this figure the height of each diagram repre-

sents 100 per cent. The abscissae are the calendar months from January
to December. Four graphs are plotted in each diagram ; the lowermost
shows for each month the percentage frequency of visibility less than

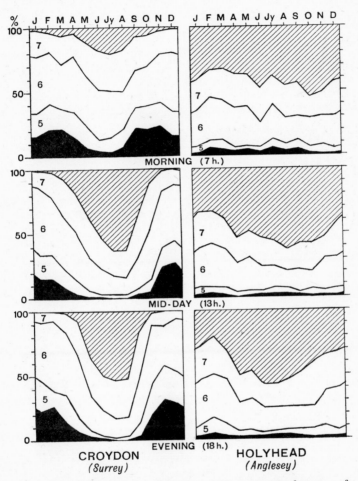

FIG. 88.—Diurnal and seasonal variations of the percentage frequency of
visibility below and above fixed limits at Croydon and Holyhead.

2,200 yards, that is to say the total frequency of mist or haze, and fog ;
the second graph represents the percentage frequency of visibility less
than $2\frac{1}{2}$ miles ; the corresponding limit is $6\frac{1}{4}$ miles for the third, and
$12\frac{1}{2}$ miles for the top graph. The area between the top graph and the

100 per cent. line is lightly shaded ; the depth of the shaded area at any point represents the percentage frequency of very good visibility. The area between the base line and the lowest graph is coloured solid black. We thus have a convenient representation of the diurnal and seasonal variations of visibility at the two stations.

The first thing that strikes the eye on looking at these graphs is the magnitude of the seasonal variation at Croydon as compared with Holyhead. The graphs also exhibit in a striking manner the low frequency of mist or fog, and the high frequency of very good visibility at Holyhead, in all months and at each of the three hours of observation. Several points on which we have already commented are illustrated by the diagrams ; in particular we may note the form of the seasonal variation of poor visibility at Croydon at 7 h., with a definite dip in December and January. We may postpone the discussion of certain other features of the graphs in view of the fact that the data for additional stations now to be given will afford a more extended basis of comparison.

130. Frequency of very good visibility. Space does not permit of our presenting visibility data for other stations in the detailed form adopted in the preceding tables and diagrams. Climatologically, the data in regard to very good visibility and low visibility are of chief interest and it is proposed, therefore, to confine attention to these subdivisions of our subject.

In Table LV we have ten-year averages of the percentage frequency of occurrence in each month of visibility more than $12\frac{1}{2}$ miles (code figures 8 and 9 combined) at 7 h., 13 h. and 18 h., for a representative selection of stations. Graphs of the values for Leuchars, Cranwell, Croydon, Holyhead and Mount Batten are given in Fig. 89. We have already commented upon the high frequency of very good visibility at Holyhead ; we now see that Holyhead shares this attribute with Leuchars in Fifeshire, Mount Batten near Plymouth and Aldergrove, an inland station in Northern Ireland. Leuchars and Mount Batten are by no means so widely separated from centres of atmospheric pollution as are Holyhead and Aldergrove ; in particular, Leuchars is only a few miles distant from the large manufacturing city of Dundee. Renfrew, in the industrial area of southern Scotland, enjoys a frequency of very clear days nearly equal to that at Felixstowe, a seaside resort on the East Anglian coast. Cranwell and South Farnborough, which may reasonably be described as rural inland sites, record fewer occasions with very good visibility than Croydon in summer months. We may judge, therefore, that proximity to a large source of atmospheric pollution is of less importance in determining the frequency of very clear days than might perhaps be thought.

The differences between stations are relatively small in summer months, except in regard to the 7 h. data, and we may say that in June, July and August the chances are rather in favour of being able to see more that 12½ miles, in the middle of the day and early evening anywhere in the British Isles. In the winter, very clear days are more frequent in the west and north than in the eastern and south-eastern districts, either coastal or inland. Judging from the Croydon results they are very infrequent in the neighbourhood of London.

The diurnal variation shows some points of interest. In general, the highest frequency of very good visibility is observed at 13 h., as might be expected, but at most stations 18 h. gives slightly the higher frequency in summer months. In the winter months, on the other hand, 18 h. tends to give a lower percentage than either of the other hours.

131. Frequency of low visibility. The percentage frequencies of occasions of low visibility, *i.e.* occasions of mist, haze or fog, are given in Table LVI for the same selection of stations; graphs will be found in Fig. 90. To some extent these results are naturally complementary to those given in Table LV; thus the stations which were outstanding in respect to the frequency of very good visibility, namely Leuchars, Holyhead, Mount Batten and Aldergrove, all show a small annual frequency of occasions of low visibility, and *vice versa*. With the exception of Aldergrove, the inland stations all show a high frequency of fog, mist or haze during the winter half-year. In the summer, Renfrew shows a high frequency of poor visibility conditions at 7 h., but the frequencies for the other stations at this hour are not markedly different. At 13 h. and 18 h. the inland stations, except Renfrew, are almost entirely immune from fog, mist or haze in the summer months.

Attention has already been drawn to the large seasonal variation at Croydon. We observe that Renfrew, Cranwell, Felixstowe and South Farnborough show similar features. Renfrew and South Farnborough both show maxima in spring and autumn at 7 h., with definitely lower values in the winter. At Croydon, low visibility is more frequent at 18 h. than at either 7 h. or 13 h. from November to February; Renfrew shows the same characteristic from December to February, but none of the other stations shows this feature.

TABLE LV

PERCENTAGE FREQUENCY OF VERY GOOD VISIBILITY (MORE THAN 12½ MILES)

Station	Hour	Jan.	Feb.	Mar.	Apr.	May	June	July	Aug.	Sept.	Oct.	Nov.	Dec.	Year
		%	%	%	%	%	%	%	%	%	%	%	%	%
Leuchars (*Fife*) - -	7 h.	34	26	34	47	45	**62**	53	49	48	50	46	41	45
	13 h.	34	31	48	57	58	**66**	61	62	60	57	45	39	51
	18 h.	31	27	44	61	58	**71**	66	63	61	50	40	37	51
Renfrew (*Renfrew*) -	7 h.	14	12	16	21	19	**36**	32	27	22	19	15	13	21
	13 h.	14	19	30	43	42	**61**	58	55	51	37	22	16	37
	18 h.	8	6	23	43	38	**68**	64	55	42	14	10	8	32
Cranwell (*Lincs.*) -	7 h.	5	12	12	9	15	**18**	17	13	13	14	8	4	12
	13 h.	13	21	27	34	40	47	39	**48**	36	30	9	8	29
	18 h.	4	11	21	30	43	47	50	**51**	28	12	4	2	25
Felixstowe (*Suffolk*) -	7 h.	11	18	19	11	19	**23**	22	18	13	22	18	9	17
	13 h.	13	30	36	38	48	**60**	54	**60**	41	41	23	20	39
	18 h.	9	21	28	38	56	66	66	**69**	35	29	11	8	36
Croydon (*Surrey*) -	7 h.	1	3	6	4	11	18	**20**	18	7	6	3	1	8
	13 h.	0·7	1	7	19	37	53	**63**	**63**	37	11	1	0	25
	18 h.	0	0	1	8	37	51	**58**	57	17	1	0·3	0·3	19
S. Farnborough - - (*Hants.*)	7 h.	12	10	13	14	25	**34**	29	30	22	13	11	13	19
	13 h.	17	15	28	36	43	49	51	**56**	40	23	16	13	32
	18 h.	12	11	21	28	45	50	52	**54**	28	15	11	10	28
Holyhead (*Anglesey*) -	7 h.	41	34	33	37	37	**48**	39	46	44	55	51	43	43
	13 h.	34	33	39	54	49	54	56	**63**	58	58	53	42	49
	18 h.	28	21	31	51	48	**57**	**57**	53	48	40	35	32	42
Mount Batten (*Devon*)	7 h.	29	25	29	37	**39**	34	36	27	25	33	32	28	32
	13 h.	31	33	46	56	54	**62**	60	59	51	46	41	31	48
	18 h.	26	19	32	55	58	**68**	55	60	51	27	26	27	42
Aldergrove (*Antrim*) -	7 h.	18	22	28	46	33	45	**52**	44	37	41	28	20	35
	13 h.	34	42	45	64	56	62	**72**	71	62	62	42	38	54
	18 h.	26	36	45	67	58	64	**72**	64	53	51	33	23	50

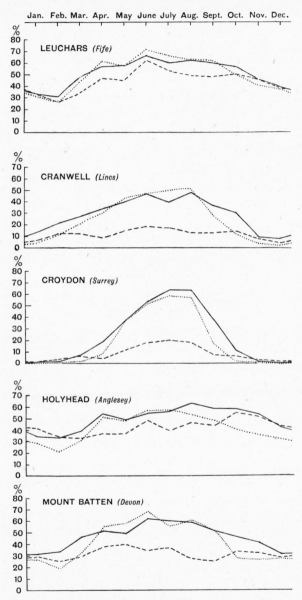

Fig. 89.—Percentage frequencies of very good visibility.
(Full line, 13 h. ; broken line, 7 h. ; dotted line, 18h.)

TABLE LVI

Percentage Frequency of Low Visibility (less than $1\frac{1}{4}$ miles)

Station	Hour	Jan.	Feb.	Mar.	Apr.	May	June	July	Aug.	Sept.	Oct.	Nov.	Dec.	Year
		%	%	%	%	%	%	%	%	%	%	%	%	%
Leuchars (*Fife*) - -	7 h.	3	7	10	3	5	3	3	2	2	5	3	2	4·1
	13 h.	4	2	4	2	0·4	0·4	0·4	0·8	0·4	1	2	2	1·7
	18 h.	5	4	5	2	3	1·5	1	0	0·7	2	2	2	2·4
Renfrew (*Renfrew*) -	7 h.	16	27	24	24	18	11	6	18	25	21	24	14	19
	13 h.	21	23	11	4	1	0·3	2	2	3	9	17	19	10
	18 h.	23	30	13	5	2	2	0·6	2	6	17	22	15	11
Cranwell (*Lincs.*) -	7 h.	18	23	17	8	7	4	5	6	14	19	21	22	13
	13 h.	12	8	2	0	0·3	0·3	0·3	0·3	0	1·5	10	14	4
	18 h.	19	13	4	0·3	0·3	0	0·3	0	1	4	13	22	6
Felixstowe (*Suffolk*) -	7 h.	19	23	15	10	5	3	5	6	10	13	14	16	12
	13 h.	12	15	3	1	1	0·5	0·4	0	0·5	4	5	11	5
	18 h.	9	13	8	3	0·5	0·5	0	0·5	1	7	7	15	5
Croydon (*Surrey*) -	7 h.	16	21	21	15	7	5	4	7	22	21	23	16	15
	13 h.	15	15	9	3	0·9	0·9	0	0	3	5	24	27	8
	18 h.	23	26	14	6	2	0·9	0	0	3	20	31	28	14
S. Farnborough - - (*Hants.*)	7 h.	17	23	24	13	4	3	3	6	22	29	28	17	16
	13 h.	11	10	5	0·7	0·7	0	0·3	0	0·3	3	14	12	5
	18 h.	13	15	6	3	0·6	0	0	0	2	10	18	14	7
Holyhead (*Anglesey*) -	7 h.	2	6	5	4	5	3	6	4	5	1·5	0·6	1	3·5
	13 h.	3	3	2	0	1	2	2	2	2	0·6	1	1	1·6
	18 h.	3	5	2	2	2	2	3	3	2	0·7	0·7	1	2·2
Mount Batten (*Devon*)	7 h.	2	3	3	2	2	2	3	6	6	6	2	3	3·5
	13 h.	5	1	1	0·6	0·6	1	1	3	1	1	2	4	1·8
	18 h.	3	2	1	2	1	0·7	2	1	1	0·3	0·3	1	1·3
Aldergrove (*Antrim*) -	7 h.	9	7	10	3	3	1	3	3	4	5	6	5	5
	13 h.	5	3	0·9	1	0	0·3	0	0	1	0·3	3	3	1·6
	18 h.	3	3	1	0	0	0	0	0	0·3	2	5	4	1·5

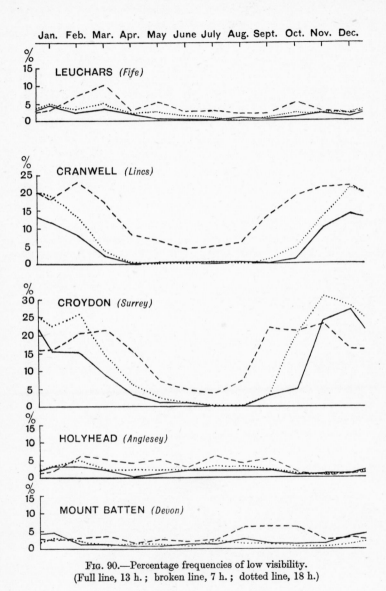

Fig. 90.—Percentage frequencies of low visibility.
(Full line, 13 h.; broken line, 7 h.; dotted line, 18 h.)

132. Days with fog. In the preceding discussions of visibility data we have considered separately the observations made in the early morning (7 h.), midday (13 h.) and evening (18 h.), and in this way we have been able to reach certain conclusions about the diurnal, as well as the seasonal, variations. It is hardly worth while pursuing the study of diurnal variation by further analysis of the data for fixed hours, and we shall find it more profitable, when dealing with the subject of fogs, to pool the observations. From data in the form of Table LIII we can say how often a fog occurs at 7 h., or at 13 h., or at 18 h. ; the figures do not, however, tell us on how many days a fog has been observed at one *or other* of those hours. To determine exactly the number of days with fog it would be necessary to keep continuous records, but we may be fairly sure that on the great majority of days when a fog has occurred between early morning and evening it would have been of sufficient duration to be observed either at 7 h., at 13 h. or at 18 h. We must bear in mind, however, that data in regard to " days with fog " derived from a scrutiny of the observations at three fixed hours are, to some extent, underestimates of the true number. In particular, many early morning fogs in the summer have disappeared by 7 h.

Graphs of ten-year averages of the number of days with fog, defined in this manner, at a selection of stations, are given in Fig. 91. It will be seen that there are very marked differences from station to station, both in the number of fogs and in the form of the seasonal variation. Starting from the top of the diagram, Lerwick in the Shetlands shows a very definite seasonal variation with a summer maximum and a winter minimum : in July there is an average of rather more than three fogs ; June has an average of two ; the winter months enjoy almost complete immunity, and there is an average of one fog in April and one in May. At Eskdalemuir at a height of 794 feet in the southern uplands of Scotland there is a maximum frequency of three fogs in December and January, and a summer minimum of 0·5 in June ; there is a minor maximum in September, but fogs are no more frequent in October and November than in July or in April. Spurn Head (Yorks.) also shows a well-marked winter maximum with five days in January, and a summer minimum of 0·5 day in August ; apart from the August minimum there is a nearly uniform frequency of one to two days per month from March to October.

Kew Observatory, on the western outskirts of London, shows the sort of annual variation we were led to expect from the data previously given for the neighbouring station of Croydon. We have a very low

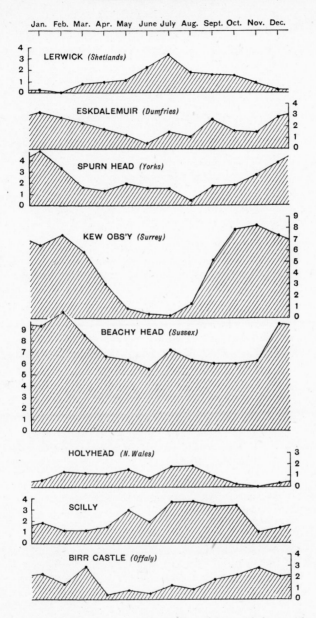

Fig. 91.—Monthly averages of the number of days with fog at either
7 h., 13 h. or 18 h.

fog frequency in the summer months, with a minimum of about one day in five years in June, and a maximum of more than eight days per month in November ; the average exceeds five per month from September to March. It is of interest to note that the spring month March has an average of six days with fog, one more than the average for September. The results for Beachy Head, the highest point on the chalk cliffs of the south coast (502 feet), are very remarkable. This appears to be among the foggiest spots in the British Isles, so far as we can tell from the available statistics. The average number of days with fog exceeds five in all months of the year and exceeds eight from December to March, with a maximum of 10·5 in February. This station shows a summer minimum of 5·5 in June, but we observe the existence of a minor maximum of seven in July. The results for Holyhead exhibit the features to be expected from our examination of the data for individual hours. The average frequency is low in all months, and is zero in November ; the maximum frequency, about two days per month, occurs in July and August. Scilly affords a representation of the open sea conditions at the mouth of the English Channel ; here we have a form of seasonal variation rather similar to that at Holyhead. In most months, however, fogs are about twice as frequent at Scilly as at Holyhead and we notice that the season of maximum frequency extends from July to October, or perhaps it would be truer to say from May to October, with an interruption in June. The lowest frequencies occur in February, March and November, each giving about one day with fog.

Birr Castle may be regarded as representative of inland conditions in the middle of Ireland. The general average of fog frequency is low, March and November being the maximum months with about three fogs each ; the period from April to August yields only about one fog per month.

133. Annual frequency of fog. In Table LVII we have averages, mainly based on a period of ten years, of the number of days with fog in each season and the whole year, at stations where observations have been made at 7 h., 13 h. and 18 h. Looking first at the annual averages we see that the frequency of fog is very low at Stornoway (three days), on the eastern coast of the island of Lewis and Harris, Outer Hebrides ; at Malin Head (six days), in the north of Ireland ; and at Valentia (three days), on the south-west coast of Ireland. At the other end of the scale we have Beachy Head with an annual average of eighty-eight days, followed by Birmingham, Harrogate, Leafield and Kew, each with more than fifty days, and Renfrew, Biggin Hill and Liverpool (Bidston Observatory), each with forty-seven days.

Fig. 92 is a sketch map showing the geographical distribution indicated by these data. In view of the rather small number of stations used we must bear in mind that it is only possible to show the distribution in very broad outline. It is quite certain that there are important variations within small areas, due partly to meteorological causes and partly to industrial activities ; thus, in the year 1935, fifty morning fogs were observed at Rickmansworth, a valley station in Hertfordshire, as compared with nine at Rothamsted and at St. Albans, only a few miles distant in the same county. Also, the effects of altitude are difficult to allow for. In Scotland the fog frequency at moderate altitudes does not appear to differ much from the sea-level value ; in fact, fog seems to be very infrequent at stations such as Braemar, Balmoral and Dalwhinnie at heights of 1,000 to 1,500 feet. At Buxton in Derbyshire and Cantref in Brecknockshire the fog frequency at about 1,000 feet also seems to differ little from the value observed at lower altitudes. On the other hand we know that fog is very frequent on the high tablelands of Devon and Cornwall ; at Princetown, Dartmoor, seventy-nine morning fogs were observed in 1935, and we may estimate that the average number of " days with fog " there is at least 100. We have also observed the very high frequency of fog at Beachy Head, at the very moderate altitude of 500 feet. It appears therefore that fog is more frequent on high land adjacent to the south coast of England than elsewhere. With these considerations in mind, the chart must be described as referring more specifically to low-lying areas.

The main features disclosed by the chart are :

(a) An area covering most of northern, central and south-eastern England in which the annual number of days with fog exceeds forty ; within this area there is a zone extending northward from London across the Midland counties to the West Riding of Yorkshire, in which the frequency exceeds fifty days.

(b) An area with more than forty days covering the lowland area of Scotland from the Clyde basin to the Firth of Forth.

(c) An Atlantic coastal area with very low fog frequency.

(d) An area of relatively high fog frequency extending from the Pembroke coast southward to Scilly and then eastward into the English Channel as far as the Channel Islands.

Apart from the south-west coasts of Great Britain which are included in area (d), fog tends to be more frequent on the east coasts than on the west coasts ; thus the frequency at Spurn Head is more than double

s

TABLE LVII

Station	Spring (March to May)	Summer (June to August)	Autumn (Sept. to Nov.)	Winter (Dec. to February)	Whole Year
Scotland					
Lerwick (*Shetlands*) - -	3	7	4	0·4	14
Wick (*Caithness*) - - -	4	6	1	0·3	11
Aberdeen (*Aberdeen*) - -	5	3	3	5	16
Leuchars (*Fife*) - - -	5	2	3	3	13
Renfrew (*Renfrew*) - - -	9	3	17	18	47
Eskdalemuir (*Dumfries*) - -	5	3	6	9	23
Inchkeith (*Fife*) - - -	6	4	4	4	18
England and Wales					
Tynemouth (*Northumberland*) -	9	8	10	15	42
Spurn Head (*Yorks.*) - -	5	3	6	12	26
Cranwell (*Lincs.*) - - -	7	4	12	19	42
Yarmouth (*Norfolk*) - -	5	2	5	9	21
Felixstowe (*Suffolk*) - -	5	1	6	11	23
Clacton (*Essex*) - - -	2	0·9	4	9	16
Birmingham (*Warwick*) - -	12	4	18	25	59
Ross-on-Wye (*Hereford*) - -	6	3	16	12	37
Harrogate (*Yorks.*) - -	13	6	14	23	56
Kew Observatory (*Surrey*) -	10	2	21	21	54
Croydon (*Surrey*) - - -	7	2	14	14	37
Biggin Hill (*Kent*) - - -	10	3	15	19	47
Lympne (*Kent*) - - -	8	5	12	19	44
Dungeness (*Kent*) - - -	4	3	6	7	20
Beachy Head (*Sussex*) - -	22	19	18	29	88
Calshot (*Hants.*) - - -	4	2	5	6	17
S. Farnborough (*Hants.*) -	9	2	15	14	40
St. Catherine's Pt. (*I. of Wight*)	7	5	3	8	23
Worthy Down (*Wilts.*) - -	7	3	8	15	33
Leafield (*Oxon.*) - - -	7	2	17	25	51
Liverpool (Bidston) (*Cheshire*) -	14	4	14	15	47
Sealand (*Flints.*) - - -	9	2	16	15	42
Holyhead (*Anglesey*) - -	4	5	1	2	12
St. Ann's Head (*Pembroke*) -	9	9	4	7	29
Portland Bill (*Dorset*) - -	5	4	1	3	13
Mount Batten (*Devon*) - -	3	4	3	3	13
Falmouth (*Cornwall*) - -	5	6	3	2	16
Scilly (St. Mary's) - - -	5	9	8	4	26
Guernsey (*Channel Islands*) -	6	7	3	6	22
Ireland					
Malin Head (*Donegal*) - -	2	2	1	1	6
Donaghadee (*Down*) - -	3	3	2	2	10
Birr Castle (*Offaly*) - -	4	2	7	6	19
Valentia (*Kerry*) - - -	1	1	0·7	0·1	3
Roche's Point (*Cork*) - -	4	5	4	3	16

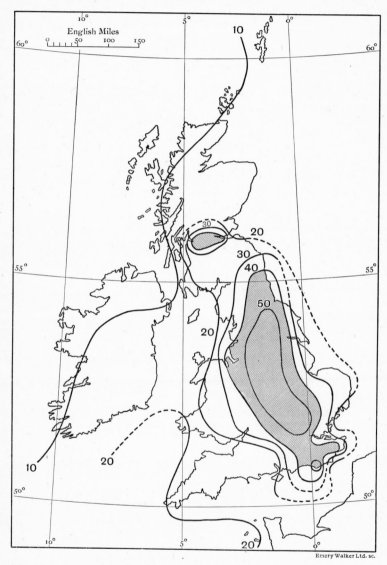

FIG. 92.—Average annual number of days with fog at either 7 h., 13 h. or 18 h.
(This chart refers to places near sea-level and up to altitudes of about 500 feet only.)

that at Holyhead in about the same latitude. The central area of high
fog frequency protrudes, however, westward to the coast over south
Lancashire, Cheshire and Flintshire. Much of this area is highly in-
dustrialized. A rather similar state of affairs exists in southern Scotland
where the region of high fog frequency also protrudes westward over
the industrial area of the Clyde basin.

134. Seasonal frequency of fog. The seasonal frequencies given in
Table LVII show that the type of variation observed at Croydon and
Kew Observatory occurs very generally in the central region of high
fog frequency, though there are some local variations in respect to the
season—autumn or winter—of maximum frequency. At most stations
winter gives the maximum number, but autumn shows the maximum
frequency in a few cases. Within this region summer is quite definitely
the season of minimum frequency, and spring occupies an intermediate
position.

The stations with a summer maximum include Lerwick in the extreme
north, Holyhead on the North Wales coast, and Mount Batten, Falmouth, Scilly, Guernsey and Roche's Point, all on the south and south-
west coasts. Beachy Head is peculiar in giving a winter maximum and
an *autumn* minimum. It is rather surprising to find that Harrogate has
an average of as many as six days with fog in the summer. Speaking
generally, however, we may say that summer fog is a coastal phenomenon, though it is relatively infrequent even at places such as Scilly and
Lerwick, where the seasonal curve reaches a definite maximum in summer. At all the stations where the maximum occurs in summer the
minimum occurs in winter, and these areas therefore show a reversal of
the seasonal variation found inland.

135. Persistent fog. In the previous sections we have considered the
data in regard to the frequency of days on which fog was observed at
one or more of the fixed hours, 7 h., 13 h. and 18 h. We may now
consider the complementary question of the frequency of days on which
fog was observed at all three hours. Such days may be described as
days of persistent fog. It is clear from the statistics we have already
examined that persistent fog is infrequent everywhere; even at inland
stations within the region of maximum fog frequency, fog is uncommon
at 13 h. and it is obvious that days with fog at all three hours must be
still less frequent.

Certain areas appear to be practically immune from persistent fog.
During the ten years ending 1930 there were no occurrences at Valentia,
only one at Holyhead, two at Leuchars and Mount Batten, three at

Stornoway, Malin Head and Portland Bill, four at Aberdeen and five at Eskdalemuir. During the same period there were sixty-two occurrences at Kew Observatory, fifty-seven at Harrogate, and forty or more at Birmingham, South Farnborough, Croydon and Biggin Hill. At Beachy Head eighty persistent fogs were observed in seven years ; thus even at this very foggy station the average frequency of persistent fogs is only about eleven per annum.

Of the sixty-two occurrences in ten years at Kew, November gave twenty, January fifteen, February eleven, December ten, March three, October two and April one. Thus we may say that persistent fogs at Kew are practically confined to the four months November to February, with occasional occurrences in October, March and April, and complete immunity from May to September. This is true generally for inland stations and also for some coastal stations such as Liverpool, Spurn Head, Yarmouth, Clacton, Felixstowe and Calshot. These stations are all in areas where we have a summer minimum of days with fog, and a maximum in autumn or winter. At stations on the south-west coasts we find a more uniform incidence. Thus at Scilly, where thirty persistent fogs occurred in the ten-year period, the seasonal distribution was : spring five days, summer eight days, autumn eleven days, winter six days ; the maximum occurred in September, with five days, and the minimum in March, with no days. At Beachy Head the eighty persistent fogs observed in seven years were distributed as follows : spring nineteen days, summer eleven days, autumn seven days, winter forty-three days. There were twenty occurrences in February, and none in October. Of all fog days at Beachy Head, about one in eight is a day of persistent fog ; the corresponding ratios at other stations are : Kew, one in nine ; Croydon, one in nine ; Birmingham, one in eleven ; Liverpool, one in thirteen ; Harrogate, one in seven ; Scilly, one in nine ; Birr Castle, one in nineteen ; Holyhead, one in 120 ; Leuchars, one in sixty-five ; Aberdeen, one in forty. We may judge, therefore, that the *proportion* of fogs which are persistent tends to be relatively high in areas where fogs are common, and low in areas where fogs are infrequent.

136. Factors in visibility. We have referred to precipitation, water droplets and solid particles in the air as the causes of low visibility. There are other physical factors which may operate to render a distant object invisible ; these include the colour and illumination of the object in relation to its background ; for example it would be much easier to see a distant range of hills when silhouetted against a brightly illumin-ated sky at sunset, than to distinguish them, when snow-covered, against a background of white cloud. We may, however, regard a factor of this sort as one of the sources of error in the observer's estimate of the visual range, rather than as a factor affecting that property of the atmosphere which the term " visibility " is intended to connote. On some occasions visibility may be more definitely impaired by variations of density in the atmosphere, giving rise either to the phenomenon known as " shimmering " or to mirage effects. Broadly speaking, we may say, however, that visibility is related to the concentration of either water droplets or solid particles ; visibility will be low when conditions favour the condensation of water droplets or an increase in the concentration of solid particles, and visibility will be good when the opposite circumstances prevail.

The physics of visibility is a difficult subject, but the meteorological factors which come into play are fairly simple. Leaving solid particles out of the question for the moment we may say that the potentiality of fog exists whenever the meteorological circumstances are such that the air near ground level may be cooled below the dew-point. The cooling may be produced in various ways : thus we may have a current of warm humid air passing over colder sea or colder land ; nocturnal radiation from the land surface may provide the cooling agency ; or again, it is possible for condensation to occur by the mixing of two masses of air at different temperatures, provided both are fairly near to the point of saturation with water-vapour (55). To these agencies, which do not involve any consideration related to altitude, we may add dynamic cooling of moist air due to the upward motion imparted to the air current when passing over rising land.

In this enumeration of the agencies concerned in the production of water fog, we have tacitly assumed that the occurrence of fog is contingent upon the air being saturated with water-vapour. It is, however, a fact that observations with the wet- and dry-bulb hygrometer do not always indicate saturation when fog prevails. The relative humidity may indeed be appreciably below 100 per cent., even in a fog which is quite typically a water fog and not a smoke fog. Various explanations have been advanced to account for this apparent anomaly ; we need not pause to consider them here, but we may take note of the fact that the number of occasions of fog is not necessarily equal to the number of occasions of relative humidity 100 per cent.

137. Sea fogs. When a current of moist air passes over colder water, the layer of air immediately in contact with the water will naturally be chilled. The chilled air will be mixed by the agency of eddy-motion with the over-lying layers of air ; we thus have a progressive cooling extending gradually to higher levels. When a considerable depth of air is cooled in this manner to a temperature below the dew-point a fog will result. The essential condition is that the temperature of the sea surface must be below the dew-point of the overrunning air. These conditions exist in a highly developed form on the Grand Banks of Newfoundland, where warm moist winds from the south pass from the region of the Gulf Stream over a sea surface chilled to a low temperature by the cold waters of the Labrador current (see Fig. 3, p. 22). The result is the formation of the dense sea fogs for which the Grand Banks are famed. Such extreme conditions are not found over the seas adjacent to the British Isles, but they occur sufficiently often off our south-west coasts to produce a fairly high frequency of sea fogs in that area. Their tendency to occur in the summer and early autumn rather than in the winter may be attributed to the fact that the excess of air temperature over sea temperature tends to be a maximum during the warmer portion of the year.

138. Coastal fogs. On a coast where the ground slopes down to sea-level, orographic effects may come into operation so as to increase the frequency of fog above that observed over the open water. The dynamic cooling due to the ascent of air near saturation would suffice in many cases to complete the process of fog formation which was begun by the passage of the moist air over cooler water. It seems clear that the high frequency of fog observed at Beachy Head during summer months must be due to this cause. On a flat shore foggy air penetrating inland would be warmed again very rapidly by the solar heating over the land area during the daytime ; thus the foggy conditions would be confined to a narrow coastal strip. When the inland area is cooled by nocturnal radiation to a temperature as low as, or lower than, the sea temperature there is no reason why the sea fog should not penetrate inland ; in these circumstances we may have a fog covering both sea and land on summer nights.

Our statistics show that sea fog is mainly a phenomenon of the summer, while inland fog is mainly a phenomenon of the winter ; thus we should expect coastal fogs to occur with off-shore winds in the winter and with on-shore winds in the summer. Actually, as we shall see presently, inland fogs occur mainly under conditions of little or no wind, and the higher night temperature due to the proximity of the sea often suffices to prevent the spread of an inland radiation fog to the coastline, in spite of the fact that the gravitational " land-breeze " would tend to facilitate such spreading. Similarly the summer diurnal sea-breeze would tend to blow sea fog on-shore. It seems probable that this tendency is the main factor in reducing the summer sunshine records of our south-west coasts below those of the south-east coasts ; in winter, when sea fog does not occur to any large extent, the highest sunshine records are found on the south-west coasts.

139. Inland water fogs. We have mentioned the passage of warm moist air over colder ground, and the cooling of moist air by nocturnal radiation as the causes of inland fogs. The former process is likely to occur most frequently when a " warm front " advances across the country in winter, and will often be associated with drizzling rain. The most typical form of inland fog is, however, that which occurs during calm cloudless nights in autumn and winter, when terrestrial radiation is the agency in cooling the moist air below the dew-point. The physical conditions under which fog occurs in these circumstances have been very completely discussed by G. I. Taylor (55), to whom we are also indebted for the elucidation of the mechanism of fog formation over the sea.

The fact that the formation of inland fog is due most frequently to nocturnal radiation, tends to result in a geographical distribution depending in a very special manner on topographical features. The fog will form most readily in areas where cold air tends to stagnate, that is to say in valley bottoms and over flat areas of low-lying land. The hill-tops are often free from fog while the valleys and low lands are enveloped in thick fog. Similarly we may see pasture lands covered with ground fog no more than a few feet deep while the air above is quite clear. The inland regions of high fog frequency are thus likely to correspond, on the whole, with those which are subject to a large daily range of temperature.

The conditions which favour the formation of inland radiation fogs occur most frequently in association with anticyclones and with the feeble barometric gradients which occur in " cols ", or regions between adjacent pairs of depressions and anticyclones. In winter and autumn the resulting fog may be very dense and widespread, but in summer the chilling of the air does not often extend high enough to produce more than a ground fog. Also, summer radiation fogs are dissipated very rapidly under the rays of the sun and are thus a phenomenon of the night and very early morning. The fact that radiation fogs occur most frequently in association with anticyclones has given rise to the widespread and well-founded belief that mist or fog in the early hours of a

summer morning is a sign of a very fine day ; the " pride of the morning " is the countryman's beautiful term for this phenomenon.   In
winter the fog may form too dense a canopy to permit of the penetration
of sufficient solar radiation to disperse it, and a persistent fog may thus
result.

While the low lands are most affected by radiation fogs, the hills are
more frequently affected by the fogs occurring in association with warm
fronts ; many such " fogs " are in fact due to the presence of low cloud
down to within a few hundreds of feet of sea-level. Every motorist is
familiar with the presence of fog patches on the hill-crests in these
circumstances. It is not surprising, therefore, that we find it difficult
to make out any clear relationship between annual fog frequency and
altitude over the British Isles as a whole.

140. The effects of smoke.   The nocturnal cooling of the ground
which leads to the formation of inland water fogs, produces an inversion
of the normal lapse-rate of air temperature ; that is to say, the temperature increases with height, instead of decreasing as is usual.   In these
circumstances vertical movement in the lower layers of the atmosphere
is very effectively prevented. Consider, for example, a small portion of
air near the ground, the temperature of which happens to be one degree
warmer than the surrounding air at the same level. Being warmer, its
density would be lower and it would tend to rise ; even if its own
temperature remained the same it would very soon arrive at a level
where the air was at a temperature one degree above that of the initial
level of the rising air, and there would be no tendency for it to rise any
further. Actually, the rising air would be cooled dynamically in the
process of rising and the height at which equilibrium was attained would
thus be reduced. In this way we see that an inversion of temperature
acts as a roof or lid, preventing passage of air from below the inversion
into higher levels. An inversion has this property whether the air
below it is foggy or not.

In these circumstances any impurity suspended in the atmosphere
must accumulate near the place of origin ; it cannot penetrate the top
of the inversion and there is no surface wind to carry it away horizon-
tally. Thus when a surface inversion of temperature occurs, the concentration of smoke particles in the air of towns increases rapidly and
progressively. We have mentioned the absence of wind, but it would
indeed require only a very small air speed to sweep smoke away fast
enough to prevent the concentration becoming sufficient to produce a
pure smoke fog. In general, the concentration of smoke serves to

augment the obscuration due to water droplets ; because the conditions which favour the formation of a radiation water fog are precisely those which favour the accumulation of smoke in the layers of air close to the ground. The smoke produces two very noticeable effects : it renders the fog dark coloured and dirty, and it acts very effectively as a screen to prevent the penetration of the sun's radiation, which would dissipate the fog if it could penetrate the overhanging canopy of fog and smoke. Thus fog may persist all day over large towns while in the surrounding country it yields to the influence of sunshine.

In the next section we shall give some information in regard to suspended impurity in the atmosphere, but it is of interest here to consider the composition of a typical London fog, where we have a mixture of water droplets and smoke suspended in an atmosphere which we will assume to be saturated with water-vapour, at a temperature of 40° F. In each cubic metre of such air we should have 6·5 grams of water in the form of vapour, and about one gram of water in the form of liquid droplets. In an exceptionally dense smoke fog the concentration of soot is as high as ten milligrams per cubic metre, but we may take five milligrams as a more usual figure. Thus in 100 cubic metres, equivalent to the contents of a good sized living room, we should find 650 grams of water-vapour (rather more than one pint if condensed to liquid), 100 grams of suspended water droplets (a small wineglass-full) and 0·5 gram of suspended soot (a small pinch). The pure air containing these ingredients would weigh about two hundredweights.

During the prevalence of fog, the surface visibility is often definitely better in large cities than in the adjacent suburban and country districts. In London it is quite common for traffic by road and rail in the suburbs to be brought to a standstill by fog, but it is uncommon for such conditions to prevail in the central areas. This effect may be attributed partly to the fact that a built-up area is less effective as a " radiating surface " than fields and grasslands, and partly to the higher temperature which prevails in the central areas of large towns as a result of artificial heating. The result of these two factors is to keep the street level relatively free from dense fog, but on many occasions the inversion extends to heights of the order of 1,000 to 2,000 feet, and in these circumstances a very black and impenetrable canopy of smoke may be formed overhead. We thus get the so-called " high fogs " which produce a darkness like that of night, at midday. For some reason which is not very clear, this phenomenon appears to have become more common in London in recent years, replacing the " London particular ", which appears to have been a dense surface fog coloured to the tint of pea-soup by a rich admixture of tarry soot derived from the imperfect combustion of bituminous coal.

141. Suspended impurity in the atmosphere. The systematic measurements made in recent years have placed us in possession of a considerable amount of information in regard to the amount and chemical composition of the impurity either suspended in or deposited from the atmosphere. At the present time the investigation is under the control of the Department of Scientific and Industrial Research, assisted by a Standing Conference of Co-operating Bodies, and a Research Committee. The observations are made by voluntary observers, employing instruments designed mainly by J. S. Owens (56), and a summary is given in an Annual Report. The data we shall quote are taken from the Twenty-first Report, covering the year ended 31st March, 1935.

The data in regard to deposited impurity are interesting in many ways, but the suspended impurity is the thing of chief interest in connection with atmospheric obscurity. It appears to consist mainly of carbon in an extremely fine state of subdivision ; so fine, indeed, that it may be regarded for practical purposes as in a permanent state of suspension, being carried about by air currents almost as if it were a gaseous constituent of the air, with little tendency to settle out by gravitational movement. The instrumental records furnish information in regard to the concentration of impurity, expressed as milligrams per cubic metre of air.

It is obvious that the concentration of impurity at a given place and time must depend partly on meteorological factors and partly on human activities ; thus if we observe a very high concentration on a given occasion it may be due to the existence of meteorological circumstances tending to favour the accumulation of smoke, or to an abnormal rate of emission of smoke by neighbouring chimneys, or to a combination of both factors. With these considerations in mind it is customary to publish separate results for ordinary week-days, Saturdays and Sundays, and for the winter and summer periods, the latter being defined as the period during which " summer time " is in operation. Also separate statistics are available for " ordinary days " and for days of " thick smoke haze ". We shall confine attention here to the results for week-days and we shall not deal with the subdivision into ordinary days and hazy days.

In Fig. 93 we have four graphs showing the diurnal variation of suspended impurity during the summer period of 1934 at Stoke-on-Trent, in the highly polluted region of the Staffordshire Potteries, Coventry, a Midland industrial city, Westminster Bridge, London, and

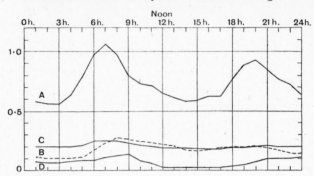

FIG. 93.—Diurnal variation of the concentration of suspended impurity in milligrams per cubic metre, on weekdays; summer half-year, April 22 to October 6, 1934.

A—Stoke-on-Trent; B—Coventry; C—Westminster Bridge, London; D—Kew Observatory.

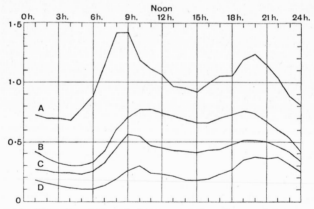

FIG. 94.—Diurnal variation of the concentration of suspended impurity in milligrams per cubic metre, on weekdays; winter half-year, October 7, 1934, to April 13, 1935.

(Same stations as in Fig. 93.)

Kew Observatory on the western outskirts of London. Fig. 94 shows corresponding graphs for the winter period of 1934 to 1935. It will be seen at once that the mean concentration is much higher during the winter period than during the summer period at each station; thus at Stoke-on-Trent we have a mean concentration of about 1·0 in winter as compared with 0·75 in summer. At the other stations the differences are relatively larger ; at Kew the winter mean is about four times the summer mean.

All four stations show a very conspicuous and interesting form of diurnal variation, with minima in the early morning and afternoon, and maxima in the forenoon and late evening. At Stoke-on-Trent this form of diurnal variation is very noticeable both in the summer and winter curves, but it will be observed that the morning maximum occurs about two hours earlier in summer than in winter. At the other stations the diurnal variation is more conspicuous in the winter curves than in the summer curves, and in each case we see an advancement of the time of recurrence of the morning maximum similar to that observed at Stoke. The times of incidence of the early morning minimum also show an advancement in the summer period, but the afternoon minimum and the late evening maximum do not seem to vary much with the season.

If the rate of emission of smoke from chimneys was absolutely constant we should expect higher concentrations in the winter than in the summer, because atmospheric turbulence, which is the chief agency by which smoke is mixed with the overlying layers of clean air, is much more active in summer than in winter. We should also expect the concentration to exhibit a form of diurnal variation in sympathy with the diurnal variation of wind velocity and turbulence ; thus we should anticipate a maximum concentration round about sunrise and a minimum in the afternoon. In actual practice the rate of emission of smoke is, of course, far from constant, and the observed form of diurnal variation differs so radically from that to be anticipated on meteorological grounds that we must regard variation of the rate of emission as the major controlling factor. From this point of view it is easy to explain the occurrence of high concentrations in the forenoon as the result of the lighting of domestic fires and the stoking up of industrial furnaces. The subsequent fall to the afternoon minimum is in accordance with expectations on meteorological grounds, but the fall is no doubt also accentuated by the lower emission of smoke from fires which are burning steadily after their ignition or major replenishment in the early morning. The rise after the afternoon minimum may be attributed partly to the decrease of wind velocity and turbulence, and partly to the increased consumption of coal on domestic fires during the evening period. In this way we reach the second maximum in the late evening ; the subsequent fall to low values during the night hours represents the effect of the low rate of emission when domestic fires are mainly dead and industrial furnaces are damped down.

In connection with the morning maximum of suspended impurity it is of interest to note that the maximum frequency of fog and mist is observed to occur about one hour after sunrise. F. Entwistle (57) found that the deterioration in visibility from one to two hours after sunrise occurred not only near large towns but also in country situations. He explains the phenomenon as being the first result of the mixing of the lower layers of the atmosphere by eddy-motion initiated by the onset of solar radiation. After a clear calm night these lower layers of air would be in a stratified condition with relative humidity perhaps slightly below saturation but with temperature increasing upwards fairly rapidly from ground level. In these circumstances the effect of mixing would be to equalize the temperature and moisture-content, and it can be shown that a saturated mixture would result on reasonable assumptions. The great output of domestic and factory smoke at about the same period would no doubt augment the effect very substantially.

BIBLIOGRAPHY

(55) G. I. Taylor, " The formation of fog and mist," London, *Q.J.R. Meteor. Soc.*, **43**, 1917, p. 241.

(56) W. N. Shaw and J. S. Owens, *The Smoke Problem of Great Cities* (Constable).

(57) F. Entwistle, " The diurnal and seasonal variations of fog," *Prof. Notes*, No. 33. (H.M.S.O.)

See also :

F. J. W. Whipple and others, Discussion on " The horizontal range of vision as a meteorological observation ", London, *Q.J.R. Meteor. Soc.*, **48**, 1922, p. 85.

F. Entwistle, " Fog," *R. Aero. Soc. Reprints*, No. 28, 1928.

CHAPTER XII

SPECIAL TYPES OF CLIMATE

COASTAL CLIMATES

142. At various points in the discussion of our climatic data we have had occasion to observe the transition between the conditions on the coast and the conditions inland. In particular, we have noted a general tendency for the coastal regions to show a relatively small diurnal range of temperature and relative humidity, and a small frequency of thunderstorms and winter fogs. It is natural to regard the coastline as a region having a special climatic character, because it marks the boundary between the sea and the land. We saw in Chapter II that seas and land masses differ meteorologically in a very characteristic manner; we should thus expect a coastal region to show climatic features intermediate between those of the open sea and the inland area. Over the open sea there is practically no diurnal variation of temperature, wind-speed or relative humidity; inland, the range of the diurnal variations of these elements may be very large. Inland, the flow of air which we recognize as wind is impeded by surface friction, due to trees, buildings and surface irregularities, which are non-existent over the open sea. Inland, also, we have hills and mountain ranges, which impart a vertical movement to the air which passes over them and so produces " orographic " rain. These are some of the more important meteorological differences between the regions divided by the coastline. In Chapter IV we devoted some space to the consideration of the diurnal sea-breeze, and in Chapter XI, coastal fogs were separately discussed; in general, however, we have not dealt with the special climatic features of the coastal regions in detail. We propose now to consider some of the points of difference between the coasts and the adjacent inland districts in regard to temperature and rainfall.

143. Temperature inland and on the coast. A glance through the charts given in earlier chapters will serve to show that in many cases a comparison between inland and coastal conditions is complicated by the effects of altitude or by the existence of geographical variations of a

TABLE LVIII

DIFFERENCES OF TEMPERATURE AT NEIGHBOURING COASTAL AND INLAND STATIONS

	Jan.	Feb.	Mar.	Apr.	May	June	July	Aug.	Sep.	Oct.	Nov.	Dec.	Year
	°F.	°F.	°F.	°F.	°F.	°F.	°F.	°F.	°F.	°F.	°F.	°F.	°F.
Scarborough-York													
Maximum -	0·0	−0·5	−1·3	−3·2	−4·6	−4·6	−3·1	−2·5	−1·8	−0·7	0·2	0·2	−1·8
Minimum -	1·6	1·4	1·4	1·3	0·6	0·5	0·4	0·9	1·8	2·3	1·9	1·4	1·3
Mean - -	0·8	0·5	0·1	−1·0	−2·0	−2·0	−1·3	−0·8	0·2	0·8	1·1	0·8	−0·2
Skegness-Lincoln													
Maximum -	0·4	−0·4	−1·9	−3·9	−4·8	−5·3	−5·0	−2·9	−1·9	−0·4	0·3	0·3	−2·1
Minimum -	0·5	0·5	0·4	0·0	0·3	−0·1	0·4	0·4	1·4	1·0	0·8	0·9	0·5
Mean - -	0·5	0·1	−0·7	−1·9	−2·2	−2·7	−2·3	−1·2	−0·3	0·3	0·6	0·6	−0·8
Yarmouth-													
Norwich													
Maximum -	0·0	−1·0	−2·3	−3·5	−5·0	−4·0	−3·3	−2·6	−2·2	−0·6	0·4	0·2	−2·0
Minimum -	0·8	0·4	0·2	1·4	1·4	1·7	1·6	1·7	2·8	2·1	1·6	1·0	1·4
Mean - -	0·4	−0·3	−1·1	−1·1	−1·8	−1·1	−0·8	−0·4	0·3	0·8	1·0	0·6	−0·3
Margate-Greenw'h													
Maximum -	0·4	−0·7	−1·8	−3·6	−4·9	−5·5	−4·6	−3·8	−2·2	−0·3	0·7	0·8	−2·2
Minimum -	0·9	1·2	1·8	2·2	2·1	1·9	1·8	2·7	3·8	3·4	2·3	1·1	2·1
Mean - -	0·7	0·3	0·0	−0·7	−1·4	−1·8	−1·4	−0·5	0·8	1·6	1·5	0·9	0·0
Means for eastern													
England													
Maximum -	0·2	−0·7	−1·8	−3·5	−4·8	−4·9	−4·0	−2·9	−2·0	−0·5	0·4	0·4	−2·0
Minimum -	0·9	0·9	0·9	1·2	1·1	1·0	1·1	1·4	2·5	2·2	1·7	1·1	1·3
Mean - -	0·6	0·1	−0·4	−1·2	−1·9	−1·9	−1·5	−0·7	0·3	0·9	1·1	0·7	−0·3
Southport (Lancs)-													
Mancht'r (Whit-													
worth Park)													
Maximum -	0·1	−0·1	−0·3	−0·5	−1·3	−1·7	−1·5	−1·0	−0·4	0·3	0·3	0·3	−0·5
Minimum -	−0·5	−0·4	−0·6	−0·4	−1·3	−0·9	−0·6	0·1	−0·3	−0·3	−0·7	−0·4	−0·5
Mean - -	−0·2	−0·2	−0·5	−0·4	−1·3	−1·3	−1·1	−0·5	−0·3	0·0	−0·2	0·0	−0·5
Sidmouth (Devon)-													
Cullompton													
Maximum -	0·5	−0·1	−1·4	−2·1	−3·6	−3·8	−3·9	−3·1	−2·1	−0·5	0·5	0·6	−1·6
Minimum -	2·1	2·0	1·8	1·5	1·2	1·4	1·6	2·0	3·0	3·3	3·1	2·1	2·0
Mean - -	1·3	1·0	0·2	−0·3	−1·2	−1·2	−1·1	−0·6	0·5	1·4	1·8	1·4	0·2
Donaghadee													
(Down)-Armagh													
Maximum -	0·8	0·1	−0·8	−2·1	−2·9	−3·3	−2·4	−1·7	−0·9	0·1	0·8	1·3	−0·9
Minimum -	1·5	1·4	1·5	2·2	1·8	1·4	1·0	1·6	2·4	2·6	2·4	1·8	1·8
Mean - -	1·1	0·7	0·3	0·1	−0·5	−0·9	−0·6	−0·1	0·7	1·3	1·6	1·5	0·5

NOTE.—A negative sign means that the temperature is lower at the coastal station than at the inland station.

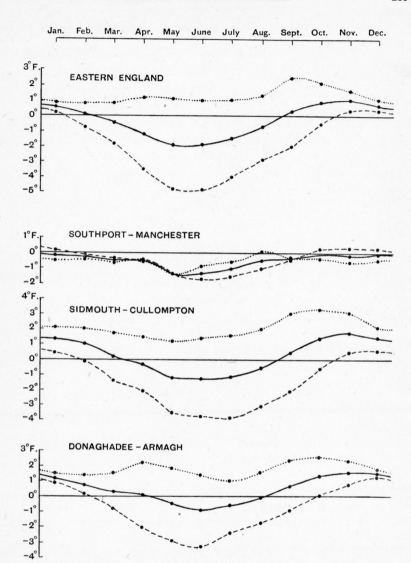

Fig. 95.—Average differences of temperature between neighbouring coastal and inland stations.

(Full line, mean for the day; broken line, mean maximum; dotted line, mean minimum. A minus sign indicates that the coastal station is colder than the inland station.)

T

more general character. Our aim at the moment is to determine the
effect at a coastal station of its special situation in proximity to the sea.
In order to eliminate other factors as far as possible, we propose to take
pairs of stations, each pair consisting of a station on the coast and a
neighbouring inland station, at a low altitude, which may fairly be
regarded as typical of the inland conditions of the region. By tabulating
the difference of temperature between the coastal station and the inland
station in each month we shall then be in a position to draw conclusions
in regard to the special features of the coastal climate in that region.

Results obtained in this way from seven pairs of stations are given
in Table LVIII. In each case the difference is regarded as positive if the
coastal temperature exceeds the inland temperature. The first four
pairs of stations are all on the eastern side of England, a region where
the hinterland is flat and low-lying almost everywhere and there is no
difficulty in selecting pairs of stations for comparison. These data are
taken from a paper read at a Congress of the Royal Institute of Public
Health (16) and were derived from averages for the period 1881-1915.
The results show a very considerable degree of resemblance and we have
therefore taken the means of the four pairs and entered them in the
table under the heading "means for eastern England". The mean
values are illustrated by graphs in Fig. 95.

Looking first at the differences of mean maximum temperature we
see that the coastal values are lower than the inland values in all months
from February to October, the difference reaching its highest value,
about 5° F., in May or June. In November, December and January
the maximum temperature on the coast exceeds the inland value by a
small fraction of a degree. On the average for the whole year the daily
maximum on the coast is about 2° F. lower than the value inland.

The results in the case of the daily minimum are distinctly different.
In general, though Skegness-Lincoln shows an exception in June, the
coastal value exceeds the inland value in all months and the greatest
difference occurs in September and October. The four eastern pairs
of stations show some differences in regard to the season when the
coastal temperature exceeds the inland temperature by the smallest
margin. The mean of the four pairs shows a smallest difference of
rather less than one degree from January to March, and a greatest
difference of 2·5° F. in September.

The mean temperature (average of maximum and minimum) is, in
general, higher inland than on the coast during the summer half-year, and
lower during the winter half-year. The averages for the four eastern pairs

of stations show a greatest difference of about 2° F. in May and June (inland warmer than coast), and about 1° F. in October and November (inland colder than coast). In early summer the mean daily range inland exceeds the value on the coast by about 6° F., mainly because the afternoons are about 5° F. warmer. In the winter the coast is slightly warmer than the inland districts, but there is little difference in the daily range.

Southport and Manchester (Whitworth Park) give similar results in respect to maximum temperature, but the differences in summer are much smaller, the highest value being no more than 1·7° F. in June. The results in the case of the minimum temperatures are altogether different from those observed in the east of England. Except in August, when there is a difference of 0·1° F. in favour of Manchester, the night temperatures are slightly lower at Southport than at Manchester in all months of the year. Also there is no clearly recognizable form of seasonal variation in the differences. There appears to be very little difference at any time of the year, by night or by day, between the temperatures of Southport and Manchester. North-west England appears to be peculiar in respect to this uniformity of coastal and inland temperatures. Thus in January we have maxima of 43·4° F. at Bolton, 44·4° F. at Hutton and 43·6° F. at Lancaster, inland, as compared with 43·9° F. at Blackpool, 43·5° F. at Morecambe and 44·7° F. at Southport, on the coast. In July we have maxima of 66·9° F. at Bolton, 67·0° F. at Hutton and 66·2° F. at Lancaster as compared with 65·7° F. at Blackpool, 66·1° F. at Morecambe and 66·5° F. at Southport.

The comparison of Sidmouth and Cullompton in Devonshire gives results more similar to those found in eastern England. In June and July the average daily maximum is nearly 4° F. higher at Cullompton than at Sidmouth ; from November to January the coastal station is about 0·5° F. warmer than the inland station in the afternoon. The mean minimum at Sidmouth exceeds that at Cullompton in all months, the greatest difference, about 3° F., occurring in the autumn, and the smallest difference in May.

Donaghadee and Armagh, in north-eastern Ireland, again give similar results, though the excess of inland maximum temperature in summer is somewhat less than in Devonshire and decidedly less than in eastern England. The seasonal variation of the difference of mean minimum temperature is generally similar to that observed in Devonshire and in eastern England, with highest values in the autumn. It will be noticed, however, that there is a tendency for the difference to be higher in spring than in winter or summer ; this feature is also seen in the results for Margate-Greenwich.

It will be observed in all these comparisons that the mean temperature for the whole year is very nearly the same at the coastal and inland station. The differences in the monthly mean temperatures are in the direction of reducing the annual range on the coast in comparison with the hinterland. The phase of the difference curves is, however, in advance of the phase of the actual temperature curves ; thus the greatest elevation of inland temperature above the coast temperature occurs about two months in advance of the warmest time of the year, and the greatest depression of inland temperature occurs about two months before the coldest time of the year. There is therefore less actual difference between the amplitude of the annual variation of temperature inland and on the coast than might be supposed from the tabulated differences.

144. Comparison with sea-surface temperature. Perhaps the most interesting facts which emerge from the comparisons of inland and coastal stations are (*a*) the tendency for the greatest differences in mean maximum temperature to appear in early summer, and (*b*) the tendency for the greatest differences in mean minimum temperature to appear in autumn. We may reasonably expect to find the explanation of these seasonal variations by comparing the inland temperature conditions with those of the open sea off the adjacent coast. By way of example we give in the upper part of Fig. 96, graphs of the mean temperature in the surface waters of the North Sea off the east coast of England, and of mean maximum and minimum temperature at Norwich, a typical inland station about twenty miles from the northern and eastern coasts of Norfolk. The first thing we notice is that under normal conditions the sea temperature falls between the average maximum and minimum for the inland station from January to October, but in November and December the sea is warmer than the inland region both by night and by day. The inland maximum curve rises high above the sea temperature curve in the spring and summer and it is of interest to see when the greatest difference occurs. In the lower part of Fig. 96 we have therefore plotted the difference, sea temperature *minus* inland maximum temperature, and also the difference, sea temperature *minus* inland minimum temperature. We see that the greatest difference in the case of the maximum occurs in May and June. The shape of this difference curve is practically identical with that of the difference curve for coastal *minus* inland maximum temperature.

The other difference curve, sea temperature *minus* inland minimum, has a maximum in the autumn, agreeing with the result found from our comparison of inland and coastal stations.   The smallest difference, however, occurs in May and June, not in the earlier months January to March.   It appears probable that the major cause of the equalization of

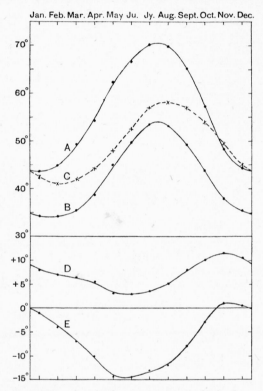

Fig. 96.—Comparison of sea-surface temperature and inland temperature.
  A—Mean maximum at Norwich.
  B—Mean minimum at Norwich.
  C—Mean temperature of western North Sea.
  D—North Sea temperature *minus* Norwich minimum.
  E—North Sea temperature *minus* Norwich maximum.

inland and coastal temperatures in winter is the prevalence of south-westerly and westerly winds, which often bring to our eastern coasts air at a temperature exceeding that of the North Sea waters.

145. The effect of the diurnal sea-breeze.   It is clear from Fig. 96 that the temperature conditions are highly favourable for the development of diurnal sea-breezes on the east coast of England in the summer

months.   In the months of May and June the inland daily maximum
exceeds the sea surface temperature by more than 14° F. under normal
conditions, and the difference amounts to 10° F. or more in every month
from April to August.   In Chapter IV some account was given of the
part played by the diurnal sea-breeze in regard to our statistics of wind
direction for different coasts.   We may now conclude that the sea-breeze
is more important as a climatic controlling factor on our eastern coasts
than elsewhere, for it is here that we find the maximum differences
between the inland day temperature and the sea surface temperature,
especially in the early summer months.   In May the North Sea is about
5° F. colder than the waters at the mouth of the English Channel or off
the west coast of Ireland.   At Cullompton (Devon) the mean maximum
temperature exceeds the sea temperature in the Channel by about 6° F.
in April, 10° F. in May, 12° F. in June, 11° F. in July and 8° F. in August.
In Ireland much smaller contrasts are found, thus at Birr Castle (Offaly),
which is nearly in the middle of Ireland, the mean maximum exceeds the
sea temperature of the Atlantic waters by about 3° F. in April, 6° F. in
May, 9° F. in June and July and 4° F. in August.

On a western shore the sea-breeze due to convection arising from
inland heating tends to augment the frequency of winds from what
would in any case be the prevailing direction ; one would therefore
expect the climatic effects of the sea-breeze to be relatively inconspicuous.
On an eastern shore, on the other hand, the sea-breeze brings in cold
air off a chilly sea on summer afternoons and it becomes a climatic factor
of major importance.   It has the effect of suppressing the diurnal rise of
temperature and raising the humidity.   We have also noted that the
maximum depression of day temperature occurs in May and June, a
time of year when a little more warmth would often be welcome.   On
the east coast the sea-breeze often reaches the velocity of a moderate
wind and there can be little doubt that the " bracing " quality for which
that coast is famous is due mainly to those winds.

146. Rainfall on the coast.   Speaking generally, the coastal regions
are the areas of lowest rainfall in the British Isles.   We saw in Chapter V
that the driest areas of Great Britain are found on the east coast around
the Thames estuary.   From that point, running northward we have a
dry coastal strip all the way up to Caithness.   On the east coast of
Ireland we have an area with an annual rainfall under thirty inches.   On
other coasts the contrast between the dry coastal strip and the adjacent
inland regions is much accentuated by the land contours ; thus in North
Wales we have the abrupt transition from an annual average of no more

than twenty-six inches at Rhyl, thirty inches at Llandudno and thirty-five inches at Holyhead to about 200 inches in Snowdonia.

It might be expected that the causes which operate to produce the seasonal variations in the difference of temperature between coastal and adjacent inland regions would also have some effect on the rainfall. There is some interest, therefore, in comparing the monthly averages of rainfall at the pairs of stations quoted in Table LVIII. For this purpose we have expressed the average monthly rainfall at the coastal station as a percentage of the value at the inland station. The results are given in Table LIX. The four pairs of stations in eastern England have been grouped together in this table.

TABLE LIX

Rainfall at Coastal Stations Expressed as a Percentage of the Rainfall at Neighbouring Inland Stations

Stations	Jan.	Feb.	Mar.	Apr.	May	June	July	Aug.	Sep.	Oct.	Nov.	Dec.	Year
Mean of four pairs of stations in eastern England	101	99	99	93	92	89	93	100	107	108	108	100	99
Southport-Manchester -	101	108	100	96	98	82	87	100	117	107	119	100	101
Sidmouth-Cullompton -	89	90	89	93	91	98	94	92	102	90	91	89	92
Donaghadee-Armagh - -	100	105	93	96	95	92	97	92	98	106	107	101	99

We see that there is a very definite tendency in eastern England for the rainfall on the coast to be less than the rainfall inland in the summer months from April to July, and for the coastal rainfall to exceed the inland rainfall in other months, but particularly in the autumn. The Southport-Manchester and Donaghadee-Armagh comparisons show a similar result, but the effect does not seem to exist in Devonshire. It seems probable that the inland transport of cool air by the sea-breeze tends to produce stable conditions on the coast during summer months, and thus reduce the rainfall due to convectional showers and thunderstorms. It is not easy, however, to see why a compensating action should occur in the autumn, unless it is due to instability set up on the coast by the relatively warm sea surface. We have seen that autumn and early winter is the time of year when the sea temperature is on the average higher than the inland temperature both by night and by day, and this fact would appear to have some significance.

147. General conclusions. We have not attempted to include all coasts of the British Isles in these comparisons ; in some areas it is indeed difficult to find suitably situated pairs of stations for which we possess comparable data. In the examples considered we have, however, noted a sufficient degree of general similarity to justify the conclusion that they represent the main climatic differences between coastal and inland areas very fairly. Gathering together the results arrived at here and in preceding chapters, we may summarize the principal features of our coastal climates as follows :

1. Low frequency of fog, particularly during autumn and winter, except in industrial areas, or where the land rises steeply from sea-level on the south coast of England.
2. A higher general level of wind-velocity than inland, with more frequent gales and less gustiness.
3. Frequent sea-breezes during the warmer portion of the day in spring, summer and early autumn.
4. Higher duration of sunshine than inland, especially in winter months.
5. Cooler afternoons except in late autumn and early winter, the greatest difference as compared with inland conditions occurring in early summer (May and June).
6. Warmer nights in all months, the greatest difference as compared with inland conditions occurring in the autumn.
7. A slightly smaller annual range of temperature.
8. Lower frequency of thunderstorms and frosts.
9. Lower rainfall in the summer but a tendency for higher rainfall in other seasons, particularly in the autumn.

VALLEY CLIMATES

148. In geographical terminology the word " valley " may mean anything between a large area of country drained by a river, as for example in the expression " the Thames valley ", and a small elongated depression between adjacent hills. In meteorology when reference is made to conditions " in a valley " the term has the latter connotation rather than the former. The valleys we have in mind in this section are, in fact, the bottoms of the depressions between ridges of hills. These low-lying areas in hilly or undulating country show interesting climatic peculiarities, but in studying these peculiarities we are handicapped by the fact that we possess little data. The reason for this lack of information is the preference given to more orthodox sites in selecting positions for meteorological stations. When a local authority, or a voluntary observer, proposes to establish a meteorological station, it is normally intended that the readings should be fairly representative of the locality ; the authority is discouraged, quite rightly, by the Meteorological Office from establishing such a station in a place which is likely to exhibit climatic peculiarities of a very local character.

In recent years it has come to be recognized that the climates of valleys and hollows are deserving of special study. Much work of this kind has been done in Austria, and quite recently encouragement has been given to similar research work in this country by the Ministry of Agriculture and Fisheries, stimulated by peculiar features in the distribution of damage to fruit crops during the disastrous frost of May 1935. We may hope for a considerable increase in our knowledge of this very important branch of climatology during the next few years. In the meanwhile we are able to form some idea of the peculiarities of valley climates by referring to a series of observations made in a Hertfordshire valley by E. L. Hawke. Mr. Hawke established a meteorological station in the garden of his residence in a valley near Rickmansworth (Herts.) in 1929, and it soon became evident that the site showed the special climatic characteristics of a valley in a conspicuous degree. For the purpose of studying these peculiarities we shall compare the Rickmansworth data with those for Rothamsted, a normally exposed station also in Hertfordshire, and we may begin by describing the situations of the two stations briefly.

149. The sites of the Rickmansworth and Rothamsted stations. The station we shall refer to as " Rickmansworth " is in a valley bottom among the foothills of the Chilterns, midway between the small towns of Rickmansworth and Chorleywood, Herts. The topography of the neighbourhood is indicated by the chart in Fig. 97, where the position of the station is indicated by the letter X. The soil consists of a foot or two of sandy gravel overlying the Chiltern chalk. The valley bottom runs at first eastward and then southward ; it is separated from the Chess Valley to the north-eastward by a ridge of high land the crest of which is about 100 feet higher than the valley bottom ; westward there is more extensive high land rising above 300 feet. At the point marked E the natural opening of the valley at its southern end is dammed by a high railway embankment carrying the main lines from Marylebone to the north. The site of the thermometer screen is 182 feet above mean sea-level and is thus not quite at the lowest point of the valley.

The Rothamsted station is on farm land at the experimental station, Harpenden, maintained by the Lawes Agricultural Trust. The site is at 420 feet above sea-level near the flattened crest of a ridge of the Chilterns. It is about fourteen miles north of Rickmansworth and the site has no peculiarities calling for special mention. The soil is a rather heavy loam with a reddish yellow subsoil over chalk.

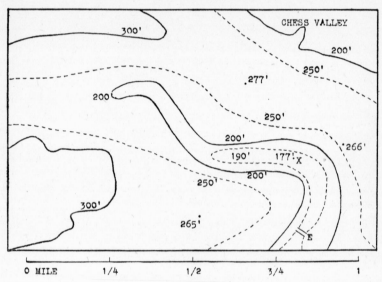

FIG. 97.—Topography of the vicinity of the Rickmansworth station.
(After E. L. Hawke.)

150. Comparison of Rickmansworth and Rothamsted.

In Table LX we have tabulated the values of the mean daily maximum temperature, mean daily minimum, daily mean, and mean daily range for the period 1931 to 1935, and we have added data in regard to the highest and lowest temperatures observed in each month of 1935, with the number of nights with ground frost at the two stations. Beginning at the top of the table we see that the mean daily maximum at Rickmansworth, the valley station, is decidedly higher than at Rothamsted in each month. On the average for the whole year the difference amounts to about 3° F., but it exceeds 4° F. in June, July and August, diminishing to 1·5° F. in December. On the other hand, the mean daily minimum at Rick-

mansworth is from 4° F. to 5° F. lower than at Rothamsted in all
months. Thus the daily mean temperature at Rickmansworth is nearly
the same as at Rothamsted throughout the year but there is a very

TABLE LX

COMPARISON OF TEMPERATURES AT RICKMANSWORTH AND ROTHAMSTED
IN HERTFORDSHIRE

	Jan.	Feb.	Mar.	Apr.	May	June	July	Aug.	Sep.	Oct.	Nov.	Dec.	Year
	°F.	°F.	°F.	°F.	°F.	°F.	°F.	°F.	°F.	°F.	°F.	°F.	°F.
Average daily maximum 1931-1935													
Rickmansworth	44·5	46·0	51·4	55·7	63·2	70·7	75·2	74·7	67·3	58·0	49·6	44·6	58·4
Rothamsted -	42·7	43·2	48·5	52·3	59·3	66·5	71·0	70·0	63·5	54·7	47·5	43·1	55·2
Average daily minimum 1931-1935													
Rickmansworth	28·7	28·2	28·3	34·6	39·5	45·2	48·5	47·4	43·8	37·2	33·6	30·9	37·2
Rothamsted -	33·2	32·7	33·8	38·6	43·3	49·8	53·6	52·7	49·1	42·7	38·1	35·1	41·9
Daily mean temperature 1931-1935													
Rickmansworth	36·6	37·1	39·9	45·1	51·3	57·9	61·9	60·9	55·5	47·6	41·6	37·7	47·8
Rothamsted -	37·9	37·9	41·1	45·5	51·3	58·1	62·3	51·3	56·3	48·7	42·8	39·1	48·5
Mean daily range 1931-1935													
Rickmansworth	15·8	17·8	23·1	21·1	23·7	25·5	26·7	27·1	23·5	20·8	16·0	13·7	21·2
Rothamsted -	9·5	10·5	14·7	13·7	16·0	16·7	17·4	17·3	14·4	12·0	9·4	8·0	13·3
Highest monthly maximum in 1935													
Rickmansworth	54	58	67	64	78	86	89	89	74	63	63	51	89
Rothamsted -	52	55	63	61	72	81	84	84	71	59	59	49	84
Lowest monthly minimum in 1935													
Rickmansworth	15	18	19	20	17	28	32	31	27	15	16	7	7
Rothamsted -	23	26	27	30	27	41	42	40	38	27	28	13	13
Number of nights with ground frost in 1935													
Rickmansworth	26	21	28	20	15	2	4	6	6	20	23	25	196
Rothamsted -	12	9	17	9	6	0	0	0	0	5	14	16	88

great difference between the stations in respect to daily range. For the
whole year the mean daily range at Rickmansworth exceeds 21° F. and
is substantially greater than that observed in any other place for which
we possess data. In the summer months the daily range exceeds 25° F.
and even in January we have at Rickmansworth a daily range nearly
equalling that observed in midsummer at Rothamsted.

The mean maximum temperatures observed at Rickmansworth are comparable with those observed at stations such as Camden Square and Westminster in the central area of London, but to find a station showing similar values of minimum temperature we have to go to the high-level stations in the north of Scotland. As a matter of interest we give below estimated values of the mean minimum at Rickmansworth for the period 1906 to 1935, with the values for Braemar, Aberdeenshire (1,111 feet), for comparison :

	Jan.	Feb.	Mar.	Apr.	May	June	July	Aug.	Sep.	Oct.	Nov.	Dec.	Year
Rickmansworth	29°	29°	29°	33°	40°	43°	47°	47°	43°	37°	32°	30°	37°
Braemar - -	29°	29°	29°	33°	37°	42°	46°	45°	41°	37°	32°	30°	36°

Thus the night climate of this Hertfordshire valley appears to be almost exactly similar to that of the Aberdeenshire plateau, which is about the coldest inhabited region in the British Isles.

The data in regard to monthly extremes in 1935 indicate that on days of exceptional warmth the temperature at Rickmansworth exceeds that at Rothamsted by about the same margin as on ordinary occasions. The results for extreme minima show, however, that on very cold nights the contrast between the two stations is even greater than usual. Thus in June 1935 the extreme minimum at Rickmansworth was 28° F. as compared with 41° F. at Rothamsted, and in several other months we have differences of 10° F. or more. At Rothamsted there was no reading of a screen minimum of 32° F. or below in June, July, August or September, but Rickmansworth recorded a freezing temperature in each of these months.

The results in respect to the frequency of ground frosts are even more striking. Rothamsted recorded eighty-eight ground frosts in 1935, which is about the normal number for that region, but Rickmansworth observed no fewer than 196. No month of the year was immune from ground frost, and as many as eighteen occurred in the four months June to September, which gave no frosts at Rothamsted. During the other months ground frosts occurred at Rickmansworth on about three nights out of four.

The average daily range of temperature at Rickmansworth is, as we have seen, very great in all months, and on some specially favourable occasions truly phenomenal changes have been observed. On 29th August the temperature rose from 34·0° F. at 5 h. 45 m. G.M.T. to 84·9° F. at 14 h. 30 m., a variation of no less than 50·9° F. in less than nine hours (58). A range of 46·7° F. was observed on 27th September,

1929, and one of 47·7° F. on 28th March, 1933 (59). A daily variation exceeding 40° F. has been registered on numerous occasions, most frequently in June, July and August.

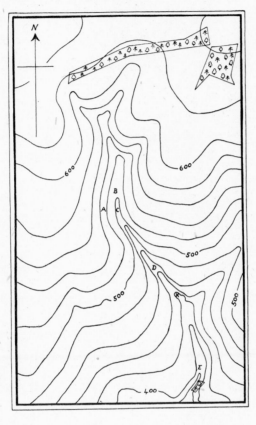

CONTOUR INTERVAL 20 FEET

SCALE 0 _____ ¼ _____ ½ MILE

FIG. 98.—Topography of a Cotswold valley near Leafield (Oxon.).
(After G. S. P. Heywood.)

151. Conditions in a valley of the Cotswolds. G. S. P. Heywood (60) has examined the conditions of katabatic air flow and the resulting temperature variations in a valley of the Cotswolds near Leafield, Oxfordshire. The contours of the valley selected for study are shown in Fig. 98 and it will be seen at once that the topography differs considerably from that of the Rickmansworth site. The station where the records were made is shown by a letter X, and it was near the south-eastern end of a valley which not only had steeply sloping sides, but the bottom of which also sloped appreciably, the drop amounting to about eighty feet in half a mile. The letters A, B, C and D on the map mark positions where smoke was liberated to determine the direction and speed of katabatic air flow.

Heywood found that a gravitational flow of cold air, that is to say a katabatic wind, tended to occur on nights when conditions were favourable for a rapid cooling of the ground by radiation, that is to say when skies were clear and there was little or no general wind current near ground level. The cold air flowed down the hillsides and along the bottom of the valley, very much like a stream of water, but the speed of the flow was always very slow, never more than about 3·5 miles per hour. It became inappreciable when the cold air had accumulated to a considerable depth over the low ground.

On radiation nights in summer Heywood found that the temperature at the observing station in the valley fell to a value about 4° F. or 5° F. lower than on the adjacent high ground ; much smaller differences were observed in the winter. On nights when the katabatic effect was not observed the minima in the valley and on the high ground usually agreed to within a fraction of 1° F.

152. General conclusions in regard to valley climates. From the results we have cited it is clear that valley situations are characterized by a tendency for the occurrence of low night temperature when conditions are favourable for vigorous nocturnal radiation. From Heywood's investigations it is clear that the cold conditions arise from the accumulation in the valley of cold air draining from the adjacent hillsides. The actual loss of heat by radiation is probably greater from the hilltops than from the valley bottoms ; on the high ground the air, chilled by contact with the cold ground, can, however, flow away downward and be replaced by warmer air from the free atmosphere at about the same level. Thus the cooling process does not operate continuously on the same mass of air and the temperature observed on the hilltop does not therefore descend to so low a value as in the valley bottoms, where the cold air accumulates and is cooled progressively so long as the loss of heat from the ground by radiation remains unimpeded. The tendency for stagnation of air in valleys would be most marked during the night, but would also be operative in the daytime because of the shelter from wind afforded by the adjacent hills. We may suppose the high day temperature observed at Rickmansworth to be due to this cause.

The topography of the Rickmansworth station is obviously such as to favour the " ponding " of cold air and the development of very low temperatures on radiation nights. The ponding is apparently due in no small measure to the railway embankment which dams the southern extremity of the valley, and it would be interesting to see the effect on the climate if the embankment were removed. There are probably not very many situations where the Rickmansworth conditions are repro- duced, and we may assume that Heywood's results give a closer ap- proximation to the conditions likely to be observed in most valleys. We may suppose also that much would depend upon the orientation of the valley in respect to the prevailing winds, on the nature of the soil, and on the presence or absence of water in the valley or hollow. Water would tend to minimize the daily range of temperature because of its high capacity for heat. At Rickmansworth the sandy, porous soil favours a large daily range of temperature independently of the topo- graphical peculiarities.

The occurrence of a large daily range of temperature is necessarily associated with the occurrence of high relative humidity at night and frequent fog in the evening and early morning. " Valley fog " is of course a well known phenomenon, and it often has a well defined upper surface marking the depth to which the air has been cooled below the dew-point. This must give rise to loss of early morning and late evening sunshine.

It is perhaps hardly necessary to state that the very remarkable climate described here as prevailing at " Rickmansworth " is peculiar to the small valley in which the meteorological station is situated. There is no reason for supposing that the town of Rickmansworth, a pleasant and popular residential area, is subject as a whole to the climatic abnormalities we have detailed.

TOWN CLIMATES

153. Workers in large cities are very familiar with the difference in the " feel of the air " which they experience when they travel into the open country ; country dwellers perhaps notice the contrast even more when they are obliged to spend a day or two in a large town. The difference is certainly not entirely climatic ; the psychological effect of the change from the grimy and often sordid surroundings of the town to the verdure and quietude of the countryside is very great, but it is nevertheless true that there are recognizable differences of climate between the two types of environment. Some of these have already come to our notice. A very conspicuous feature of large towns, especially manufacturing towns, is the smoke-pall by which they are often over-hung. This reduces the amount of sunshine, gives rise to smoke fogs, and also, as is now well known, acts as a very effective screen, cutting off the ultra-violet radiation from the sun. In addition, the large buildings of towns shelter the streets from the wind and their frictional resistance greatly reduces the wind velocity even when the measurement is made well above the level of the housetops. Mention has also been

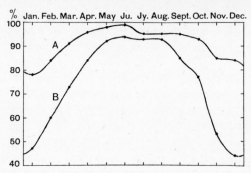

Fig. 99.—Percentage of country sunshine recorded by London stations.
A—Suburbs ; B—Central area.

made of the higher temperature in towns due at least in part to artificial heating.

We propose here to examine some climatological data for the purpose of determining the extent to which these effects are discernible in different seasons. In selecting an area for examination the obvious choice is the London area, not only because it is the largest " town " area of the world, and therefore more likely than any other to show the anticipated characteristics, but also for two other reasons. The first reason is that the London area is relatively flat, thus minimizing the complications introduced by variations in altitude ; the second reason is that we have more meteorological data for the London area than for any other city.

154. **London sunshine.** The daily duration of sunshine, averaged over the whole year, varies from 4·06 hours at Hampstead on the north-western outskirts of London, to 3·36 hours at Bunhill Row in the heart

of the city. The outer suburban areas have averages similar to Hampstead; thus we have 4·00 hours at Enfield in the north, 4·02 hours at Kew Observatory in the west and 3·97 hours at Greenwich in the east. Tottenham, in the more closely built-up area of north London, has an average of 3·87 hours. Coming nearer to the centre of London we have 3·59 hours at Regent's Park and 3·68 hours at Westminster. There is thus a very definite falling off in average daily sunshine as we go from the suburbs to the central districts. To form a basis of comparison we need to know the average daily sunshine in the country districts around London. For that purpose we may take the average of the three stations,

TABLE LXI

COMPARISON OF LONDON AND COUNTRY SUNSHINE (MONTHLY MEANS OF DAILY DURATION, AND PERCENTAGE VALUES)

Area	Jan.	Feb.	Mar.	Apr.	May	June	July	Aug.	Sep.	Oct.	Nov.	Dec.	Year
	hrs.	hrs.	hrs.	hrs.	hrs.	hrs.	hrs.	hrs.	hrs.	hrs.	hrs.	hrs.	hrs.
Country stns. (1)	1·70	2·50	3·88	5·05	6·58	6·98	6·53	6·10	5·16	3·42	2·09	1·38	4·29
Suburbs (2)	1·33	2·09	3·54	4·84	6·43	6·91	6·23	5·81	4·90	3·20	1·78	1·16	4·03
Per cent. of country	*78*	*84*	*91*	*96*	*98*	*99*	*95*	*95*	*95*	*93*	*85*	*84*	*94*
Central area (3)	0·79	1·50	2·83	4·25	6·07	6·52	6·03	5·66	4·39	2·63	1·12	0·61	3·54
Per cent. of country	*47*	*60*	*73*	*84*	*92*	*94*	*93*	*93*	*85*	*77*	*53*	*44*	*82·5*

(1) Mean of Rothamsted, Wisley and Tunbridge Wells
(2) Mean of Hampstead, Kew and Enfield
(3) Mean of Bunhill Row, Regent's Park and Westminster

Rothamsted in Hertfordshire, Wisley in Surrey and Tunbridge Wells in Kent. The mean of these three stations gives a daily average of 4·29 hours. Adopting this method of estimating what the sunshine of London would be in the absence of town smoke, we see that there is a daily loss varying from 0·23 hour (five per cent.) at Hampstead to 0·93 hour (twenty-two per cent.) at Bunhill Row.

For the purpose of comparing the sunshine of London with that of the country districts in individual months we have grouped the London stations as follows: " suburban " (mean of Hampstead, Enfield and Kew) and " central area " (mean of Regent's Park, Westminster and Bunhill Row). In Table LXI we have set out the monthly mean values for the country stations, and for the two London groups, and we have also expressed the London values as percentages of the country values. The percentages are shown graphically in Fig. 99.

u

From these data and curves we see at once that London's loss of sunshine is most serious in the winter months. In June the sunshine recorded in the suburbs is practically equal to that recorded at the country stations, and even the central area receives ninety-four per cent. of the country duration. The percentage exceeds ninety in the suburbs from March to October, and in the central area from May to August. In December and January, however, the duration of sunshine in the central area is less than half the country duration, and in January the loss

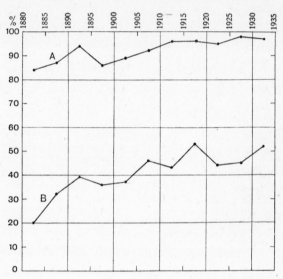

Fig. 100.—Five-yearly means of sunshine duration in Central London, expressed as a percentage of the duration at Kew Observatory.
A—Summer (June and July) ; B—Winter (December and January).

exceeds twenty per cent. even in the suburbs. Further examination of the data shows that the loss in the central area averages nearly one hour per day from November to March, and about half an hour per day from May to August.

We may presume that the losses occur mainly when the altitude of the sun is low, because a large thickness of hazy air has to be traversed by the sun's rays under those conditions. From the curves showing the diurnal variation of suspended impurity in the atmosphere (Figs. 93 and 94, p. 284) it is also clear that the major portion of the loss must occur during the early forenoon, when the penetration of solar radiation is hindered not only by the low altitude of the sun but also by the high concentration of suspended impurity at that time.

During the past half-century continuous efforts have been made to reduce the amount of atmospheric pollution by industrial and domestic smoke. That these efforts have borne fruit will be seen from an inspection of Fig. 100. For the purpose of drawing the two graphs the duration of sunshine in central London was expressed as a percentage of the duration at Kew Observatory in each five-year period from 1881-1885 to 1931-1935. "Winter" refers to the two months December and January, and "summer" to the two months June and July. It will be seen that both graphs show a general upward trend, though there are some superposed irregularities. The rise is particularly marked in the case of the "winter" graph. In the five years 1881-1885 the central stations recorded only twenty per cent. of the duration measured at Kew; in the five years 1931-1935 the corresponding figure was fifty per cent. Meanwhile the percentage for the summer months has risen from eighty-four in 1881-1885 to within two or three units of 100 per cent. We may say therefore that there has been a very definite improvement in the London atmospheric conditions during the past fifty years; all will agree, nevertheless, that the position cannot yet be regarded as satisfactory, when about half the winter sunshine of central London is cut off by smoke.

155. London temperatures. In Table LXII we give two sets of data by which the temperature conditions in the central area of London may be compared with the conditions in the surrounding districts. In the upper part of the table Westminster (St. James's Park) is compared with Wisley in Surrey; both sets of data are 30-year averages of extremes for periods of twenty-four hours. We see that the maximum temperatures at the two stations agree closely in the summer months from May to August; in the autumn and winter from October to February the average maximum at Westminster is about 1° F. higher than at Wisley. The differences in the case of the mean minimum are distinctly greater; on the average for the whole year the Westminster minimum is 2·5° F. higher than the Wisley minimum and the difference exceeds 3° F. from May to October. The mean temperature at Westminster is 1·5° F. higher than at Wisley and there is little variation from this figure in individual months.

In the lower part of the table we have a comparison of Croydon Aerodrome and Kensington Palace Gardens, based on 15-year averages of day maximum and night minimum. It is perhaps rather invidious to describe Croydon as a country district, but the meteorological conditions on the aerodrome certainly resemble those of the country rather than the town. The results in this case are rather different from those of the Wisley and Westminster comparison. Here the town station shows higher temperatures both by night and by day in practically all months, and the variations in the case of the maximum are very similar to those

TABLE LXII

COMPARISON OF TEMPERATURES IN LONDON AND THE COUNTRY

Station	Jan.	Feb.	Mar.	Apr.	May	June	July	Aug.	Sep.	Oct.	Nov.	Dec.	Year
	° F.	° F.	° F.	° F.	° F.	° F.	° F.	° F.	° F.	° F.	° F.	° F.	° F.
Wisley, max. -	44·9	45·7	49·9	55·0	63·7	68·3	71·6	70·8	65·9	58·0	49·1	45·7	57·4
Westminster, max.	46·0	46·7	50·5	55·7	63·9	68·1	71·4	70·9	66·4	58·8	50·2	46·9	58·0
Difference -	1·1	1·0	0·6	0·7	0·2	−0·2	−0·2	0·1	0·5	0·8	1·1	1·2	0·6
Wisley, min. -	34·9	34·3	35·6	38·6	44·6	48·8	52·8	52·5	48·3	43·3	37·3	36·2	42·3
Westminster, min.	36·4	36·2	37·6	41·1	47·7	52·2	55·9	55·6	51·7	46·3	39·6	37·8	44·8
Difference -	1·5	1·9	2·0	2·5	3·1	3·4	3·1	3·1	3·4	3·0	2·3	1·6	2·5
Wisley, mean -	39·9	40·0	42·7	46·8	54·1	58·5	62·2	61·7	57·1	50·7	43·2	40·9	49·9
Westm'ster, mean	41·2	41·5	44·1	48·4	55·8	60·1	63·7	63·3	59·1	52·5	44·9	42·3	51·4
Difference -	1·3	1·5	1·4	1·6	1·7	1·6	1·5	1·6	2·0	1·8	1·7	1·4	1·5
Croydon, max. -	44·9	45·2	50·3	54·3	61·7	67·4	71·9	70·1	65·6	57·0	49·1	44·4	56·8
Kensington, max.	45·6	45·7	50·9	55·3	63·3	68·7	73·2	71·3	66·5	58·3	48·9	45·0	57·7
Difference -	0·7	0·5	0·6	1·0	1·6	1·3	1·3	1·2	0·9	1·3	−0·2	0·6	0·9
Croydon, min -	37·1	35·9	36·7	39·9	45·3	50·3	54·6	54·0	50·5	45·1	39·4	37·5	43·9
Kensington, min.	37·7	36·5	38·0	41·3	46·8	51·9	56·2	55·1	51·6	46·3	40·3	38·0	45·0
Difference -	0·6	0·6	1·3	1·4	1·5	1·6	1·6	1·1	1·1	1·2	0·9	0·5	1·1
Croydon, mean -	41·0	40·5	43·5	47·1	53·5	58·9	63·3	62·1	58·1	51·1	43·3	40·9	50·3
Kensington, mean	41·7	41·1	44·5	48·3	55·1	60·3	64·7	63·2	59·1	52·3	44·6	41·5	51·3
Difference -	0·7	0·6	1·0	1·2	1·6	1·4	1·4	1·1	1·0	1·2	0·3	0·6	1·0

Wisley and Westminster values are averages for 1906-1935 ; Croydon and Kensington values are averages of day maximum and night minimum for the period 1921-1935.

in the case of the minimum. The difference of mean temperature throughout the year is 1° F., Kensington being the warmer ; there is a variation of the difference from about 1·5° F. in summer to 0·6° F. in winter.

In comparisons of this sort something must be allowed for local peculiarities of topography and differences of altitude. The height of the Croydon station above sea-level exceeds that of the Kensington station by 137 feet ; this difference would account for Kensington being on the average about 0·5° F. warmer than Croydon. Wisley is 123 feet higher than Westminster and we should thus expect a difference due to altitude of about 0·4° F. Even with these allowances we see, however, that the town stations are definitely warmer than the country stations, particularly at night and in the summer.

These results are, on the whole, in accordance with popular impressions. It seems probable that the maintenance of relatively high temperature in towns on summer nights is due partly to the retention of heat by the brick and stonework of buildings, and partly to the fact that the very presence of the buildings tends to prevent free radiation of heat from the ground at night. The differences of temperature in winter months are smaller than we might perhaps have expected. Londoners are familiar with the fact that in winter there are many occasions when snow whitens the landscape in the outer suburbs, while in the city the precipitation is in the form of a cold rain, mixed perhaps with a little melting snow. We have referred also to the tendency for the higher temperature within the town to prevent the occurrence of dense fog at street level. The conditions certainly tend to be colder in the parks and open spaces, from which meteorological statistics are in the main derived.

156. London winds. Mention has been made of the reduction of wind speed in towns due to the presence of buildings, which break up the surface and impede the flow of air. The magnitude of this effect in the central London area may be judged by comparing the wind speeds recorded at South Kensington and at Kew Observatory and Croydon Aerodrome on the outskirts of London. Of the three anemometers, that at Croydon, mounted at a height of 105 feet above ground level and 313 feet above sea-level, on the control tower of the airport of London has the most open exposure. At Kew the anemometer is on the observatory roof seventy-five feet above ground level ; the immediate surroundings are open parkland but the site is low-lying and unfavourably placed for the measurement of wind. At South Kensington the anemometer is mounted thirty feet above the roof of the Science Museum and 110 feet above ground level ; it may be regarded as giving a fair representation of the winds above the general roof-level of London. Some results for the year 1935 are set out in Table LXIII. The limits of velocity in the table correspond with " strong winds ", " moderate to fresh winds ", " light winds " and " light airs and calms ". It will be seen that in 1935 there were only thirteen hours of strong wind at South Kensington as compared with ninety-five hours at Kew and 371 hours at Croydon. In respect of moderate and fresh winds the differences between the three stations are not so great, but South Kensington shows a very high frequency of light winds (four to twelve miles per hour) as compared with the other two stations. When we come to light airs and calms (less than four miles per hour), however, we find a result of a different kind, these very low velocities being much less frequent at South Kensington than at either of the other stations. In 1935 they averaged only two hours per day at South Kensington as compared with four hours per day at Kew. The results for other years show the same feature, and we may conclude that calm or nearly calm conditions are

TABLE LXIII

NUMBER OF HOURS OF WINDS OF STATED MEAN VELOCITIES RECORDED AT LONDON STATIONS IN 1935

Station	Exceeding 24 m.p.h.	13 to 24 m.p.h.	4 to 12 m.p.h.	Less than 4 m.p.h.
South Kensington - - -	13	1,723	6,322	702
Per cent. of total - -	*0·15*	*20*	*72*	*8*
Kew Observatory - - -	95	2,083	5,025	1,557
Per cent. of total - -	*1·1*	*24*	*57*	*18*
Croydon Aerodrome - -	371	2,969	4,177	1,243
Per cent. of total - -	*4·2*	*34*	*48*	*14*

only about half as frequent in a large city as in the surrounding country. It seems probable that this phenomenon is related to the maintenance of warmth in cities during the night hours, because the lull of wind at night is a consequence of the setting up of the nocturnal inversion of temperature near the ground.

Although winds of high mean velocity are rare at South Kensington, gusts of high velocity are not uncommon, as the reader will see by referring back to paragraph 32, p. 60. Hoardings and chimney pots are almost as liable to be blown down in the middle of a large city as anywhere else.

BIBLIOGRAPHY

(58) E. L. Hawke, "A diurnal temperature range of 50·9° F.," *Meteorological Magazine*, **71**, 1936, p. 186.

(59) E. L. Hawke, "The extreme diurnal range of temperature in the British Isles," *Q.J.R. Meteor. Soc.*, **59**, 1933, p. 261.

(60) G. S. P. Heywood, "Katabatic winds in a valley," *Q.J.R. Meteor. Soc.*, **59**, 1933, p. 47.

Fig. 101.—Index chart showing positions of stations for which climatic
tables are given in the Appendix.

APPENDIX

CLIMATIC TABLES FOR REPRESENTATIVE STATIONS

LIST OF STATIONS

SCOTLAND

Northern Islands
    Lerwick (*Shetland*)
    Deerness (*Orkney*)

East Coast
    Aberdeen Observatory
    Inchkeith (*Fife*)

West Coast
    Stornoway (*Hebrides*)
    Rothesay (*Bute*)

Inland
    Fort William (*Inverness*)
    Glasgow (*Lanark*)
    Colmonell (*Ayr*)

ENGLAND, WALES AND THE ISLE OF MAN

East Coast
    Tynemouth (*Northumberland*)
    Spurn Head (*Yorks.*)
    Great Yarmouth (Gorleston) (*Norfolk*)
    Shoeburyness (*Essex*)

West Coast
    Douglas (*Isle of Man*)
    Liverpool (Bidston Observatory)
    Holyhead (*Anglesey*)
    St. Ann's Head (*Pembroke*)
    Cardiff (*Glamorgan*)

South Coast
    Dungeness (*Kent*)
    Portsmouth (*Hants.*)
    Portland Bill (*Dorset*)
    Plymouth (*Devon*)
    Falmouth (*Cornwall*)

Inland
    York (*Yorks.*)
    Cambridge (*Cambs.*)
    Buxton (*Derby*)
    Birmingham (Edgbaston) (*Warwick*)
    Oxford (Radcliffe Observatory) (*Oxford*)
    Kew Observatory (*Surrey*)
    Stonyhurst College (*Lancs.*)

English Channel
    Scilly (St. Mary's)
    Jersey (*Channel Islands*)

IRELAND

North Coast
    Malin Head (*Donegal*)

East Coast
    Dublin (Phœnix Park) (*Dublin*)

South Coast
    Roche's Point (*Cork*)

West Coast
    Valentia Observatory (*Kerry*)

Inland
    Armagh (*Armagh*)
    Markree Castle (*Sligo*)
    Birr Castle (*Offaly*)

The positions of the stations are shown in Fig. 101.

NOTES ON THE TABLES

Cloudiness is expressed in tenths of the sky covered ; the values given are means for combinations of hours stated in the footnotes.

Relative Humidity is given where averages are available for an individual hour, preferably 13 h.

Days with Fog. Unless otherwise stated the values given are averages (mainly for periods of about ten years) of the number of days with fog at either 7 h., 13 h. or 18 h. A fog is defined as an occasion with horizontal visibility less than 1,100 yards.

Days with thunder and *days with snow.* The values are averages of the number of days on which thunder or snow was observed at any time during the civil day, midnight to midnight.

Temperature. The letter D after " daily maximum " indicates that the values refer to the day period 7 h. to 18 h.; the letter N indicates that the minimum values refer to the night period 18 h. to 7 h. For these stations the values of daily maximum, daily minimum and " average " are derived from readings during the period 1921-1935. For other stations the corresponding values are mainly thirty-year averages. The lines marked " monthly maximum " and " monthly minimum " give the average of the highest and lowest readings each year in the month named ; in these lines the entries under " year " are averages of the highest and lowest temperatures observed in each year. The lines marked " extreme maximum " and " extreme minimum " show the highest and lowest temperatures ever observed in the month named. These values are derived from all available readings down to the year 1935.

Rainfall. The entries under " average fall " and " number of days " refer to the standard period 1881-1915. The entries under " most in a day " are derived from all available records down to the year 1935.

Sunshine. The values given are mainly averages for thirty years ending 1935.

Principal sources of data :

(M.O. 407)—Averages of Temperature for periods ending 1935.

(M.O. 408)—Averages of Bright Sunshine for periods ending 1935.

The Book of Normals (Sections I, IV and V).

Admiralty Pilots.

Meteorological Office manuscript records.

The data from official publications are reproduced by kind permission of the Controller of H.M. Stationery Office.

SCOTLAND

Station—LERWICK (Shetlands).   Lat. 60° 9′ N. ;   Long. 1° 8′ W. ;   156 feet above Mean Sea Level.

Element	Jan.	Feb.	Mar.	Apr.	May	June	July	Aug.	Sep.	Oct.	Nov.	Dec.	Year
Cloudiness * - -	7·7	7·8	7·7	7·3	7·2	7·5	7·7	7·7	7·4	7·5	7·5	7·4	7·5
Days with fog -	0·2	0·0	0·8	0·9	1	2	3	2	2	1	0·8	0·2	14
Days with thunder -	0·1	0·1	0·0	0·1	0·0	0·1	0·1	0·3	0·1	0·1	0·1	0·1	1
Days with snow -	4	4	6	3	0·8	0·0	0·0	0·0	0·0	0·8	2	4	25
TEMPERATURE (° F.)													
Average - -	40	39	40	41	45	49	53	53	51	46	43	41	45
Daily maximum D	43	42	43	45	49	53	57	57	54	49	46	44	49
Daily minimum N	40	39	40	41	45	49	53	53	51	46	43	41	45
Monthly maximum	49	48	49	52	57	62	63	63	61	56	52	50	65
Monthly minimum	27	25	25	29	36	38	42	42	39	34	30	28	22
Extreme maximum	53	53	57	62	66	70	71	82	69	63	58	53	82
Extreme minimum	16	17	18	21	27	33	37	38	32	26	21	19	16
RAINFALL (inches)													
Average fall -	4·3	3·2	3·1	2·3	2·1	1·8	2·3	3·0	3·0	3·9	4·2	4·8	38·0
Number of days -	27	23	25	19	18	15	17	20	20	24	25	27	260
Most in a day -	1·6	1·4	1·2	1·3	1·3	1·4	3·4	2·8	1·7	1·7	1·8	1·5	3·4
SUNSHINE													
Hours per day -	0·7	1·5	3·0	4·2	5·0	5·5	4·4	3·8	3·7	2·3	1·2	0·4	3·0
Per cent. of possible	11	17	26	29	29	30	25	24	28	23	16	7	24

* 7 h.

Station—DEERNESS (Orkney).   Lat. 58° 56′ N. ;   Long. 2° 45′ W. ;   160 feet above Mean Sea Level.

Element	Jan.	Feb.	Mar.	Apr.	May	June	July	Aug.	Sep.	Oct.	Nov.	Dec.	Year
Cloudiness * - -	7·4	7·3	7·5	7·2	7·3	7·6	8·0	7·9	7·7	7·2	7·4	7·4	7·5
Rel. Humidity (%) *	87	88	85	84	82	85	86	86	86	87	85	89	86
Days with fog * -	0·1	1	1	1	1	1	3	2	0·9	0·4	0·4	0·1	12
Days with thunder	0·9	0·6	0·1	0·2	0·3	0·8	0·5	2	0·6	0·4	0·5	0·5	7
Days with snow -	6	6	6	4	1	0·0	0·0	0·0	0·1	0·9	3	4	31
TEMPERATURE (° F.)													
Average - -	40	39	40	42	46	50	54	54	51	46	43	41	45
Daily maximum -	43	43	44	47	51	55	58	58	55	49	46	44	49
Daily minimum -	36	36	36	38	42	46	49	50	47	42	40	38	42
Monthly maximum	49	48	50	54	60	64	66	65	62	57	53	50	68
Monthly minimum	27	26	27	30	34	40	43	44	41	36	31	29	24
Extreme maximum	54	56	60	61	66	74	76	71	71	66	58	56	76
Extreme minimum	8	12	13	22	29	34	36	37	32	29	23	20	8
RAINFALL (inches)													
Average fall -	3·5	3·0	2·8	2·1	2·0	1·8	2·6	2·9	2·9	3·8	3·9	4·2	35·5
Number of days -	21	18	20	16	14	13	14	17	18	21	20	23	215
Most in a day -	1·3	1·7	1·3	1·2	1·8	1·1	1·9	3·6	1·5	1·7	1·5	1·7	3·6
SUNSHINE													
Hours per day -	1·0	1·9	3·1	4·6	5·3	5·3	4·3	3·8	3·3	2·5	1·3	0·6	3·1
Per cent. of possible	14	20	26	32	31	29	25	25	24	24	17	10	25

* 9 h.

Station—ABERDEEN OBSERVATORY. Lat. 57° 10′ N. ; Long. 2° 6′ W. ; 37 feet above Mean Sea Level.

Element	Jan.	Feb.	Mar.	Apr.	May	June	July	Aug.	Sep.	Oct.	Nov.	Dec.	Year
Cloudiness * - -	6·3	6·6	6·5	6·6	6·6	6·5	7·0	7·1	6·4	6·4	6·2	6·1	6·5
Rel. Humidity (%) †	78	75	73	71	72	71	71	71	72	76	79	80	74
Days with fog -	1	2	2	2	2	1	0·9	1	1	0·7	0·8	1	16
Days with thunder	0·0	0·0	0·0	0·2	0·7	1	2	1	0·4	0·1	0·1	0·1	6
Days with snow -	7	7	7	3	0·8	0·0	0·0	0·0	0·1	1	3	5	34
TEMPERATURE (° F.)													
Average - -	39	39	40	43	48	53	57	56	53	48	42	40	47
Daily maximum -	43	43	45	48	53	59	62	62	58	52	46	43	51
Daily minimum -	35	35	36	38	43	47	51	51	47	43	38	36	42
Monthly maximum	52	53	59	62	68	72	73	73	69	64	56	53	76
Monthly minimum	22	22	24	29	33	38	42	40	36	31	26	22	15
Extreme maximum	59	64	70	74	75	80	86	83	82	77	63	61	86
Extreme minimum	4	6	10	21	29	30	38	33	30	25	13	6	4
RAINFALL (inches)													
Average fall -	2·2	2·1	2·4	1·9	2·3	1·7	2·8	2·7	2·2	3·0	3·0	3·2	29·5
Number of days -	18	17	20	17	17	15	17	18	17	20	19	19	214
Most in a day -	1·4	1·5	1·4	2·2	1·1	2·0	1·9	1·9	2·5	1·9	2·8	1·7	2·8
SUNSHINE													
Hours per day -	1·5	2·5	3·5	4·8	5·5	6·0	4·9	4·5	4·2	3·0	1·9	1·2	3·6
Per cent. of possible	20	26	30	34	33	34	29	30	33	30	24	18	30

* 9 h., 15 h. and 21 h.   † 13 h.

Station—INCHKEITH (Fife). Lat. 56° 2′ N. ; Long. 3° 8′ W. ; 190 feet above Mean Sea Level.

Element	Jan.	Feb.	Mar.	Apr.	May	June	July	Aug.	Sep.	Oct.	Nov.	Dec.	Year
Cloudiness * - -	6·8	7·4	7·4	7·7	7·7	7·3	7·6	7·8	7·4	7·3	7·0	7·1	7·4
Rel. Humidity (%) †	83	83	78	75	79	75	78	76	77	77	83	85	79
Days with fog -	0·9	2	3	2	2	1	1	1	1	1	2	1	18
Days with thunder													
(a) - - -	0·2	0·1	0·1	0·2	0·5	1	2	1	0·2	0·2	0·0	0·0	5
Days with snow (a)	4	3	5	1	0·4	0·0	0·0	0·0	0·0	0·2	0·9	3	17
TEMPERATURE (° F.)													
Average - -	41	40	42	44	49	54	58	57	54	49	44	41	48
Daily maximum D	44	44	46	49	54	59	63	62	59	53	47	44	52
Daily minimum N	38	37	37	39	44	49	53	53	50	45	41	39	44
Monthly maximum	53	52	56	57	63	70	72	70	67	62	56	53	74
Monthly minimum	29	29	30	33	36	42	48	47	43	36	33	31	27
Extreme maximum	56	54	62	63	73	79	81	79	79	69	61	57	81
Extreme minimum	24	20	23	30	33	40	43	43	39	31	29	26	20
RAINFALL (inches)													
Average fall -	1·5	1·3	1·3	1·5	2·0	2·0	2·7	3·0	2·3	2·3	1·8	1·6	23·3
Number of days -	15	12	13	14	15	13	16	16	14	16	14	14	172
Most in a day (a) -	1·7	1·4	1·7	1·3	1·8	1·7	2·7	2·8	1·4	2·6	1·4	1·0	2·8
SUNSHINE													
Hours per day -	1·8	2·4	3·8	4·7	5·5	7·1	5·6	4·9	4·5	3·3	2·1	1·2	3·9
Per cent. of possible	24	26	33	33	34	41	33	33	35	32	25	17	32

* 7 h., 13 h. and 18 h.   † 13 h.   (a) At Leith and Inchkeith.

Station—STORNOWAY (Hebrides). Lat. 58° 11′ N.; Long. 6° 21′ W.; 34 feet above Mean Sea Level.

Element	Jan.	Feb.	Mar.	Apr.	May	June	July	Aug.	Sep.	Oct.	Nov.	Dec.	Year
Cloudiness * - -	7·6	7·6	7·2	7·1	7·2	7·6	7·8	7·7	7·5	7·5	7·5	7·4	7·5
Rel. Humidity (%) †	88	86	82	78	76	77	79	80	80	84	87	89	82
Days with fog -	0·0	0·0	0·6	0·1	0·0	0·4	0·1	0·6	0·3	0·3	0·0	0·2	3
Days with thunder	0·5	0·2	0·1	0·1	0·2	0·3	0·4	0·4	0·1	0·1	0·4	0·5	3
Days with snow -	5	5	5	3	0·8	0·0	0·0	0·0	0·0	0·9	2	4	25
TEMPERATURE (° F.)													
Average - -	41	41	42	43	47	52	56	55	52	47	43	42	47
Daily maximum D	45	45	47	49	53	57	61	60	57	52	47	45	51
Daily minimum N	38	37	37	38	42	47	51	50	47	43	40	39	42
Monthly maximum	51	51	53	58	64	69	69	67	64	60	54	52	72
Monthly minimum	26	26	25	29	33	39	41	40	37	32	29	26	21
Extreme maximum	55	55	59	67	75	78	76	75	77	70	58	56	78
Extreme minimum	11	12	13	16	26	31	32	33	32	26	20	12	11
RAINFALL (inches)													
Average fall -	5·2	4·5	4·1	3·0	2·6	2·3	3·0	4·0	3·9	5·2	5·8	6·3	49·9
Number of days -	25	22	24	19	19	17	21	22	21	23	24	26	263
Most in a day -	2·8	1·6	1·5	1·2	1·9	1·1	1·7	2·7	1·9	2·1	1·9	1·6	2·8
SUNSHINE													
Hours per day -	0·9	1·9	3·5	5·0	5·8	5·5	4·7	4·1	3·7	2·5	1·5	0·7	3·3
Per cent. of possible	12	21	30	35	35	31	27	27	29	24	19	11	27

* 7 h., 13 h. and 18 h. † 13 h.

Station—ROTHESAY (Bute). Lat. 55° 50′ N.; Long. 5° 4′ W.; 200 feet above Mean Sea Level.

Element	Jan.	Feb.	Mar.	Apr.	May	June	July	Aug.	Sep.	Oct.	Nov.	Dec.	Year
Days with thunder	0·4	0·4	0·3	0·4	1	0·8	1	1	0·5	0·4	0·3	0·4	7
Days with snow -	3	3	3	1	0·5	0·0	0·0	0·0	0·0	0·3	0·7	2	14
TEMPERATURE (° F.)													
Average - -	40	40	41	45	50	55	57	57	53	49	43	41	48
Daily maximum -	44	44	47	51	57	62	64	63	59	53	47	45	53
Daily minimum -	36	36	36	38	43	47	51	51	48	44	39	37	42
Monthly maximum	52	51	56	62	71	76	74	73	70	62	56	53	79
Monthly minimum	25	26	26	30	34	40	42	42	38	32	28	26	21
Extreme maximum	56	56	64	71	78	85	84	83	81	69	61	57	85
Extreme minimum	12	11	20	22	30	33	39	36	32	25	20	19	11
RAINFALL (inches)													
Average fall -	4·5	4·0	3·6	3·0	3·0	3·1	4·0	4·9	4·0	4·4	5·1	5·4	49·0
Number of days -	21	19	19	17	17	15	19	20	17	20	21	23	228
Most in a day -	2·2	1·6	1·6	1·6	2·3	2·0	1·6	2·4	1·9	1·9	2·2	1·7	2·4
SUNSHINE													
Hours per day -	1·1	1·9	3·3	4·9	5·6	6·4	5·0	4·4	3·9	2·5	1·7	1·0	3·5
Per cent. of possible	15	19	28	35	35	37	30	29	31	24	20	15	28

Station—FORT WILLIAM (Inverness).   Lat. 56° 49′ N. ;   Long 5° 7′ W. ;   171 feet above Mean Sea Level.

Element	Jan.	Feb.	Mar.	Apr.	May	June	July	Aug.	Sep.	Oct.	Nov.	Dec.	Year
Cloudiness * - -	8·1	7·6	7·5	7·2	7·3	7·2	7·9	8·2	7·8	7·5	7·8	8·0	7·7
Rel. Humidity (%) †	78	77	71	64	61	67	70	74	73	75	78	80	72
TEMPERATURE (° F.)													
Average - -	39	39	41	44	51	55	57	57	53	48	42	40	47
Daily maximum -	44	44	47	51	58	63	65	64	60	54	47	44	53
Daily minimum -	35	35	35	37	43	47	50	50	47	42	37	35	41
Monthly maximum	52	51	55	62	71	76	76	72	70	62	56	54	78
Monthly minimum	21	21	24	28	33	40	42	40	35	30	25	22	16
Extreme maximum	57	56	63	73	83	86	84	85	85	74	63	66	86
Extreme minimum	5	10	11	20	26	35	37	36	30	22	11	11	5
RAINFALL (inches)													
Average fall -	9·6	7·4	6·6	4·4	3·9	3·5	4·8	6·1	6·3	7·0	8·1	10·1	77·8
Number of days -	23	19	20	18	18	15	20	22	19	21	21	24	240
Most in a day -	3·7	3·8	2·9	2·6	1·7	1·8	3·3	2·7	2·8	4·5	3·3	3·7	4·5
SUNSHINE													
Hours per day -	0·8	1·8	3·1	4·6	5·8	5·8	4·2	3·6	3·3	2·4	1·0	0·4	3·1
Per cent. of possible	10	19	26	33	35	33	25	24	26	24	12	6	25

* 9 h. and 21 h.   † 13 h.

Station—GLASGOW (Lanark).   Lat. 55° 52′ N. ;   Long. 4° 17′ W. ;   85 feet above Mean Sea Level.

Element	Jan.	Feb.	Mar.	Apr.	May	June	July	Aug.	Sep.	Oct.	Nov.	Dec.	Year
Cloudiness * - -	8·3	8·2	7·5	7·4	7·7	7·3	7·7	8·0	7·3	7·9	8·2	8·3	7·8
Rel. Humidity (%) †	84	80	74	67	65	67	69	71	73	76	81	84	74
Days with fog (a) -	6	6	5	2	2	0·8	0·5	2	5	5	7	6	47
Days with thunder	0·3	0·2	0·3	0·3	1	1	2	1	0·4	0·1	0·2	0·4	7
Days with snow -	4	3	4	0·7	0·1	0·0	0·0	0·0	0·0	0·2	1	3	16
TEMPERATURE (° F.)													
Average - -	39	40	41	45	51	56	59	58	54	48	43	40	48
Daily maximum -	43	44	46	51	57	62	65	64	60	53	47	44	53
Daily minimum -	36	36	36	39	44	49	52	52	48	44	38	37	43
Monthly maximum	50	51	55	61	68	75	75	73	67	61	55	52	78
Monthly minimum	24	29	26	31	35	41	45	43	38	31	27	24	19
Extreme maximum	55	56	62	70	77	85	85	84	83	71	60	56	85
Extreme minimum	8	7	19	21	29	36	41	35	31	24	15	8	7
RAINFALL (inches)													
Average fall -	3·3	2·9	2·7	2·1	2·6	2·5	3·1	3·9	3·0	3·4	3·6	4·1	37·2
Number of days -	19	16	17	14	15	14	17	18	16	17	18	21	202
Most in a day -	1·4	1·8	1·1	1·3	1·4	2·2	2·1	2·4	1·8	1·7	1·8	1·4	2·4
SUNSHINE													
Hours per day -	0·8	1·6	2·7	4·3	5·2	5·6	4·8	4·2	3·4	2·1	1·0	0·5	3·0
Per cent. of possible	10	17	23	31	32	33	29	28	27	20	12	7	25

* 9 h. and 21 h.   † 13 h.   (a) At Renfrew.

Station—COLMONELL (Ayr). Lat. 55° 8′ N. ; Long. 4° 53′ W. ; 170 feet above Mean Sea Level.

Element	Jan.	Feb.	Mar.	Apr.	May	June	July	Aug.	Sep.	Oct.	Nov.	Dec.	Year
Cloudiness * - -	7·0	6·9	6·1	6·0	6·2	6·3	6·6	6·7	6·3	6·6	6·4	6·9	6·5
Rel. Humidity (%) *	90	89	85	82	79	80	83	85	86	87	88	89	85
Days with Fog * -	4	3	2	3	1	2	1	2	2	1	2	3	26
TEMPERATURE (° F.)													
Average - -	40	40	42	45	51	55	58	57	54	49	43	41	48
Daily maximum -	45	45	48	52	59	62	65	64	61	55	49	46	54
Daily minimum -	36	35	35	38	43	48	51	51	47	43	37	37	42
Monthly maximum	52	52	56	63	73	73	74	73	70	65	56	53	78
Monthly minimum	24	24	24	27	30	38	42	40	34	28	23	24	19
Extreme maximum	55	56	67	72	82	82	82	88	77	74	63	60	88
Extreme minimum	13	12	16	16	26	33	34	28	28	21	12	14	12
RAINFALL (inches)													
Average fall -	4·3	3·9	3·4	2·5	2·6	2·5	3·1	4·0	3·5	4·5	5·0	5·6	44·8
Number of days -	23	16	15	15	16	15	18	21	19	21	19	22	220
Most in a day -	1·5	1·8	1·9	1·5	1·2	2·7	1·2	1·3	1·9	2·0	1·7	2·0	2·7

* 9 h.

ENGLAND, WALES AND THE ISLE OF MAN

Station—TYNEMOUTH (North'd). Lat. 55° 0′ N. ; Long. 1° 25′ W. ; 108 feet above Mean Sea Level

Element	Jan.	Feb.	Mar.	Apr.	May	June	July	Aug.	Sep.	Oct.	Nov.	Dec.	Year
Cloudiness * -	7·1	7·7	7·0	7·0	7·0	6·9	7·0	6·9	6·7	6·7	6·6	6·7	6·9
Days with fog -	6	4	4	3	3	3	2	3	3	2	4	5	42
Days with thunder	0·1	0·1	0·1	0·3	0·8	1	2	1	0·4	0·3	0·1	0·1	7
Days with snow -	5	5	5	2	0·3	0·0	0·0	0·0	0·0	0·4	1	3	23
TEMPERATURE (° F.)													
Average - -	41	41	42	45	49	55	59	59	55	50	44	41	48
Daily maximum D	44	44	47	49	54	60	65	64	60	55	47	44	53
Daily minimum N	37	37	38	40	44	49	54	53	50	45	40	38	44
Monthly maximum	53	54	59	62	68	73	75	75	71	64	57	54	78
Monthly minimum	23	25	25	30	34	40	44	44	39	33	28	25	20
Extreme maximum	60	60	70	73	81	82	85	83	88	77	67	59	88
Extreme minimum	6	7	15	17	29	36	39	38	34	27	20	10	6
RAINFALL (inches)													
Average fall -	1·6	1·4	1·8	1·4	2·0	2·0	2·4	2·8	1·8	3·0	2·1	2·2	24·5
Number of days -	15	14	16	15	14	13	14	16	13	17	16	16	179
Most in a day -	1·3	1·0	1·4	1·3	3·0	2·6	2·5	2·4	1·6	3·2	2·4	1·3	3·2

* 7 h., 13 h. and 18 h.

*Station—*SPURN HEAD (Yorks.).   Lat. 53° 34′ N. ;   Long. 0° 7′ E. ;   29 feet above Mean Sea Level.

Element	Jan.	Feb.	Mar.	Apr.	May	June	July	Aug.	Sep.	Oct.	Nov.	Dec.	Year
Cloudiness * - -	7·3	7·4	7·3	6·9	6·8	6·8	7·2	7·0	6·8	7·0	7·0	7·2	7·1
Days with fog -	5	3	2	1	2	2	1	0·4	2	2	3	4	26
Days with thunder	0·1	0·1	0·4	0·7	2	3	3	3	0·9	0·4	0·1	0·1	13
TEMPERATURE (° F.)													
Average - -	40	40	42	45	51	56	61	61	57	51	45	41	49
Daily maximum D	43	43	47	50	56	61	67	66	62	56	48	44	53
Daily minimum N	37	37	37	41	45	51	55	55	53	47	41	38	45
Monthly maximum	50	51	55	60	67	73	75	75	70	63	56	52	80
Monthly minimum	27	29	30	33	38	44	49	49	45	38	33	28	24
Extreme maximum	55	61	62	70	76	83	86	87	80	74	63	56	87
Extreme minimum	13	19	24	30	34	34	44	45	37	33	28	19	13
RAINFALL (inches)													
Average fall -	1·7	1·5	1·7	1·4	1·9	1·9	2·2	2·6	1·7	2·9	2·3	2·4	24·2
Number of days -	15	14	15	13	12	12	12	14	12	17	16	16	168
Most in a day -	1·1	0·8	0·8	0·7	1·2	1·3	1·8	1·7	2·1	1·3	1·5	1·8	2·1
SUNSHINE													
Hours per day -	1·7	2·5	4·0	4·9	5·9	6·4	6·4	5·9	4·9	3·6	2·1	1·5	4·2
Per cent. of possible	21	25	34	35	38	38	39	40	39	34	24	19	34

* 7 h., 13 h. and 18 h.

*Station—*GREAT YARMOUTH (Gorleston) (Norfolk).
Lat. 52° 35′ N. ;   Long. 1° 43′ E. ;   5 feet above Mean Sea Level.

Element	Jan.	Feb.	Mar.	Apr.	May	June	July	Aug.	Sep.	Oct.	Nov.	Dec.	Year
Cloudiness * - -	7·0	7·6	6·6	7·1	6·7	6·7	6·4	6·4	6·4	6·9	6·9	6·9	6·8
Days with fog -	3	3	2	1	2	0·8	1	0·3	1	2	2	3	21
Days with thunder	0·1	0·1	0·3	0·5	1	2	2	3	0·8	0·4	0·2	0·1	11
Days with snow -	4	3	4	1	0·4	0·0	0·0	0·0	0·0	0·1	0·7	2	17
TEMPERATURE (° F.)													
Average - -	41	40	42	46	51	57	62	61	58	52	45	41	50
Daily maximum D	44	44	47	51	57	63	68	68	64	57	49	44	55
Daily minimum N	37	36	37	41	46	51	55	55	52	47	41	38	45
Monthly maximum	51	52	57	62	68	73	76	75	70	60	57	53	78
Monthly minimum	25	26	27	33	36	43	47	46	42	36	30	26	21
Extreme maximum	57	60	66	72	81	81	87	89	82	74	64	60	89
Extreme minimum	10	13	18	19	31	37	42	41	33	27	23	15	10
RAINFALL (inches)													
Average fall -	1·7	1·5	1·8	1·5	1·7	1·8	2·3	2·5	2·0	2·9	2·4	2·4	24·5
Number of days -	18	15	17	14	13	12	13	14	13	18	18	18	183
Most in a day -	1·1	0·8	0·7	1·3	1·2	1·7	2·1	4·8	2·6	2·2	1·5	2·5	4·8
SUNSHINE													
Hours per day -	1·8	2·6	4·1	5·5	7·2	7·0	6·8	6·4	5·3	3·7	2·2	1·3	4·5
Per cent. of possible	22	27	35	39	46	42	42	44	41	35	25	17	36

* 7 h., 13 h. and 18 h.

Station—SHOEBURYNESS (Essex).   Lat. 51° 32′ N. ;   Long. 0° 49′ E. ;   11 feet above Mean Sea Level.

Element	Jan.	Feb.	Mar.	Apr.	May	June	July	Aug.	Sep.	Oct.	Nov.	Dec.	Year
Cloudiness * - -	6·6	6·9	6·3	6·2	5·7	5·9	5·7	6·1	5·9	6·0	6·5	6·5	6·2
TEMPERATURE (° F.)													
Average - -	40	40	43	47	53	58	63	63	59	52	44	40	50
Daily maximum D	45	46	50	54	61	67	72	71	67	58	49	45	57
Daily minimum N	35	35	35	39	45	50	54	54	51	45	39	36	43
Monthly maximum	53	54	59	64	74	77	79	79	74	67	57	54	83
Monthly minimum	24	26	28	30	37	42	46	47	40	34	29	25	20
Extreme maximum	58	59	68	72	88	84	92	89	86	78	63	57	92
Extreme minimum	11	16	20	22	30	37	39	40	30	25	19	9	9
RAINFALL (inches)													
Average fall -	1·4	1·2	1·3	1·2	1·3	1·8	1·8	1·8	1·7	2·4	2·1	1·8	19·8
Number of days -	14	12	13	11	11	10	10	12	10	16	15	15	149
Most in a day -	1·0	0·8	0·9	0·8	1·0	2·1	2·0	1·6	1·9	2·5	1·2	1·1	2·5
SUNSHINE													
Hours per day -	1·8	2·7	4·5	5·1	7·2	7·5	7·3	6·8	5·4	4·0	2·2	1·6	4·7
Per cent. of possible	22	28	38	37	47	46	45	47	43	37	25	20	38

* 7 h., 13 h. and 18 h.

Station—DOUGLAS (Isle of Man).   Lat. 54° 10′ N. ;   Long. 4° 28′ W. ;   284 feet above Mean Sea Level.

Element	Jan.	Feb.	Mar.	Apr.	May	June	July	Aug.	Sep.	Oct.	Nov.	Dec.	Year
Cloudiness * - -	7·4	7·1	6·6	6·2	6·3	6·5	6·8	6·8	6·3	6·9	7·0	7·3	6·8
Days with thunder	0·1	0·2	0·2	0·3	1	2	1	1	0·8	0·7	0·5	0·3	9
Days with snow -	4	3	4	1	0·1	0·0	0·0	0·0	0·0	0·3	1	2	17
TEMPERATURE (° F.)													
Average - -	41	41	42	45	51	55	58	58	55	50	45	43	49
Daily maximum -	45	45	47	51	56	60	63	63	60	54	49	46	53
Daily minimum -	38	37	37	40	45	49	52	53	50	46	41	39	44
Monthly maximum	51	51	54	60	67	72	72	70	67	61	55	53	75
Monthly minimum	27	27	27	31	34	40	44	43	44	33	30	27	23
Extreme maximum	55	55	65	69	74	81	79	81	77	70	59	59	81
Extreme minimum	12	11	18	23	28	36	39	35	32	26	25	13	11
RAINFALL (inches)													
Average fall -	3·4	3·2	3·0	2·4	2·5	2·4	3·1	3·8	3·3	4·5	4·7	4·9	41·2
Number of days -	20	18	18	16	15	13	14	17	14	19	19	21	204
Most in a day -	2·0	1·3	1·7	1·2	2·6	1·6	1·8	3·3	4·7	2·2	2·6	2·1	4·7
SUNSHINE													
Hours per day -	1·7	2·4	4·2	5·9	6·5	7·2	6·3	5·5	5·1	3·2	2·2	1·4	4·3
Per cent. of possible	21	25	35	42	41	42	38	37	40	31	26	19	35

* 9 h. and 21 h.

X

THE CLIMATE OF THE BRITISH ISLES

Station—LIVERPOOL (Bidston Observatory).

Lat. 53° 24′ N. ; Long. 3° 4′ W. ; 198 feet above Mean Sea Level.

Element	Jan.	Feb.	Mar.	Apr.	May	June	July	Aug.	Sep.	Oct.	Nov.	Dec.	Year
Cloudiness * -	7·1	6·8	6·7	6·1	5·9	5·9	6·6	6·7	6·5	6·6	6·4	7·1	6·5
Days with fog	4	6	8	3	3	0·8	1	2	4	4	6	5	47
Days with thunder	0·1	0·2	0·3	0·6	1	2	1	1	0·7	0·4	0·1	0·3	8
Days with snow	3	2	3	0·7	0·1	0·0	0·0	0·0	0·0	0·1	0·8	2	11
TEMPERATURE (° F.)													
Average - -	41	40	42	46	52	57	60	59	56	50	44	41	49
Daily maximum -	45	44	47	51	58	63	65	65	61	55	48	45	54
Daily minimum -	37	36	37	41	46	51	55	54	51	45	40	38	44
Monthly maximum	53	54	57	63	71	76	77	75	71	63	59	54	80
Monthly minimum	25	27	29	33	37	34	49	48	42	35	30	26	22
Extreme maximum	58	62	66	75	83	86	89	87	87	73	62	59	89
Extreme minimum	9	12	21	23	30	38	44	41	34	27	25	17	9
RAINFALL (inches)													
Average fall -	2·1	1·7	1·9	1·6	1·9	2·2	2·6	3·1	2·4	3·3	2·5	2·6	27·9
Number of days -	17	16	17	14	15	13	15	17	15	18	18	19	194
Most in a day -	1·5	1·2	1·1	1·0	2·1	2·1	1·6	1·7	1·4	1·7	1·8	1·1	2·1
SUNSHINE													
Hours per day -	1·7	2·3	3·4	5·2	6·2	6·7	6·0	5·2	4·4	2·9	2·0	1·3	4·0
Per cent. of possible	21	24	29	37	40	40	36	36	34	28	24	18	32

* 7 h., 13 h., 18 h. and 21 h.

Station—HOLYHEAD (Anglesey). Lat. 53° 19′ N. ; Long. 4° 37′ W. ; 26 feet above Mean Sea Level.

Element	Jan.	Feb.	Mar.	Apr.	May	June	July	Aug.	Sep.	Oct.	Nov.	Dec.	Year
Cloudiness * - -	7·1	7·0	6·8	6·2	6·1	6·2	6·5	6·2	6·1	6·7	6·8	7·2	6·6
Days with fog -	0·6	1	1	1	1	0·8	2	2	1	0·2	0·0	0·3	12
Days with thunder	0·0	0·2	0·3	0·2	0·8	1·1	1·0	1·1	0·5	0·8	0·2	0·2	6
Days with snow	2	1	2	0·4	0·0	0·0	0·0	0·0	0·0	0·1	0·4	0·8	7
TEMPERATURE (° F.)													
Average - -	44	43	44	46	51	55	59	59	57	53	47	45	50
Daily maximum D	46	46	48	50	55	59	63	63	61	55	50	47	54
Daily minimum N	42	40	40	42	47	51	55	55	53	49	44	43	47
Monthly maximum	51	51	55	60	66	71	72	71	69	63	56	53	76
Monthly minimum	29	30	32	35	40	45	49	49	45	39	34	31	27
Extreme maximum	55	59	67	75	76	83	85	86	78	76	62	56	86
Extreme minimum	20	17	26	26	32	40	43	45	40	32	29	26	17
RAINFALL (inches)													
Average fall -	2·9	2·4	2·6	2·1	2·0	2·1	2·6	3·2	2·7	4·0	4·1	4·2	34·9
Number of days -	19	17	18	14	14	13	16	17	15	19	19	20	201
Most in a day -	1·3	1·4	1·5	1·2	1·2	1·1	3·3	2·7	2·2	2·9	2·7	1·5	3·3
SUNSHINE													
Hours per day -	1·7	2·7	4·0	5·8	6·5	7·2	6·2	5·5	4·7	3·1	2·1	1·3	4·3
Per cent. of possible	21	27	34	42	41	43	38	38	37	30	25	18	35

* 7 h., 13 h. and 18 h.

Station—St. Ann's Head (Pembroke).

Lat. 51° 41′ N. ; Long. 5° 11′ W. ; 142 feet above Mean Sea Level.

Element	Jan.	Feb.	Mar.	Apr.	May	June	July	Aug.	Sep.	Oct.	Nov.	Dec.	Year
Cloudiness * - -	7·2	6·8	6·4	5·8	5·9	5·8	6·1	6·2	6·0	6·6	6·9	7·0	6·4
Days with fog -	3	3	2	2	4	2	3	3	3	1	0·7	2	29
Days with thunder	0·1	0·0	0·0	0·2	0·4	0·5	0·4	0·5	0·5	0·4	0·2	0·1	3
Days with snow -	2	1	2	0·3	0·0	0·0	0·0	0·0	0·0	0·0	0·2	0·8	6
TEMPERATURE (° F.)													
Average - -	45	43	44	46	51	56	59	59	57	53	48	45	51
Daily maximum D	47	46	48	51	55	61	63	63	60	56	51	48	54
Daily minimum N	42	40	40	42	47	51	55	55	53	49	45	43	47
Monthly maximum	51	50	52	58	66	71	70	69	66	61	56	54	74
Monthly minimum	29	31	32	35	39	45	50	50	45	39	34	31	27
Extreme maximum	54	56	64	70	75	79	82	84	74	69	60	57	82
Extreme minimum	19	22	22	28	32	38	43	45	40	33	28	19	19
RAINFALL (inches)													
Average fall -	3·3	2·7	2·6	1·9	1·9	2·0	2·5	3·1	2·7	4·2	3·8	4·5	35·2
Number of days -	20	17	17	15	14	13	14	16	14	19	20	22	201
Most in a day -	1·3	1·7	1·1	1·3	1·4	1·9	2·4	1·9	1·9	1·7	1·9	2·1	2·4
SUNSHINE													
Hours per day -	1·7	2·6	4·1	5·7	6·4	7·2	6·6	5·7	4·7	3·1	2·2	1·5	4·3
Per cent. of possible	20	27	35	41	41	44	41	39	38	29	25	19	35

* 7 h., 13 h., 18 h.

Station—Cardiff (Glamorgan). Lat. 51° 28′ N. ; Long. 3° 10′ W. ; 202 feet above Mean Sea Level.

Element	Jan.	Feb.	Mar.	Apr.	May	June	July	Aug.	Sep.	Oct.	Nov.	Dec.	Year
Days with thunder	0·5	0·2	0·3	0·5	1	0·3	2	2	0·5	0·3	0·4	1	9
TEMPERATURE (° F.)													
Average - -	41	41	43	47	53	58	61	60	57	51	44	42	49
Daily maximum -	45	45	49	53	61	65	68	67	63	56	49	46	56
Daily minimum -	36	35	36	40	45	50	53	53	50	45	39	37	43
RAINFALL (inches)													
Average fall -	3·7	2·9	3·1	2·5	2·5	2·5	3·1	4·2	3·1	4·7	4·1	5·0	41·4
Number of days -	19	16	16	15	14	13	15	17	14	18	18	21	196
SUNSHINE													
Hours per day -	1·7	2·7	3·9	5·5	6·5	7·5	6·8	6·0	4·9	3·5	2·2	1·6	4·4
Per cent. of possible	21	27	33	40	42	45	42	41	39	32	25	20	36

Station—DUNGENESS (Kent). Lat. 50° 55′ N. ; Long. 0° 58′ E. ; 20 feet above Mean Sea Level.

Element	Jan.	Feb.	Mar.	Apr.	May	June	July	Aug.	Sep.	Oct.	Nov.	Dec.	Year
Cloudiness * - -	6·8	7·0	6·8	6·5	5·9	6·2	6·4	6·3	6·0	6·6	6·8	7·0	6·5
Days with fog (*a*) -	6	6	4	2	2	1	2	2	4	4	4	7	44
Days with thunder	0·1	0·1	0·3	0·6	1	2	2	2	1	0·8	0·1	0·2	10
Days with snow -	3	3	3	0·9	0·1	0·0	0·0	0·0	0·0	0·1	0·4	2	12
TEMPERATURE (° F.)													
Average - -	41	41	43	46	52	57	62	62	59	53	46	42	50
Daily maximum D	45	45	48	52	58	63	67	68	65	58	50	46	55
Daily minimum N	38	37	37	41	46	51	56	56	53	47	41	38	45
Monthly maximum	50	52	54	60	68	72	74	74	71	64	58	53	77
Monthly minimum	23	25	26	30	36	42	46	46	40	33	29	24	19
Extreme maximum	55	57	62	67	77	76	83	83	81	72	63	57	83
Extreme minimum	11	9	12	24	26	37	40	38	32	22	17	12	9
RAINFALL (inches)													
Average fall -	1·9	1·6	1·8	1·4	1·3	1·6	1·8	2·0	2·0	3·5	2·7	2·8	24·4
Number of days -	16	15	15	13	11	11	12	13	13	17	16	17	169
Most in a day -	1·9	1·3	1·9	1·0	1·3	2·0	1·9	1·8	1·5	2·4	1·2	1·1	2·4
SUNSHINE (*b*)													
Hours per day -	2·1	3·1	4·5	5·8	7·5	7·6	7·3	6·9	5·9	4·0	2·5	1·8	4·9
Per cent. of possible	25	31	38	43	49	46	46	48	47	37	28	22	40

* 7 h., 13 h. and 18 h.　　　　(*a*) At Lympne.　　　　(*b*) At Hastings.

Station—PORTSMOUTH (Hants.). Lat. 50° 48′ N. ; Long. 1° 6′ W. ; 15 feet above Mean Sea Level.

Element	Jan.	Feb.	Mar.	Apr.	May	June	July	Aug.	Sep.	Oct.	Nov.	Dec.	Year
Cloudiness * - -	6·9	6·3	5·9	5·5	5·0	5·3	5·3	5·3	5·1	5·9	6·4	7·3	5·9
Rel. Humidity (%) *	89	87	84	77	74	74	75	77	80	85	87	90	82
Days with fog * -	5	2	0·6	0·8	0·0	0·0	0·0	0·0	0·0	0·2	2	3	14
TEMPERATURE (° F.)													
Average - -	41	41	44	48	55	59	63	63	59	53	46	43	51
Daily maximum -	46	46	50	55	62	66	70	70	66	59	51	47	57
Daily minimum -	37	37	38	41	48	52	56	57	53	47	41	39	46
Monthly maximum	53	54	59	65	75	76	79	77	73	67	58	55	82
Monthly minimum	25	28	29	32	39	45	49	48	43	36	30	28	24
Extreme maximum	57	58	65	73	79	83	90	90	84	76	64	57	90
Extreme minimum	17	20	20	27	31	38	46	44	35	26	23	17	17
RAINFALL (inches)													
Average fall -	2·4	2·0	2·0	1·6	1·7	1·8	2·0	2·2	2·2	3·7	3·0	3·1	27·7
Number of days -	15	14	14	12	11	11	12	13	11	16	16	18	163
Most in a day -	1·9	1·0	0·9	1·1	1·5	1·9	1·7	1·4	2·4	1·9	1·7	1·7	2·4
SUNSHINE													
Hours per day -	2·0	3·0	4·5	5·8	7·5	7·6	7·3	6·7	5·7	3·9	2·6	1·8	4·9
Per cent. of possible	24	30	38	43	48	47	46	46	45	37	29	22	40

* 9 h.

Station—PORTLAND BILL (Dorset).   Lat. 50° 32′ N. ;   Long. 2° 27′ W. ;   32 feet above Mean Sea Level.

Element	Jan.	Feb.	Mar.	Apr.	May	June	July	Aug.	Sep.	Oct.	Nov.	Dec.	Year
Cloudiness * - -	7·0	6·8	6·5	5·9	5·9	5·8	6·0	6·0	5·8	6·5	6·6	7·0	6·3
Days with fog -	0·8	1	1	1	3	1	2	1	0·7	0·2	0·1	0·8	13
Days with thunder	0·2	0·1	0·3	0·2	1	0·6	1	0·6	0·5	0·3	0·2	0·1	5
TEMPERATURE (° F.)													
Average - -	45	43	44	47	52	57	61	61	59	55	48	45	51
Daily maximum D	48	46	48	51	56	61	65	65	63	58	52	48	55
Daily minimum N	42	40	41	43	48	53	57	58	56	51	45	42	48
Monthly maximum	52	51	53	59	67	68	72	70	68	64	58	54	75
Monthly minimum	30	31	31	35	41	47	52	52	47	41	34	32	27
Extreme maximum	57	54	66	71	76	78	83	83	75	68	62	58	83
Extreme minimum	23	24	21	28	36	43	47	45	40	34	24	24	21
RAINFALL (inches)													
Average fall -	2·2	1·9	1·9	1·5	1·4	1·5	1·7	1·9	1·9	3·3	2·8	3·1	25·1
Number of days -	16	13	15	13	11	10	11	12	12	17	14	19	163
Most in a day -	1·0	1·7	1·2	0·7	1·5	1·1	1·6	3·9	1·8	1·8	1·6	2·1	3·9
SUNSHINE													
Hours per day -	2·1	3·0	4·5	6·0	7·0	7·7	7·3	6·7	5·5	3·7	2·6	1·7	4·8
Per cent. of possible	24	30	38	44	45	47	46	46	44	35	29	22	39

* 7 h., 13 h. and 18 h.

Station—PLYMOUTH (Devon).   Lat. 50° 22′ N. ;   Long. 4° 8′ W. ;   117 feet above Mean Sea Level.

Element	Jan.	Feb.	Mar.	Apr.	May	June	July	Aug.	Sep.	Oct.	Nov.	Dec.	Year
Cloudiness * - -	7·3	6·9	6·2	5·8	5·8	6·2	6·2	6·0	5·7	6·5	6·8	7·3	6·4
Days with fog (a) -	0·8	1	1	1	3	1	2	1	0·7	0·2	0·1	0·8	13
TEMPERATURE (° F.)													
Average - -	43	43	45	48	53	58	61	61	58	53	47	45	51
Daily maximum -	48	47	50	54	59	64	67	67	64	58	51	49	57
Daily minimum -	39	39	39	42	48	52	55	55	52	48	42	40	46
Monthly maximum	55	54	58	64	71	77	77	77	75	72	66	59	79
Monthly minimum	27	29	29	33	38	44	47	47	42	36	30	29	25
Extreme maximum	59	58	69	73	78	85	87	85	84	78	62	62	87
Extreme minimum	17	19	22	28	32	37	42	42	36	29	24	23	17
RAINFALL (inches)													
Average fall -	3·3	2·9	2·9	2·2	2·1	2·1	2·8	3·0	2·4	3·9	3·6	5·0	36·2
Number of days -	19	15	16	14	13	12	14	15	14	18	18	22	190
Most in a day -	1·5	1·4	1·5	1·1	1·6	2·2	1·8	1·9	1·5	2·2	2·2	1·7	2·2
SUNSHINE													
Hours per day -	1·9	2·9	4·4	5·9	6·5	7·4	6·8	6·1	5·3	3·7	2·5	1·7	4·6
Per cent. of possible	22	29	37	43	42	46	43	43	42	34	28	21	38

* 9 h. and 21 h.   (a) At Mount Batten.

Station—FALMOUTH (Cornwall). Lat. 50° 9′ N. ; Long. 5° 5′ W. ; 167 feet above Mean Sea Level.

Element	Jan.	Feb.	Mar.	Apr.	May	June	July	Aug.	Sep.	Oct.	Nov.	Dec.	Year
Cloudiness * - -	6·7	6·6	6·7	5·2	5·2	5·5	5·5	5·3	5·5	6·1	6·4	6·8	6·0
Rel. Humidity (%) †	81	77	75	72	72	73	72	73	76	75	79	81	76
Days with fog -	0·6	0·8	1	1	2	1	2	3	2	1	0·7	0·5	16
Days with thunder	0·3	0·4	0·3	0·2	0·4	0·5	0·8	0·6	0·4	0·7	0·2	0·3	5
Days with snow -	1	1	2	0·2	0·1	0·0	0·0	0·0	0·0	0·1	0·3	0·6	5
TEMPERATURE (° F.)													
Average - -	44	44	45	48	53	57	61	61	58	53	47	45	51
Daily maximum -	48	48	50	53	59	63	67	67	63	58	52	49	56
Daily minimum -	40	39	40	43	48	52	55	55	53	48	43	41	46
Monthly maximum	53	53	55	60	66	70	73	71	68	62	57	54	75
Monthly minimum	30	31	32	36	40	46	50	50	45	39	35	32	29
Extreme maximum	57	58	63	70	75	82	85	83	78	72	62	58	85
Extreme minimum	20	22	23	29	30	40	44	44	36	32	23	24	20
RAINFALL (inches)													
Average fall -	4·2	3·7	3·5	2·6	2·2	2·3	2·8	3·3	2·9	5·0	4·8	6·3	43·6
Number of days -	20	17	18	15	14	13	15	16	15	21	20	23	207
Most in a day -	1·7	2·1	1·8	1·5	1·1	1·7	2·8	2·8	1·9	3·3	2·4	2·3	3·3
SUNSHINE													
Hours per day -	1·9	2·8	4·4	6·2	6·7	7·6	7·0	6·3	5·3	3·7	2·5	1·8	4·7
Per cent. of possible	23	28	37	46	44	47	44	44	42	34	28	22	38

* 9 h. and 21 h.   † 13 h.

Station—YORK (Yorks.). Lat. 53° 57′ N. ; Long. 1° 5′ W. ; 57 feet above Mean Sea Level.

Element	Jan.	Feb.	Mar.	Apr.	May	June	July	Aug.	Sep.	Oct.	Nov.	Dec.	Year
Cloudiness * - -	6·9	6·8	6·2	6·1	6·3	6·0	6·6	6·6	5·5	6·1	6·2	6·7	6·3
Rel. Humidity (%) †	87	86	80	74	72	70	73	77	80	83	86	87	80
Days with thunder	0·1	0·1	0·1	1	2	1	3	3	0·7	0·4	0·2	0·3	12
Days with snow -	3	3	3	0·8	0·1	0·0	0·0	0·0	0·0	0·1	1	3	14
TEMPERATURE (° F.)													
Average - -	39	40	42	46	53	57	61	60	56	50	43	40	49
Daily maximum -	44	45	48	53	61	66	69	68	64	56	48	44	55
Daily minimum -	35	35	36	39	44	49	53	52	48	43	38	35	42
Extreme maximum	60	61	73	78	82	88	89	90	92	78	66	60	92
Extreme minimum	3	3	8	11	24	34	37	37	30	23	14	−5	−5
RAINFALL (inches)													
Average fall -	1·8	1·5	1·7	1·6	2·0	2·1	2·5	2·5	1·6	2·7	2·1	2·2	24·3
Number of days -	17	15	16	14	14	13	14	16	13	18	18	18	186
Most in a day -	1·1	1·6	1·1	1·0	2·8	1·7	2·3	1·2	1·9	1·8	1·6	1·5	2·8
SUNSHINE													
Hours per day -	1·1	1·9	3·1	4·3	5·1	5·8	5·3	4·9	4·3	2·9	1·6	0·9	3·4
Per cent. of possible	14	19	26	31	32	34	32	33	33	27	19	12	28

* 9 h. and 21 h.   † 9 h.

Station—CAMBRIDGE (Cambs.). Lat. 52° 12′ N. ; Long. 0° 8′ E. ; 41 feet above Mean Sea Level.

Element	Jan.	Feb.	Mar.	Apr.	May	June	July	Aug.	Sep.	Oct.	Nov.	Dec.	Year
Cloudiness * - -	6·6	6·6	6·0	5·9	5·9	5·9	6·3	6·0	5·3	5·7	6·2	6·4	6·1
Days with thunder	0·1	0·1	0·4	0·9	2	3	3	3	1	0·5	0·1	0·1	14
TEMPERATURE (° F.)													
Average - -	39	40	42	46	53	58	62	61	57	50	43	40	49
Daily maximum -	45	46	50	55	63	68	71	71	66	58	49	45	57
Daily minimum -	34	33	34	38	44	48	52	52	48	42	37	35	41
Monthly maximum	54	56	63	69	75	81	84	83	78	68	59	55	87
Monthly minimum	20	21	23	26	30	38	43	42	36	29	24	21	15
Extreme maximum	59	67	70	84	88	88	95	96	93	80	65	60	96
Extreme minimum	4	6	12	21	25	32	36	38	28	23	8	0	0
RAINFALL (inches)													
Average fall -	1·5	1·3	1·5	1·3	1·8	2·1	2·2	2·3	1·6	2·4	1·9	1·9	21·8
Number of days -	15	13	14	13	13	12	13	14	11	15	14	16	163
Most in a day -	1·4	1·4	1·3	1·7	1·7	2·4	2·2	1·5	1·8	1·9	1·3	1·5	2·4
SUNSHINE													
Hours per day -	1·7	2·5	3·9	4·9	6·4	6·8	6·2	6·0	4·9	3·5	2·0	1·3	4·2
Per cent. of possible	21	25	33	36	41	41	38	41	39	33	23	17	34

* 9 h. and 21 h.

Station—BUXTON (Derby). Lat. 53° 16′ N. ; Long. 1° 55′ W. ; 1,007 feet above Mean Sea Level.

Element	Jan.	Feb.	Mar.	Apr.	May	June	July	Aug.	Sep.	Oct.	Nov.	Dec.	Year
Days with thunder	0·2	0·3	0·2	0·9	2	2	2	2	0·8	0·3	0·2	0·2	10
Days with snow -	8	8	8	3	1	0·0	0·0	0·0	0·0	0·9	3	6	38
TEMPERATURE (° F.)													
Average - -	36	37	39	43	49	54	57	57	53	47	41	37	46
Daily maximum -	41	41	44	49	57	61	64	64	59	52	45	41	52
Daily minimum -	32	32	33	36	41	46	50	50	46	41	36	33	40
Monthly maximum	49	54	56	63	71	76	77	75	70	62	54	50	80
Monthly minimum	15	17	20	25	30	35	40	39	33	25	23	17	9
Extreme maximum	56	58	66	73	79	83	89	88	86	77	61	58	89
Extreme minimum	0	−11	1	8	19	30	31	33	29	18	12	−4	−11
RAINFALL (inches)													
Average fall -	4·5	3·8	4·1	2·9	3·1	3·2	3·9	4·4	3·2	4·9	4·7	5·7	48·4
Number of days -	19	18	19	16	16	14	16	19	15	19	19	21	211
Most in a day -	2·2	2·0	1·7	1·9	1·5	2·8	2·1	1·8	1·7	2·4	2·2	1·8	2·8
SUNSHINE													
Hours per day -	1·0	1·7	2·9	4·2	5·5	5·9	5·3	4·7	4·1	2·6	1·4	0·7	3·3
Per cent. of possible	12	17	24	30	34	35	32	32	32	25	17	9	27

Station—BIRMINGHAM (Edgbaston) (Warwick).

Lat. 52° 29' N. ; Long. 1° 56' W. ; 535 feet above Mean Sea Level.

Element	Jan.	Feb.	Mar.	Apr.	May	June	July	Aug.	Sep.	Oct.	Nov.	Dec.	Year
Cloudiness * - -	7·2	7·0	6·6	6·4	6·5	6·5	6·9	6·4	6·0	6·6	7·0	7·3	6·7
Days with fog -	7	7	7	3	2	1	3	1	5	5	8	10	59
Days with thunder	0·1	0·1	0·4	0·5	1	2	2	2	0·7	0·5	0·0	0·0	10
Days with snow -	4	2	4	2	0·2	0·0	0·0	0·0	0·0	0·2	1	4	17
TEMPERATURE (° F.)													
Average - -	40	39	42	46	51	57	62	60	56	49	43	39	49
Daily maximum D	43	43	49	52	59	65	69	68	63	55	47	43	55
Daily minimum N	36	35	36	39	44	49	54	53	50	44	39	36	43
Monthly maximum	54	53	60	65	74	77	81	75	74	66	57	53	84
Monthly minimum	26	25	27	31	37	42	47	46	41	33	29	27	21
Extreme maximum	58	62	70	79	82	85	92	94	91	79	62	58	94
Extreme minimum	11	8	19	26	31	37	39	41	33	28	20	14	8
RAINFALL (inches)													
Average fall -	2·0	1·7	1·9	1·7	2·2	2·3	2·3	2·7	1·8	2·8	2·4	2·7	26·5
Number of days -	14	13	14	13	14	12	14	16	12	17	15	16	170
Most in a day -	1·2	0·9	1·0	0·9	1·5	1·4	1·9	2·2	1·5	1·7	1·2	2·0	2·2
SUNSHINE													
Hours per day -	1·4	2·0	3·1	4·2	5·5	6·0	5·5	5·2	4·1	2·9	1·5	1·1	3·6
Per cent. of possible	17	21	26	30	35	36	34	36	32	28	18	15	29

* 9 h. and 21 h. to 1923 ; subsequently 7 h. and 18 h.

Station—OXFORD (Radcliffe Observatory).

Lat. 51° 46' N. ; Long. 1° 16' W. ; 208 feet above Mean Sea Level.

Element	Jan.	Feb.	Mar.	Apr.	May	June	July	Aug.	Sep.	Oct.	Nov.	Dec.	Year
Cloudiness * - -	7·2	7·0	6·7	6·4	6·2	6·4	6·4	6·4	6·0	6·5	6·9	7·2	6·6
Days with thunder	0·1	0·1	0·3	0·8	2	2	2	2	0·9	0·4	0·0	0·1	11
Days with snow -	4	4	4	0·9	0·1	0·0	0·0	0·0	0·0	0·1	1	3	17
TEMPERATURE (° F.)													
Average - -	40	40	43	47	54	58	62	61	57	51	43	41	50
Daily maximum -	45	46	50	55	63	67	71	70	65	57	49	45	57
Daily minimum -	35	35	36	39	45	49	53	53	49	44	38	36	43
Monthly maximum	54	55	61	67	75	79	82	80	76	66	58	55	84
Monthly minimum	22	23	25	29	33	40	45	44	37	30	25	23	17
Extreme maximum	58	64	72	81	86	89	93	95	92	81	63	58	95
Extreme minimum	6	7	15	23	29	34	41	38	31	23	16	8	6
RAINFALL (inches)													
Average fall -	1·8	1·6	1·6	1·6	1·9	2·2	2·4	2·3	1·7	2·9	2·3	2·5	24·8
Number of days -	15	14	14	13	13	12	14	14	11	16	15	17	168
Most in a day -	1·4	1·4	1·3	1·7	1·4	2·4	2·2	2·8	1·7	1·9	1·3	1·5	2·8
SUNSHINE													
Hours per day -	1·8	2·5	3·7	4·9	5·9	6·7	6·1	5·7	4·8	3·3	2·2	1·5	4·1
Per cent. of possible	22	26	32	36	38	40	38	39	38	31	25	19	34

* 9 h., 12 h. and 21 h.

Station—KEW OBSERVATORY (Surrey).

Lat. 51° 28′ N. ;   Long. 0° 19′ W. ;   18 feet above Mean Sea Level.

Element	Jan.	Feb.	Mar.	Apr.	May	June	July	Aug.	Sep.	Oct.	Nov.	Dec.	Year
Cloudiness * - -	7·5	7·2	6·8	6·5	6·1	6·4	6·6	6·6	5·8	6·5	7·0	7·3	6·7
Rel. Humidity (%) †	80	75	69	62	61	60	60	61	65	73	79	82	69
Days with fog -	7	7	6	3	0·9	0·4	0·2	1	5	8	8	7	54
Days with thunder	0·1	0·1	0·7	1	2	2	3	3	1	0·6	0·1	0·1	14
Days with snow -	3	3	3	1	0·1	0·0	0·0	0·0	0·0	0·0	0·6	2	13
TEMPERATURE (° F.)													
Average - -	41	41	43	47	55	59	63	62	57	51	44	41	50
Daily maximum -	45	46	49	55	63	68	71	70	65	57	49	46	57
Daily minimum -	36	36	37	40	46	51	55	54	50	45	39	37	44
Monthly maximum	53	54	60	67	75	80	82	81	75	65	58	54	85
Monthly minimum	22	24	26	31	35	42	47	45	38	32	28	25	19
Extreme maximum	57	62	68	80	87	88	90	94	92	83	63	59	94
Extreme minimum	9	11	17	26	30	37	43	41	31	25	20	11	9
RAINFALL (inches)													
Average fall -	1·8	1·5	1·7	1·5	1·7	2·1	2·2	2·2	1·9	2·7	2·2	2·3	23·8
Number of days -	16	13	14	13	12	12	12	13	12	17	16	17	167
Most in a day -	1·6	1·1	0·9	1·2	1·8	2·4	2·3	1·8	1·6	1·4	1·3	1·5	2·4
SUNSHINE													
Hours per day -	1·4	2·2	3·5	4·9	6·4	6·8	6·3	5·9	4·9	3·1	1·8	1·2	4·0
Per cent. of possible	17	22	30	35	41	41	39	41	39	29	20	15	33

* 9 h., 15 h. and 21 h.   † 13 h.

Station—STONYHURST COLLEGE (Lancs.).

Lat. 53° 51′ N. ;   Long. 2° 28′ W. ;   377 feet above Mean Sea Level.

Element	Jan.	Feb.	Mar.	Apr.	May	June	July	Aug.	Sep.	Oct.	Nov.	Dec.	Year
Cloudiness * - -	7·9	7·5	7·1	7·0	6·9	6·8	7·3	7·7	6·8	6·7	7·2	7·9	7·2
Days with thunder	0·3	0·2	0·6	1	3	3	3	3	2	1	0·6	0·3	18
Days with snow -	6	5	6	2	0·6	0·0	0·0	0·0	0·0	0·6	1	4	26
TEMPERATURE (° F.)													
Average - -	39	39	41	45	51	56	59	58	54	49	42	40	48
Daily maximum -	43	43	46	51	58	63	66	64	60	54	47	44	53
Daily minimum -	35	34	35	38	44	49	53	52	48	43	37	36	42
Monthly maximum	50	51	56	61	70	76	77	74	69	61	55	52	79
Monthly minimum	23	23	25	29	34	40	44	43	37	31	27	23	17
Extreme maximum	60	58	68	72	80	87	88	84	84	74	62	59	88
Extreme minimum	5	9	11	14	24	35	40	38	32	20	18	9	5
RAINFALL (inches)													
Average fall -	4·3	3·3	3·7	2·7	2·9	3·1	3·9	5·1	3·8	4·5	4·5	4·8	46·6
Number of days -	20	17	18	15	15	14	17	19	15	18	18	20	206
Most in a day -	1·6	2·0	1·5	1·3	1·6	1·7	2·5	2·3	2·1	2·5	2·3	1·8	2·5
SUNSHINE													
Hours per day -	1·1	1·9	3·3	4·7	5·6	6·0	5·3	4·7	4·2	2·7	1·6	0·9	3·5
Per cent. of possible	14	20	27	34	35	35	32	32	33	26	19	13	29

* 9 h. and 21 h.

Station—SCILLY (St. Mary's).   Lat. 49° 56′ N. ;   Long. 6° 18′ W. ;   163 feet above Mean Sea Level.

Element	Jan.	Feb.	Mar.	Apr.	May	June	July	Aug.	Sep.	Oct.	Nov.	Dec.	Year
Cloudiness * - -	7·6	7·5	7·2	6·3	6·3	6·6	6·6	6·3	6·5	6·9	7·3	7·4	6·9
Days with fog -	2	1	1	2	3	2	4	4	3	3	1	1	27
Days with thunder	0·5	0·5	0·5	0·1	0·4	0·5	0·8	0·8	0·3	0·6	0·3	0·4	6
Days with snow -	0·8	0·8	0·9	0·2	0·0	0·0	0·0	0·0	0·0	0·0	0·2	0·2	3
TEMPERATURE (° F.)													
Average - -	47	45	47	48	52	57	61	61	59	54	49	47	52
Daily maximum D	49	49	50	52	57	62	65	65	63	57	52	50	56
Daily minimum N	44	43	43	44	48	52	56	56	54	51	46	45	48
Monthly maximum	54	54	55	58	62	67	70	70	67	63	58	55	71
Monthly minimum	34	35	35	39	43	48	52	53	49	43	39	37	31
Extreme maximum	57	57	60	66	74	78	82	76	74	69	61	58	82
Extreme minimum	25	27	30	30	38	41	47	48	40	36	29	30	25
RAINFALL (inches)													
Average fall -	3·0	2·6	2·4	1·9	1·7	1·7	2·2	2·6	2·4	3·7	3·3	4·4	31·9
Number of days -	21	17	18	15	13	13	15	16	15	21	20	23	207
Most in a day -	2·8	1·5	1·6	2·0	1·3	1·3	1·4	2·0	1·8	2·3	3·1	1·3	3·1
SUNSHINE													
Hours per day -	2·0	2·9	4·5	6·3	6·6	7·4	6·8	6·3	5·3	3·8	2·5	1·7	4·7
Per cent. of possible	23	29	38	46	43	46	43	44	42	35	28	21	38

* 7 h., 13 h. and 18 h.

Station—JERSEY (Channel Isles).   Lat. 49° 11′ N. ;   Long. 2° 6′ W. ;   28 feet above Mean Sea Level.

Element	Jan.	Feb.	Mar.	Apr.	May	June	July	Aug.	Sep.	Oct.	Nov.	Dec.	Year
Cloudiness * - -	7·1	6·6	6·2	5·4	5·4	5·7	5·5	5·4	5·2	6·5	6·9	7·4	6·1
Days with fog (a) -	2	2	2	2	2	2	3	2	3	0·6	0·4	1	22
Days with thunder	1	0·5	0·2	0·8	1	1	1	1	1	0·7	0·5	0·9	11
TEMPERATURE (° F.)													
Average - -	43	43	45	49	55	59	62	63	61	55	49	45	53
Daily maximum -	47	47	51	54	61	65	68	69	67	60	53	49	58
Daily minimum -	40	39	40	44	49	53	57	58	55	50	44	42	47
Monthly maximum	53	54	59	65	72	77	79	79	76	67	60	56	83
Monthly minimum	27	30	31	35	40	46	49	50	45	39	34	31	25
Extreme maximum	58	62	67	84	81	87	90	96	89	78	66	61	96
Extreme minimum	12	18	21	28	33	39	44	45	40	30	16	19	12
RAINFALL (inches)													
Average fall -	2·9	2·4	2·5	1·9	1·8	2·1	2·1	2·5	2·4	4·6	4·1	4·2	33·5
Number of days -	20	17	18	15	13	12	13	14	14	20	21	22	199
Most in a day -	1·3	1·2	1·3	1·8	1·5	1·9	1·7	3·2	2·0	2·4	1·5	1·8	3·2
SUNSHINE													
Hours per day -	2·2	3·3	4·8	6·4	7·1	8·0	7·7	7·3	6·0	4·1	2·6	1·7	5·1
Per cent. of possible	25	33	41	47	47	50	49	51	48	38	28	20	42

* 7 h., 13 h. and 18 h.   (a) At Guernsey.

IRELAND

Station—MALIN HEAD (Donegal).   Lat. 55° 23′ N. ;   Long. 7° 24′ W. ;   84 feet above Mean Sea Level.

Element	Jan.	Feb.	Mar.	Apr.	May	June	July	Aug.	Sep.	Oct.	Nov.	Dec.	Year
Cloudiness * - -	7·4	7·3	6·8	6·4	6·4	6·7	6·9	6·9	7·9	7·0	7·2	7·2	6·9
Days with fog -	0·3	0·4	0·9	0·3	0·6	1	0·6	0·2	0·2	0·6	0·3	0·4	6
Days with thunder	0·3	0·2	0·2	0·2	0·5	1·2	0·7	0·9	0·2	0·1	0·4	0·1	5
Days with snow -	2	2	3	0·6	0·1	0·0	0·0	0·0	0·0	0·1	0·7	2	11
TEMPERATURE (° F.)													
Average - -	43	42	43	45	49	53	57	57	54	50	45	43	49
Daily maximum -	46	45	47	49	53	57	61	61	58	54	48	46	52
Daily minimum -	40	39	39	41	45	49	53	53	51	47	42	41	45
Monthly maximum	51	51	54	59	63	69	69	69	68	61	55	53	74
Monthly minimum	30	30	31	34	38	44	48	48	43	37	34	32	27
Extreme maximum	55	59	63	69	73	78	80	80	84	73	71	56	84
Extreme minimum	21	20	23	25	31	39	42	42	36	32	30	27	20
RAINFALL (inches)													
Average fall -	2·6	2·4	2·3	2·0	2·0	2·1	2·8	3·5	2·6	3·0	3·3	3·4	32·0
Number of days -	22	19	21	19	17	16	19	21	17	20	21	24	236
Most in a day -	2·1	1·3	1·1	0·9	0·8	1·7	2·8	1·8	1·4	1·5	1·6	1·0	2·8
SUNSHINE													
Hours per day -	1·1	2·3	3·8	5·5	6·3	5·7	4·9	4·3	4·0	2·5	1·8	1·0	3·6
Per cent. of possible	15	24	32	39	39	33	29	29	32	24	21	15	30

* 7 h., 13 h. and 21 h.

Station—DUBLIN (Phoenix Park).   Lat. 53° 22′ N. ;   Long. 6° 21′ W. ;   155 feet above Mean Sea Level.

Element	Jan.	Feb.	Mar.	Apr.	May	June	July	Aug.	Sep.	Oct.	Nov.	Dec.	Year
Cloudiness * - -	6·4	6·4	5·9	5·8	6·0	6·2	6·8	6·3	5·8	6·0	6·2	6·3	6·2
Days with thunder	0·1	0·2	0·2	0·4	0·9	2	2	2	0·5	0·4	0·2	0·1	8
Days with snow -	4	4	5	1	0·3	0·0	0·0	0·0	0·0	0·2	1	2	18
TEMPERATURE (° F.)													
Average - -	41	41	42	45	51	55	59	58	54	49	43	41	48
Daily maximum -	47	47	49	53	59	64	67	66	62	57	50	47	56
Daily minimum -	35	35	35	37	42	47	51	50	46	42	37	36	41
Monthly maximum	54	55	58	63	67	73	75	74	71	64	59	56	78
Monthly minimum	21	23	24	27	31	37	41	40	35	28	25	21	16
Extreme maximum	62	65	72	69	80	82	86	85	82	73	67	60	85
Extreme minimum	4	8	16	19	26	31	35	33	29	22	15	7	4
RAINFALL (inches)													
Average fall -	2·3	1·8	1·9	1·8	2·1	2·0	2·7	3·2	1·9	2·6	2·8	2·5	27·6
Number of days -	21	18	19	17	16	15	18	19	16	19	19	21	218
Most in a day -	1·3	1·4	1·2	1·3	1·7	1·2	2·2	3·3	1·7	3·0	2·4	1·7	3·3
SUNSHINE													
Hours per day -	1·8	2·7	3·7	5·3	5·8	6·1	5·5	4·9	4·3	3·1	2·3	1·5	3·9
Per cent. of possible	23	27	31	38	37	36	33	34	34	30	27	20	32

* 9 h. and 21 h.

Station—ROCHE'S POINT (Cork).   Lat. 51° 47′ N. ;   Long. 8° 15′ W. ;   22 feet above Mean Sea Level.

Element	Jan.	Feb.	Mar.	Apr.	May	June	July	Aug.	Sep.	Oct.	Nov.	Dec.	Year
Cloudiness * - -	7·5	7·5	7·2	6·7	7·0	6·9	7·1	7·4	7·2	7·3	6·8	6·7	7·1
Days with fog -	1	1	0·9	1	2	0·6	2	2	2	2	0·6	0·1	16
Days with thunder	0·2	0·2	0·1	0·5	0·7	0·6	0·7	1	0·2	0·3	0·2	0·1	5
Days with snow -	0·8	0·8	0·9	0·2	0·0	0·0	0·0	0·0	0·0	0·0	0·2	0·2	3
TEMPERATURE (° F.)													
Average - -	45	44	45	47	52	57	60	59	57	52	47	45	51
Daily maximum D	48	48	49	52	57	62	65	64	62	57	51	48	55
Daily minimum N	41	41	41	42	47	51	55	54	52	48	43	42	47
Monthly maximum	53	54	56	59	66	70	71	70	68	62	57	54	73
Monthly minimum	29	30	32	35	39	45	48	47	44	37	33	31	27
Extreme maximum	57	56	61	72	73	80	84	80	74	69	65	58	84
Extreme minimum	20	25	27	27	35	39	43	41	39	32	27	25	20
RAINFALL (inches)													
Average fall -	4·1	3·7	3·0	2·7	2·4	2·7	2·9	3·8	3·0	4·1	4·2	5·3	41·9
Number of days -	21	18	18	16	15	14	15	18	16	19	19	23	212
Most in a day -	1·8	1·6	1·7	2·6	1·3	1·9	2·5	2·8	3·0	2·1	1·8	1·9	3·0
SUNSHINE (a)													
Hours per day -	1·6	2·4	3·8	5·4	5·8	6·3	5·9	5·1	4·5	3·1	2·1	1·4	4·0
Per cent. of possible	19	25	32	39	37	38	36	35	36	29	24	18	32

* 7 h., 13 h. and 18 h.   (a) At Ballinacurra.

Station—VALENTIA OBSERVATORY (Kerry).

Lat. 51° 56′ N. ;   Long. 10° 15′ W. ;   30 feet above Mean Sea Level.

Element	Jan.	Feb.	Mar.	Apr.	May	June	July	Aug.	Sep.	Oct.	Nov.	Dec.	Year
Cloudiness * - -	7·8	7·7	7·0	6·8	7·2	7·4	7·5	7·5	7·2	7·3	7·2	7·8	7·4
Rel. Humidity (%) †	84	82	78	76	74	75	78	79	78	79	82	85	79
Days with fog -	0·0	0·0	0·4	0·4	0·2	0·6	0·4	0·3	0·2	0·2	0·3	0·1	3
Days with thunder	0·8	0·6	0·5	0·4	0·5	0·7	0·5	0·6	0·3	0·5	0·5	0·6	7
Days with snow -	1	1	1	0·3	0·1	0·0	0·0	0·0	0·0	0·1	0·1	0·7	5
TEMPERATURE (° F.)													
Average - -	45	44	45	47	52	56	59	59	56	52	47	45	51
Daily maximum -	48	48	49	52	57	61	64	63	61	56	51	49	55
Daily minimum -	41	40	41	42	47	51	54	55	52	48	43	42	46
Monthly maximum	53	54	56	61	68	72	71	71	69	62	57	55	76
Monthly minimum	29	30	31	34	38	43	46	46	42	35	32	30	26
Extreme maximum	57	58	66	70	75	81	81	81	79	71	63	57	81
Extreme minimum	20	22	25	29	34	37	40	41	35	28	27	24	20
RAINFALL (inches)													
Average fall -	5·5	5·2	4·5	3·7	3·2	3·2	3·8	4·8	4·1	5·6	5·5	6·6	55·7
Number of days -	24	21	21	19	18	17	21	22	18	22	23	26	252
Most in a day -	2·8	2·4	1·7	1·6	1·5	1·7	1·9	2·3	2·5	3·1	2·7	1·9	3·1
SUNSHINE													
Hours per day -	1·4	2·3	3·7	5·4	5·9	5·8	5·1	4·8	4·2	2·9	2·1	1·3	3·7
Per cent. of possible	17	24	32	39	38	35	32	33	34	27	24	16	31

* 9 h., 15 h. and 21 h.   † 13 h.

Station—ARMAGH (Armagh).   Lat. 54° 21′ N. ;   Long. 6° 39′ W. ;   204 feet above Mean Sea Level.

Element	Jan.	Feb.	Mar.	Apr.	May	June	July	Aug.	Sep.	Oct.	Nov.	Dec.	Year
Cloudiness * - -	7·3	6·9	6·5	5·9	6·5	6·7	7·3	7·0	6·3	6·5	6·7	6·9	6·7
Days with thunder	0·0	0·1	0·0	0·3	0·7	1·1	1·5	1·1	0·2	0·0	0·0	0·1	5
Days with snow -	3	2	2	0·3	0·1	0·0	0·0	0·0	0·0	0·1	0·6	2	9
TEMPERATURE (° F.)													
Average - -	41	41	42	45	51	56	59	58	54	49	43	41	48
Daily maximum -	45	46	49	53	59	64	66	65	61	55	48	45	55
Daily minimum -	36	35	38	38	43	48	51	51	47	43	37	36	42
Monthly maximum	51	53	58	65	69	78	75	73	69	63	57	54	78
Monthly minimum	22	25	26	29	33	39	43	42	36	30	26	23	17
Extreme maximum	57	59	67	70	78	83	87	82	82	73	62	58	87
Extreme minimum	6	5	19	19	29	34	32	36	31	22	17	7	5
RAINFALL (inches)													
Average fall -	2·5	2·2	2·4	2·1	2·4	2·5	2·9	3·6	2·5	2·7	2·8	3·1	31·7
Number of days -	19	17	19	17	16	16	18	19	16	18	19	21	215
Most in a day -	1·1	1·2	1·1	1·3	1·6	2·2	2·1	2·6	1·7	2·2	1·7	1·3	2·6
SUNSHINE													
Hours per day -	1·5	2·3	3·5	5·0	5·3	5·6	4·7	4·3	3·9	2·8	2·1	1·3	3·5
Per cent. of possible	19	24	30	36	34	33	28	29	31	27	25	17	29

* 9 h. and 21 h.

Station—MARKREE CASTLE (Sligo).

Lat. 54° 11′ N. ;   Long. 8° 27′ W. ;   122 feet above Mean Sea Level.

Element	Jan.	Feb.	Mar.	Apr.	May	June	July	Aug.	Sep.	Oct.	Nov.	Dec.	Year
Cloudiness * - -	7·6	7·4	7·0	6·5	7·0	7·3	7·6	7·6	7·2	7·2	7·4	7·6	7·3
Days with thunder	0·7	0·7	0·2	0·4	0·9	1	1	1	0·2	0·1	0·1	0·2	7
TEMPERATURE (° F.)													
Average - -	41	41	42	45	51	55	58	57	54	49	43	41	48
Daily maximum -	47	47	50	53	59	63	65	65	62	56	50	47	55
Daily minimum -	35	35	35	37	43	47	50	50	46	42	36	36	41
Monthly maximum	53	54	58	63	70	75	74	73	70	63	56	54	78
Monthly minimum	20	22	23	27	31	36	39	38	34	26	23	21	15
Extreme maximum	57	59	68	71	78	83	85	82	80	73	62	59	85
Extreme minimum	−2	2	14	18	25	30	33	32	28	17	12	5	−2
RAINFALL (inches)													
Average fall -	3·9	3·5	3·5	2·7	2·8	3·0	3·5	4·3	3·3	4·1	4·2	4·7	43·5
Number of days -	22	19	21	18	18	17	21	22	19	20	22	25	244
Most in a day -	1·5	1·3	1·5	1·4	0·9	1·8	1·9	2·3	2·0	2·1	1·4	1·2	2·3
SUNSHINE													
Hours per day -	1·3	2·2	3·4	4·9	5·5	5·3	4·6	4·0	3·7	2·6	1·9	1·1	3·4
Per cent. of possible	17	23	29	35	35	31	28	27	29	25	22	15	28

* 9 h. and 21 h.

Station—BIRR CASTLE (Offaly). Lat. 53° 6′ N. ; Long. 7° 56′ W. ; 173 feet above Mean Sea Level.

Element	Jan.	Feb.	Mar.	Apr.	May	June	July	Aug.	Sep.	Oct.	Nov.	Dec.	Year
Cloudiness * - -	7·9	7·9	7·5	7·4	7·4	7·4	7·7	7·8	7·6	7·8	7·8	7·8	7·7
Days with fog -	2	1	3	0·4	0·8	0·5	1	0·9	2	2	3	2	19
Days with thunder	0·3	0·1	0·3	0·5	0·5	1	0·6	1	0·2	0·3	0·3	0·0	5
Days with snow -	3	3	3	0·9	0·1	0·0	0·0	0·0	0·0	0·2	0·6	2	13
TEMPERATURE (° F.)													
Average - -	42	41	43	46	51	56	60	58	55	50	43	42	49
Daily maximum D	46	47	50	53	59	65	67	65	62	56	49	46	55
Daily minimum N	37	36	37	38	43	48	53	51	48	44	38	38	43
RAINFALL (inches)													
Average fall -	2·8	2·3	2·4	2·2	2·2	2·3	3·0	3·8	2·3	2·9	3·1	3·3	32·6
Number of days -	20	17	18	16	16	15	17	19	15	18	19	21	211
SUNSHINE													
Hours per day -	1·6	2·3	3·6	5·1	5·5	5·3	4·8	4·4	4·0	2·9	2·0	1·4	3·6
Per cent. of possible	20	24	30	36	35	32	30	30	31	28	23	18	29

* 7 h., 13 h. and 18 h.

INDEX

(Numbers refer to pages.)

Abbotsinch (see Renfrew)
Aberdeen Observatory, 36, 46, 47, 55, 56, 57, 59, 64, 72, 88, 89, 105, 106, 107, 112, 113, 117, 146, 148, 150, 153, 158, 162-5, 172, 174, 185, 192, 193, 197 ff, 212 ff, 219, 220, 221, 224, 239, 247, 253, 274, 277, 316
Aberdeenshire, 175, 300
Abergavenny, (The Chain) 114
Abergwesyn (Nantneuadd), 108
Abnormally wet or dry periods, 95 ff, 99 ff
— cold or warm periods, 159 ff, 174 ff
Absolute extremes of temperature, 173 ff
Absolute humidity, 206, 220, 228 ff
— — extremes, 228 ff
Absorption of radiation 19, 149
Admiralty Pilots, 47, 51, 52, 314
Advection, 150
Afternoon sunshine, 201 ff
Air conditioning, 2, 206, 230
Aldergrove, 58, 60, 65, 264 ff
Allt-a-Mhuillin, 242
Altitude, effect on fog-frequency 273, 280, 281 ; humidity, 221, 226 ; rainfall, 77, 103 ; snow-frequency, 240, 241 ; sunshine, 183 ; temperature, 142, 144, 158, 169, 308
Altitude of the sun 15, 162, 177 ff, 200, 201, 306
Alton, 245, 246
Anemometers, 3, 52 ff
Anglesey, 16, 32, 158, 262
Annual evaporation, 121 ff
— rainfall, 75 ff, 122
— — fluctuations of, 80 ff
Annual range of mean temperature, 147, 151, 296
Annual (or seasonal) variations (see under respective subjects in Contents, p. vii).
Anticyclone, 20-2, 25, 27, 29, 31, 36, 37, 40, 41, 101, 243, 248, 280
Anticyclonic weather, 40, 41, 101, 149
Antrim, 16, 18

Apparent time, local, 181, 202
April, droughts, 95
— exceptional rain, 108
— exceptional sunshine, 195
— exceptional temperature, 161, 170
Aqueous vapour, 119, 205 ff, 278, 282
— pressure of (see Vapour pressure)
Ardsley, 122, 128
Argyllshire, 77, 78, 105, 113
Armagh, 18, 110
Armagh Observatory, 65, 85, 107, 112, 117, 146, 148, 150, 174, 237, 239, 247, 253, 288 ff, 333
Ashburton, 95
Ashford, 245
Atlantic Ocean, 16, 20-5, 31, 100, 150, 273, 294
Atlas, Rainfall, of the British Isles, 80, 89, 90, 91
Atmosphere, general circulation of, 15, 102
Atmospheric obscurity, 257 ff
— pollution, 183, 194, 204, 262, 264, 265, 281 ff, 307
August, cyclone, 1917, 34
— exceptional rain, 100, 101, 108, 110, 114, 254
— exceptional sunshine, 195
— exceptional temperature 161, 170, 174, 175, 228, 229
— thunderstorm, 1924, 101, 254
Autographic records, 3, 6, 8, 9, 140
Auxiliary climatalogical stations, 6
Averages and normals, 11ff
Averages of Bright Sunshine, v, 187, 204, 314
Averages of Temperature, v, 176, 314
Avon, River, 89
Azimuth, sun's, 180, 181
Azores anticyclone, 20 ff, 41, 100

Balk, J. G., vi.
Ballinacurra, 332
Balmakewan, 64

Balmoral, 169, 175, 236, 237, 239 ff, 273
Baltasound, 158, 192
Banbury, 250
Bantry Bay, 18
Baring Gould, S., 241
Barometric gradient, 22, 30 ff, 69, 100, 101, 280
— pressure, 1, 20 ff, 100, 101
(see also Pressure distribution)
Bartley, 128
Barton Airport, 61, 64
Basingstoke, 245
Battersea power station, 75
Baxendell, J., 70, 71
Beachy Head, 270 ff, 277, 279
Beaufort scale, 3-5, 30 ff, 42 ff
Beddington Corner, 114
Bell Rock Lighthouse, 53, 54, 58, 62-4, 73, 74
Belvoir Castle, 46, 47, 49, 236, 237, 253
Ben Alder, 78
Ben Nevis, 15, 17, 78, 103, 142, 173, 174, 183, 184, 192, 238 ff, 242
Benson (Oxford), 72
Bergen school of meteorologists, 32
Berkhamsted, 236, 237
Berkshire, 95
Berwickshire, 175
Bidston Observatory (see Liverpool)
Bigelstone, H. S., 83, 119
Biggin Hill, 246, 272, 274, 277
Bilham, E. G., 14, 74, 120, 197, 204, 256
Birmingham (Edgbaston) 57, 58, 59, 64, 237, 272, 274, 277, 328
Birr Castle, 107, 236, 237, 239, 270 ff, 277, 294, 334
Bjerknes, J. 32, 34
Blackadder, 175
Black-bulb thermometer, 3
Blackford Hill (see Edinburgh)
Blackpool, 291
Blacksod Point, 46, 47, 49
Blaenau Festiniog (Oakley Q.), 108
— (Llechwedd Q.), 108
Blizzard, 34
Blue colour of haze, 258
Bognor Regis, 172, 184
Bolton, 183, 192, 291
Bonacina L.C.W., 241, 256
Book of Normals, v, 76, 247, 250, 314
Borrowdale, 78, 110
Boscombe Down, 64
Boston (Black Sluice), 108

Botton Head, 18
Bournemouth, 189, 192
Bracing climate of the east coast, 294
Bradford, 183
Braemar, 17, 107, 169, 172, 175, 229, 239, 241, 273, 300
Braeriach, 243
Brecknockshire Beacons, 18
Breezes, land and sea, 68 ff, 165, 279, 280
Breton, H. H., 241, 245, 256
Bristol Channel, 65, 66, 68, 85, 110, 189, 249
British Association, 2, 139
British Isles, geography, 16-9
British Rainfall, 8, 75, 104, 106, 107, 108, 111, 114, 115, 117, 118, 119, 121, 122, 128, 246, 248, 254, 256
British Rainfall Organization, 76
British Summer Time, 6, 180, 283
Brooks, C.E.P., 155, 176, 186
Brundall (Blofield Rd.), 108
Bruton (Sexey's School), 100, 108
Buchan, Alexander, 154, 176
Buchan's periods, 152 ff
Buncrana, 94
Bunhill Row (London), 183, 189, 192, 304, 305
Burnley, 183, 192
Butt of Lewis, 57 ff
Buttermere (Hassness) 108
Buxton, 146, 173, 174, 175, 237, 239, 273, 327

Cader Idris, 18
Cahirciveen (see Valentia Observatory)
Cairngorm Hills, 17, 243, 256
Cairn Mor Dearg, 242
Caithness, 294
Calculated evaporation, 127, 128
Caledonian Canal, 17
Calm, 3-5, 35, 43 ff, 232, 280, 309, 310
Calshot, 61, 64, 117, 274, 277
Camden Square (London), 112, 113, 114, 116, 117, 122, 123, 124, 125, 127, 128, 132, 133, 159, 168, 300
Cambridge, 107, 146, 158, 168, 173, 174, 175, 198 ff, 236, 237, 327
Cambridgeshire, 79. 92
Campbell-Stokes sunshine recorder, 9, 177, 185, 194
Canalization of wind currents, 49
Cannington, 101, 108, 254
Cannock Sewage Works, 114

Canterbury (Harbledown), 114
Cantire, Mull of, 16
Cantref, 273
Cardiff, 189, 192, 323
Cardington, 61, 64, 114, 226
Carnedd Llewelyn, 243
Carnsore Point, 16
Carsphairn, Shiel, 114
Castleton, 110
Casual variations, 13, 140, 142
Catchment area, 85, 131, 138
Catterick, 61, 64
Celestial equator, 178
Central Plain of Ireland, 19
Chagford (Dartmoor Sanatorium), 114
Chalk formation, 130, 137
Channel Islands, 16, 87, 142, 158, 168, 181, 184, 189, 192, 273
Chatham (Woolman's Wood), 114
Chelmsford, 168
Cheshire, 276
Chess Valley, 297
Cheviots, 17
Chilgrove well, 126, 130
Chilterns, 18, 72, 77, 297
Christmas snowstorm, 1927, 238, 241, 243 ff
Churchstoke, 105, 107
Clackmannan, 110
Clacton-on-Sea, 42, 43, 79, 158, 237, 274, 277
Clare (Co.), 60
Classification of heavy rainfalls, 115, 116, 119, 254
— of weather types, 26 ff
Climate, 1, 15 ff
— coastal, 287 ff
— town, 41, 183, 186, 303 ff
— valley, 72, 169, 296 ff
Climatic tables, 313-34
Climatology, 1 ff
Cloudiness, 184 ff, 192, 196, 197, 202, 203, 204
Clouds, 10, 31, 38, 40, 177, 184 ff, 194, 201, 204, 232, 281
Clyde, River, 273, 276
Coastal climates, 287 ff
— fog, 279
— waters, temperature, 23, 24, 31, 148, 149, 279, 287
Cockle Park, 107, 236, 237
Code, visibility, 11, 257
Col, 280
Cold anticyclone, 37, 41

Cold front, 32, 34, 249, 254
Cold periods, Buchan's, 154 ff
Colmonell, 319
Compton, 128
Condensation, 8, 31, 119, 124, 137, 209, 278, 282
Configuration, in relation to rainfall, 77, 99
Continent, Eurasian, 16, 20, 27, 159, 161
Continentality, 159
Continents, meteorological characteristics of, 19, 20
Convection, 69 ff, 99, 119, 253, 294, 295
Cooling (Broomy Farm), 114
Cooling, dynamic, 31, 99, 119, 278, 279, 281
— radiative, 19, 20, 149, 159, 232, 278, 281, 302
Cork, 18, 65
Cornwall, 18, 92, 158, 245, 273
Correlation, 122, 133
Corsewall, 95
Cotswolds, 18, 301, 302
Country conditions, 282, 304 ff
Coventry, 284
Cowbridge, Ash Hall, 114
Craibstone, 128
Cranwell Aerodrome, 61, 64, 114, 117, 249, 264 ff, 274
Cray Reservoir, 112, 113
Crewe (Betley Hall), 114
Cross Fell, 17, 92
Croydon Aerodrome, 39, 54, 61, 64, 117, 118, 169, 183, 259 ff, 274, 277, 308 ff
Cullompton, 288 ff
Cumberland, 18, 31, 78
Cumulus clouds, 69
Currents, in N. Atlantic Ocean, 22 ff, 279
Cyclone, 27 ff, 99 ff (see also, Depression)
Cyclonic rain, 34, 99 ff
Cyclonic weather, 32 ff

Dagenham Sanatorium, 79
Daily averages of temperature, 153
Daily range of temperature, 7, 141, 165 ff, 280, 291, 300, 303
Daily Weather Report, 25
Dalwhinnie, 273
Damp heat, 228, 229, 252
Dansey, R. P. 242, 256
Dartmoor, 18, 92, 241, 245, 273
Data, climatological, 2 ff
Day darkness, 41, 282
Daylight, duration of, 162, 177 ff
Day maximum temperature, 6, 7, 166, 307

Days with fog, 270 ff
— gale, 65 ff
— hail, 247
— rain, 8, 102 ff
— rainfall exceeding stated values, 104 ff
— snow, 238 ff
— snow lying 240, 241
— sunshine between stated limits, 197 ff
— thunder, 250 ff
December, exceptional rain, 108, 110
— exceptional sunshine, 195
— exceptional temperature, 161, 162, 170, 175
— gales, 63
— snowstorms, 238, 241, 243 ff
Declination, solar, 164, 177 ff
Deerness, 46-9, 88, 89, 104, 107, 146, 147, 148, 150, 172, 173, 174, 185, 188, 192, 197, 239, 247, 248, 252, 253, 315
Density, 278, 281
Depression, 20, 25, 27, 31 ff, 99 ff, 243, 248, 249, 254 (see also Cyclone)
Depth of snow, 241, 245
Derbyshire, 17, 273
Deviation from normal, 12 ff
Deviation, standard, 12, 14
Devonshire, 18, 92, 166, 273, 291, 295
Devon-Cornwall peninsula, 18, 78
Dew, 137
Dew-point, 8, 31, 137, 207 ff, 211, 218 ff, 226, 227, 228, 232, 278, 279, 303
Dew ponds, 137 ff
Dewar, D., 14
Diffusion, molecular, 206
Dight, F. H., 228, 230
Dines Anemometer, 53 ff
Dingle Bay, 18
Discontinuity, 32
— in records of temperature, 7
Dispersion of rainfall fluctuations, 83, 94
Diurnal range of temperature, 38, 141, 164, 170
— relative humidity, 212, 213
— vapour-pressure, 215
— wind velocity, 38
Diurnal variation of cloudiness, 202, 203
— dew point, 211, 218 ff
— humidity, 209 ff
— moisture content, 211, 215
— saturation deficit, 211, 217
— sun's altitude and azimuth, 180, 181
— sunshine, 200, 201
— suspended impurity, 284

Diurnal variation of temperature, 19, 38, 73, 140, 163 ff, 209, 217
— vapour pressure, 211, 215 ff
— visibility, 259 ff
— wind direction, 68 ff
— wind velocity, 35, 38, 72 ff
Dolgelly, 88
Donaghadee, 46, 47, 239, 274, 288 ff
Doncaster (Pumping Station), 108
Donegal, 18, 60, 85, 94
Doodson, A. T., 83, 119
Dorchester (Water Works), 114
Douglas (I. of Man), 105, 106, 107, 146, 174, 185, 237, 239, 247, 253, 321
Douglas, C.K.M., 254, 256
Dover, 47, 59, 64, 185, 245
Down (Co.), 18
Downs (North and South), 18, 245
Downlands, 77, 137
Drainage, 96, 116, 126 ff, 255
Driest areas, 79, 294
Driest and wettest years, 80 ff
Drift, North Atlantic, 22, 23
Drifts, snow, 241 ff
Drizzle, 111
Drops, water, 258, 278, 282
Drought, 40, 95 ff, 122, 135, 139
Drought conditions in Thames basin, 135 ff
Dry air, 39, 226 ff
Dry-bulb thermometer, 3, 6, 8, 205
Dry-heating of air, 230
Drying power of the air, 206, 218
Dry periods, 95 ff
Dry weather flow of streams, 129, 137
Dublin, 47, 80, 85, 88, 92, 104, 107, 146, 174, 185, 236, 237, 239, 247, 253, 331
Dundee, 107, 172, 264
Dunfanaghy Road, 60, 63, 65
Dungeon Ghyll, 108
Dungeness, 146, 174, 239, 274, 324
Dunnet Head, 16
Dunrobin Castle, 107
Duration of daylight, 162, 177 ff
— rainfall, 9, 111 ff
— sunshine, 9, 177 ff
Durham 17, 88, 104, 148, 150
Dust, 258
Duxford, 249
Dynamic cooling, 31, 99, 119, 278, 279, 281
— warming, 41

Earth temperature, 3, 237, 278
Eastbourne, 184, 187, 188, 189, 192

East Fortune, 79
East Ham, 168
East winds, 38, 39
Eddy motion, 53, 73, 221, 232, 278, 286
Eden, River, 18
Edgbaston (see Birmingham)
Edinburgh, 79, 85, 88
Edinburgh (Blackford Hill), 57-9, 64, 79, 158, 172, 187
Effective height of anemometer, 3, 54
Eight-point scale of wind direction, 48
Elements climatological, 3 ff
Elkington Hall, 255
Elvedon Hall, 114
Elwes, Captain R. P., 250
Enfield, 183, 228, 305
Enfield (Carisbrooke), 114
England and Wales, geography, 16-8
English Channel, 16, 31, 32, 49, 65, 66, 87, 149, 243, 272, 273, 294
Entwistle, F., 286
Environment, meteorological, 20 ff
Epsom (Ashley Road), 114
Equinoxes, 56, 178 ff, 200
Equivalents, velocity, of Beaufort scale, 3, 5, 54
Error of average value, 12 ff
— probable, 12 ff
Eskdalemuir Observatory, 55, 56, 61, 63, 64, 99, 112, 113, 117, 118, 197 ff, 212 ff, 241, 253, 270, 271, 274, 277
Essex, 79, 192, 252
Eurasian Continent, 16, 20, 27, 159, 161
Europe, 16, 20 ff
Evaporation, 9, 121 ff, 206, 230
Evaporation-tank, 9, 121 ff
Evaporimeters, 121
Exmoor, 18, 92
Exposure, 3, 8, 231, 236
Extremes of absolute humidity, 228 ff
— rainfall, 93 ff, 105, 108 ff, 114 ff
— relative humidity, 226 ff
— sunshine, 195 ff
— temperature, 7, 172 ff
Extreme winds, 61 ff

Factors causing variations of temperature, 140
— geographical and environmental, 15 ff
— in visibility, 277 ff
Falmouth Observatory, 105, 107, 112, 146, 148, 150, 188, 197 ff, 212 ff, 237, 239, 241, 247, 252, 253, 274, 326
Y 2

Fareham (The Mount), 114
Farlington, 128
Fearn, 79
February, droughts, 93, 95, 101
— gales, 63
— exceptional rain, 108
— exceptional sunshine, 195
— exceptional temperature, 161, 162, 170, 175
— snowstorm, 1929, 241
Felixstowe, 64, 79, 117, 264 ff, 274, 277
Fens, 79
Fettercairn, 114
Fidra, 79
Firth of Forth, 17, 49, 79, 255, 273
— of Tay, 17, 53
— Moray, 17, 79, 89
Fishtoft School, 79
Fleetwood, 64
Flintshire, 276
Flood, 100, 255
Flood periods, 100
Fluctuations, 1, 12, 154, 165
see also List of Tables, p. xvii
Fog, 10, 11, 41, 177, 185, 256 ff, 270 ff, 296, 303
— coastal, 279, 287
— inland, 280, 281
— persistent, 276, 277, 281
— radiation, 278, 279 ff
— sea, 278, 279
— smoke, 281 ff, 304
— town, 41, 282
— valley, 303
— warm-front, 280, 281
— water, 258, 278, 280
Föhn effect, 221
Folkestone, 172
Forecasting, 1, 103
Forenoon sunshine, 201 ff
Fort Augustus, 192
Fortrose, 79
Fort William, 17, 103, 104, 142, 146, 158, 174, 318
Frequency (see under respective subjects in Contents, p. vii)
Friction, reduction of wind-speed due to, 61, 309
Fronts, cold and warm, 32
Frost, 37, 231 ff, 296
Frost, glazed, 243
Frost, hoar, 232
Frosts, severe, 37, 41, 175, 176

Frost (see also Ground frost)
Frostgraupeln, 246

Gales, 4, 33, 34, 35, 42, 43, 44, 56, 58, 60 ff, 296
— frequency of, 64 ff
— severe, 65 ff
Galty Mountains, 18
Galway, 18
Garbett, Capt. L. G., 49
Garforth, 96
Garry, River, 78
General circulation of the atmosphere, 15, 102
General rainfall, 76, 77
Geography of British Isles, 16-9
Geography, related to climatology, 2, 15
Geophysical Memoirs, v
Gethin Jones, J. R. 243
Glasgow Observatory, 105, 106, 107, 146, 159, 160, 174, 212 ff, 233 ff, 237, 239, 247, 253, 318
Glaslyn, 78
Glasspoole, J., vi, 14, 78, 84, 85, 94, 96, 98, 102, 119, 120, 197, 204
Glazed frost, 243
Glencorse, 128
Glenleven (Blackwater Dam), 112, 113
Glen More, 17
Glen Nevis, 242
Glen-na-Smoel, 110
Glen Prosen, 110
Glenquoich, 14,
Gliding, 69
Gold, E., 26, 62
Goldie, A. H. R., 74
Gordon, Seton, 243, 256
Gorleston (see Yarmouth)
Gradient, barometric, 22, 30 ff, 69, 100, 101, 280
— thermal, 144
Graduation curves of rainfall, 83, 94
Grampians, 17, 144, 166, 221, 226
Grand Banks of Newfoundland, 279
Granular snow, 246
Grass-minimum temperature, 231 ff
— thermometer, 231, 232, 236
Great Billing, 250
Great Britain (geography), 16-8
Great Glen, 17
Great Wakering, 79
Great Whernside, 18
Greenwich Mean Time, 6

Greenwich, Royal Observatory, 46, 47, 49, 50, 52, 146, 153, 173, 174, 175, 183, 185, 237, 288, 292, 305,
Gregory, Sir Richard, 155
Grêle, 246
Grésil, 246
Ground fog, 280
Ground frost, 231 ff, 299, 300
Guernsey, 168, 184, 188, 189, 192, 237, 274, 276, 330
Guernsey (St. Martin's Road), 114
Gulf Stream, 22, 23, 279
Gust, 53 ff, 310
Gustiness, 53, 61, 295
Gust level, 60, 61
Gusts, extreme, 61 ff

Hagel, 246
Hail, 8, 34, 246 ff
Hailstones, large, 119, 246, 249, 250
Hailstorm of Sept. 22nd, 1935, 248 ff
Hair, human, affected by variations of humidity, 207
Halstead, 168, 175
Hampshire, 95, 241, 245
Hampstead (London) 158, 163, 183, 189, 240, 304, 305
Hancock, D. A., 197, 204
Harrogate, 121, 122, 127, 128, 274, 276, 277
Hartland Point, 192
Hastings, 324
Hatfield (Broad Oak, Barrington), 114
Haverfordwest, 88, 187
Hawke, E. L., 297, 298, 311
Hay, R. F. M., 256
Haze, 10, 11, 185, 186, 194, 204, 257 ff
Heat, specific, 19
Heavy rainfall in short periods, 114 ff, 254
Hebrides, 16, 31, 103, 183, 272
Hellmann's formula, 54
Helvellyn, 18
Herefordshire, 85
Hertfordshire, 40, 297
Heywood, G. S. P., 301, 311
High fog, 282
Highlands of Scotland, 17, 189, 238, 241
High Willhays, 18
Hillington, 107
Hoar frost, 232
Holme Chase, Dartmoor, 241
Holyhead, 46, 47, 51, 52, 54, 57, 58, 60, 61, 65, 112, 117, 146, 174, 185, 239, 240, 248, 249, 253, 261 ff, 274, 276, 277, 295, 322

Houghall, 175
Hourly readings, 8, 55, 56, 59, 140, 163, 169, 200 ff, 211, 212, 227
Hours of observation, 6
Howard, Luke, 121
Hull, 172
Humber, 18, 89, 249, 255
Humidity, 8, 205 ff
— absolute, 206, 220, 228 ff
— — extremes of, 228 ff
— relative, 8, 206 ff, 217, 220 ff, 226 ff, 278, 303
— — extremes, 206 ff
— — geographical distribution, 221 ff
Hurricane, 3, 4
Hutton, 291
Hygrograph, 8, 207, 229
Hygrometer, 207, 278
Hygrometric state of the atmosphere, 206
Hygrometric Tables, 8, 14, 230

Icelandic low, 20 ff, 100
Ilfracombe, 114
Illumination, in relation to visibility, 277
Impervious rocks and surfaces, 129
Impurity, suspended, 258, 281 ff, 306
Inchkeith, 47, 49, 51, 52, 79, 274, 316
Industrial uses of water, 75
Inland Water Survey, 139
Inner Hebrides, 16, 17, 189
Insolation, 253 (see also Solar radiation)
Instability, 35, 40, 252, 253, 295
Intensity of rainfall, 9, 114 ff, 254
International Standard Atmosphere, 142
Inveraray Castle, 88, 89
Inverness, 172, 184, 185
Inverness-shire, 77, 78
Inversion of temperature, 19, 281, 282
Ipswich (Bishop's Hill), 114
Ireland, geography, 16, 18
Irish Sea, 16, 66, 92
Irregularities in annual variation of temperature, 152 ff
Irthlingborough, 250
Isle of Man, 16, 76, 77, 183
— — Rum, 144
— — Skye, 144
— — Thanet, 98, 99
— — Wight, 16, 184, 189, 192, 241
Isobars, 21, 30 ff
Isohyets, 77
Isomeric charts, 89
Isotherms, 15, 23, 24, 143, 144, 156, 157

January, gales, 63
— exceptional rain, 108
— exceptional sunshine, 195
— exceptional temperature, 161, 162, 170
— snowstorm, 1881, 241
Jersey, 174, 175, 184, 330
July, droughts, 95
— exceptional rain, 108, 110, 114
— exceptional sunshine, 195, 196
— exceptional temperature, 161, 170, 228, 229
— thunderstorm, 1923, 254
June, droughts, 95
— exceptional rain, 93, 100, 108, 110, 114, 254
— exceptional sunshine, 195
— exceptional temperature, 161, 170
— thunderstorm, 1917, 254

Katabatic winds, 72, 302
Kelley, A. L., vi
Kelso, 175
Kenmare Bay, 18
Kennick, 122, 128
Kensington Palace (London), 308
Kensington, South (London), 61, 64, 309, 310
Kent, 79, 94, 95, 158, 174, 187, 245, 246
Kerry, 18
Keswick, 18
Ketins, 175
Kew Observatory, 7, 39, 55-61, 64, 73, 88, 104 ff, 111, 113, 117 ff, 146, 147, 150, 152 ff, 158, 161 ff, 168 ff, 183, 189, 197 ff, 210 ff, 227 ff, 237, 239 ff, 247, 248, 253, 256, 270, 271, 274, 276, 277, 284, 305 ff, 329
Kilmarnock, 86, 105, 107
Kingstown, 60, 65
Kingussie, 175
Kinlochquoich Lodge, 79
Kinross, 110
Kirkcudbright, 17
Kirkwall, 59, 64, 187
Knockmealdown Mountains, 18
Knox-Shaw, H, vi

Lake District, 18, 78, 92
Lake Eigiau (Dam Site), 108
Lancashire, 126, 183, 189, 192, 276
Lancaster, 291
Land and sea breezes, 68 ff, 165, 279, 280
Land masses, meteorology of, 19
Land's End, 16

Lapse-rate of temperature, 35, 40, 69, 142, 249, 252
Larkhill, 61, 64
Latent heat, 232
Latitude, 15, 16, 177 ff, 194
Lea, River, 95
Leafield, 272, 274, 301
Leeds, 96
Leicestershire, 236
Leith, 44, 46, 47, 146, 185, 239, 252, 253, 316
Lerwick, 42-9, 51, 52, 55-60, 62-4, 112, 146, 169, 185, 252, 270, 274, 276, 315
Leuchars, 117, 264 ff, 276, 277
Lewis, Miss L. F., 197, 204
Leyland (Worden Hall), 114
Lightning, 250
Limerick, 18, 237
Lincoln, 288, 290
Lincolnshire, 79, 252, 255
— Wolds, 18, 77, 255
Line-squall, 34, 254
Liverpool (Bidston Observatory), 42, 43, 47, 63, 64, 83, 237, 239, 272, 274, 277, 322
Lizard, 16, 31, 63, 65
Llandudno, 295
Lloyd, A. C., 120
Llynfan Fach (Nant Coch), 108
Loan (Loch Quoich), 78
Local apparent time, 181, 202
Lochan Sgoir, 78
Lochbuie, 108
Loch Carron, 108
— Linnhe, 17
— Lochy, 17
— Oich, 17
— Ness, 17
— Quoich, 78, 108
Logie Coldstone, 175
London, 14, 15, 32, 41, 75, 96, 110, 112, 113, 117, 121, 126, 159, 168, 172, 175, 183, 184, 189, 192, 200, 245, 254, 259, 264, 270, 282, 284, 300, 304 ff
— (See also Bunhill Row, Camden Square, Enfield, Greenwich, Hampstead, Kensington Palace, Kew, Regent's Park, South Kensington, Tottenham, Westminster.)
Londonderry, 18, 110
Londonderry, Lough Swilly and Letterkenny Railway Co., 60
Longford, 110
Loss, in relation to run-off, 129, 131 ff
Louth (Lincs), 255

Lower Laithe, 128
Lowestoft, 172
Lud, River, 255
Lugnaquilla, 18
Lull of wind, 35, 53, 310
Luton Pumping Station, 114
Lympne, 61, 64, 117, 274, 324

Macgillicuddy's Reeks, 18
Maidenhead (Lowood), 14
Malin Head, 16, 88, 89, 185, 224, 225, 239, 247, 253, 272, 274, 277, 331
Malvern, 114, 192
Manchester (Oldham Road), 183, 188, 192
— (Whitworth Park), 288 ff
March, droughts, 95
— gales, 63
— exceptional sunshine, 195
— exceptional temperature, 161, 170, 175
— snowstorm, 1891, 241
Margate, 188, 288, 292
Market Deeping, 79
Markree Castle, 88, 104, 107, 185, 333
Marine Observer, 146
Marlborough, 114
Marshall, W. A. L., 250, 256
Martin, E. A., 137, 139
Maximum temperature, 6 ff, 141, 142, 165 ff
— thermometer, 3, 141, 166
May, exceptional rain, 93, 108, 110, 114
— exceptional sunshine, 195
— exceptional temperature, 161, 170
— frost of 1935, 37, 297
— thunderstorm and floods, 1920, 255
Mayo, 18
Mean temperature, 6, 141 ff
Mean wind, 53 ff
Mediterranean Sea, 16
Melksham (Beechfield), 114
Mendip Hills, 18
Merionethshire, 18
Merrick, 17
Meteorological environment of British Isles, 20 ff
Meteorological Magazine, 37, 228
Meteorological Office, v, 2, 3, 13, 54, 142, 236, 238, 241, 250, 297, 314
Meteorology of seas and land masses, 19
— synoptic, 1
Metropolitan Water Board, 131, 135, 139
Middleton-in-the-Wolds, 114
Midland Counties, 85, 87, 152, 159, 175, 183, 192, 224, 225, 243, 248, 273

Mildenhall, 114
Mill, H. R., 89, 111, 119, 120
Minimum temperature, 6 ff, 141, 165 ff, 220, 226, 233 ff
— thermometer, 3, 141, 166, 232
Ministry of Agriculture and Fisheries, 297
Mirage, 278
Mirrlees, S. T. A., 155, 176
Miscellaneous phenomena, 231 ff
Mist, 10, 11, 137, 185, 257 ff
Mizen Head, 16
Moffat, 95
Moisture-content, 119, 206 ff, 211, 215, 216, 228 ff
Monthly means, 13
Monthly rainfall, 86 ff
— — fluctuations of, 93 ff
Monthly Weather Report, 13, 221
Moray Firth, 17, 79, 89
Morecambe, 291
Morning and afternoon sunshine, 201 ff
Morpeth (see Cockle Park)
Mountain systems, 17
Mount Batten, 117, 264 ff, 274, 276, 325
Mourne Mountains, 18
Mull of Cantire, 16

Nairn, 79
Neige roulée, 246
Nene, River, 248
Newnham, E. V., 72, 74, 253, 256
Nights of ground frost, 231, 236, 237, 299, 300
Night minimum temperature, 6, 7, 166, 307
Norfolk, 19, 187, 292
Norfolk floods (1912), 100, 105, 110
No rainfall, months with, 95
Normal, 11 ff
Normal climatological stations, 6
Northampton, 249, 250
Northamptonshire, 248
Northamptonshire Natural History Society, vi
North Atlantic Drift, 22, 23
North Berwick, 79
North Channel, 16
North Downs, 18, 245
Northeasterly type of weather, 26, 37-9
Northerly type of weather, 26, 36, 37
Northern Highlands of Scotland, 17
North Foreland, 16, 192
North Sea, 16, 65, 66, 72, 149, 292 ff

North Shields, 146, 239, 247, 253
Northumberland, 99, 236
Northwesterly type of weather, 26, 35
Norwich, 88, 100, 175, 187, 292, 293
Noteworthy rainfalls, 115, 119, 254
Nottingham, 112, 113
Nottinghamshire, 85
November, exceptional rain, 108, 110
— exceptional sunshine, 195
— exceptional temperature, 161, 170, 175
— gales, 63

Objects, visibility, 10, 11, 257, 258
Observations, climatological, 2 ff
Observatories, 6, 8, 55, 141, 205 ff
Observer's Handbook, 2, 53, 258
Occlusion, 33
Octagonal wind-roses, 49, 50
October, exceptional rain, 108, 110
— exceptional sunshine, 195
— exceptional temperature, 161, 170
— gales, 63
Offaly, 18, 110
Okehampton, 88
Orkneys, 16, 103, 149, 168, 172, 187
Ormesby, St. Michael, 128
Orographic rain, 31, 32, 99 ff, 287
Orwell, River, 79
Otterbourne, 121, 122, 128
Outer Hebrides, 16, 58, 272
Overcast sky, 38, 184
Oxford (Radcliffe Observatory) vi, 12, 83, 85, 94, 145 ff, 150, 159 ff, 174, 185, 186, 188, 192 ff, 233, 237, 239, 328
Oxfordshire, 72, 192, 301

Paisley (Coats Observatory), 62, 63, 64
Peak, The, of Derbyshire, 18, 183
Pembroke (see St. Ann's Head)
Pembrokeshire, 273
Pendennis Castle, 63, 65
Pennines, 17, 78, 92, 183
Pentland Firth, 16
Pen-y-Gwrhyd, 78, 108
Penzance, 158, 168, 172
Percentage of cloud, 184 ff, 192 ff
— of possible sunshine, 184 ff, 192 ff
— of sky free from cloud, 184 ff, 192 ff
— (refer also to pp. vii-xix)
Percolation, 126 ff
— gauges, 126
Periodicity, 13, 140, 147
Periods, Buchan's, 152 ff

Persistent fog, 276, 277, 281
Perth, 175
Pervious rocks and surfaces, 129, 131
Petersfield, 245
Phenomena, miscellaneous, 231 ff
Physical effects of wind, 3, 52, 310
Physics, in relation to climatology, 2
Plymouth, 63, 65, 107, 325
Polar winds, 35, 245, 253
Pollard, A. E., 249
Pollution, atmospheric, 183, 194, 204, 262, 264, 265, 281 ff, 307
Ponding of cold air, 72, 280, 303
Portland Bill, 32, 46, 47, 49, 274, 277, 325
Portland (H.M. Breakwater), 110
Portsmouth, 237, 324
Precipitation (see Hail, Rainfall, Snow)
Predominating weather types, 26 ff
Pressure distribution, normal, 20 ff, 30
— — variations of, 25, 26 ff
— of saturated vapour, 8, 206, 208, 209
— vapour, 8, 206 ff, 211, 214 ff, 220, 225 ff
Preston, 114
Prevailing winds, 20 ff, 48, 150, 161, 221, 225, 242, 294, 303
" Pride of the morning ", 281
Princetown, 241, 245, 273
Probable error, 12 ff
Professional Notes, v

Quantock Hills, 100
Queen Mary Reservoir, 121
Quoich, Loch, 78, 108
Quilty, 60, 62, 63, 65

Radcliffe Observatory (see Oxford)
Radiation, solar, 19, 20, 141, 149, 159, 162, 164, 225, 279, 281, 282, 286
— terrestrial, 19, 20, 141, 149, 165, 232, 236, 278 ff, 302, 303, 309
Rain, days of, 8, 102 ff
Rainfall, 1, 8, 9, 75 ff, 121 ff
— coastal and inland, 294 ff
— cyclonic, 33, 34, 99 ff
— orographic, 31, 32, 99 ff, 287
— thunderstorm, 40, 99 ff, 119, 254
Rainfall Atlas of the British Isles, 80, 89
Rain-gauge, 8, 9, 109, 111, 116, 137, 238
— recording, 9, 111, 116
Recordable rainfall, 11, 137
Regent's Park, London, 183, 305
Regnault's formula, 8
Reifgraupeln, 246

Relative humidity, 8, 206 ff, 217, 220 ff, 226 ff, 278, 303,
— — extremes, 226 ff
— — geographical distribution, 221 ff
Remarkable rainfalls, 115, 119
Renfrew (Abbotsinch), 61, 63, 64, 117, 197, 264 ff, 272, 274, 318
Revesby, 128
Rhondda (Lluest Wen Res), 108
Rhyl, 295
Rhythms and patterns, 1
Richmond (Surrey) (see Kew Observatory)
Rickmansworth, 273, 297 ff
Rivers, flow of, 131
Robinson cup anemometer, 54
Roche's Point, 239, 240, 247, 274, 332
Roscommon, 110
Ross-on-Wye, 175, 225, 274
Rothamsted, 40, 127, 128, 273, 297 ff
Rothbury, 99
Rothesay, 146, 174, 237, 239, 248, 317
Rounton, 236, 237
Royal Meteorological Society, vi, 62, 89, 155
Rum, Isle of, 144
Run-off, 129 ff
Rushden, 249

St. Albans, 273
St. Ann's Head (Pembroke), 46, 47, 65, 185, 239, 248, 274, 323
St. Catherine's Point, 274
St. David's Head, 16
St. George's Channel, 16
Sale (Brooklands), 114
Salter, M. de Carle S., 89, 119
Sandown, 189, 192
Saturated vapour, 8, 119, 206 ff, 278, 279, 282
Saturation-deficit, 206, 208, 211, 214, 217, 218
Scafell Pike, 18, 78
Scarborough, 107, 288
Scilly Isles, 15, 31, 37, 42 ff, 51, 52, 57 ff, 87, 142, 146, 158, 168, 172, 173, 174, 184, 185, 192 ff, 239, 240, 249, 271 ff, 276, 277, 330
Scotland, geography of, 17
Screen, Stevenson, 3, 8, 232
Sea breeze, 40, 68 ff, 280, 293, 295
Sealand, 65, 117, 274
Seas, meteorology of, 19
Seasonal variations (see under respective subjects in Contents, p. vii)

Sea-surface temperatures, 3, 19, 20, 23, 24, 31, 69, 70, 148, 149, 278, 279. 292 ff
Seathwaite, 31, 32, 78, 79, 88, 89, 108, 110
Secular trend, 13, 140.
September droughts, 95
— gales, 63
— exceptional rain, 96, 100, 108, 114
— exceptional sunshine, 195
— exceptional temperatures, 161, 170
— hailstorm, 1935, 248 ff
Sequences of dry or wet months, 96 ff
Seton Gordon, 243, 256
Sevenoaks, 246
Severn, River, 224
Sgurr na Ciche, 78
Shad Thames Pumping Station, 114
Shade temperature, 3
Shaw, Sir Napier, 49, 72
Sheffield, 183, 237, 239
Shetlands, 16, 44, 58, 103, 142, 152, 158, 159, 168, 172, 179, 181, 187, 189, 252, 270
Shimmering, 278
Shoeburyness, 61, 64, 79, 104, 321
Shrewsbury, 168
Sidmouth, 288 ff
Silchester House, 114
Simpson, Sir George C., v, 14
Sixteen-point scale of wind direction, 42, 48
Skegness, 288, 290
Skelwith Bridge, 108
Skew frequency distribution, 81
Sleet, 36, 238
Slieve Bloom Mountains, 18
Slieve Donard, 18
Slieve Gullion, 18
Sligo, 110
Smoke, 41, 183, 185, 186, 194, 195, 200, 204, 258, 262, 264, 281 ff, 304 ff
Smoke-fog, 281 ff, 304
Snow, 8, 33, 34, 35, 36, 37, 127, 238 ff, 309
Snow-beds, permanent, 241 ff
Snow, depth of, 241, 245, 246
Snowdon, 18, 78, 144, 243
Snowdonia, 78, 96, 295
Snowdon (Llydaw Copper M.), 108
— (Pen-y-Gwryd), 78, 108
Snow, drifting of, 241, 245, 246
Snow lying, 238, 240, 241
Snow-storm of Christmas, 1927, 238, 241, 243 ff
Soft hail, 246

Soil, evaporation from, 9, 127 ff
Solar radiation, 19, 20, 141, 149, 159, 162, 164, 225, 279, 281, 282, 286, 306
Solar radiation thermometer, 3
Solstices, 56, 68, 123, 149, 164, 179 ff, 200
Somerset, 100, 101
Southampton, 107, 146, 174
South Downs, 18
Southeasterly type of weather, 27, 39, 40
Southend, 79, 152, 159
Southern Uplands of Scotland, 17
South Farnborough, 117, 226, 264 ff, 274, 277
South Kensington (London), 61, 64, 309, 310
Southport, 61, 63, 64, 70, 71, 72, 112, 117, 122, 124, 126, 128, 146, 174, 237, 239, 288 ff
South Shields, 59, 64
Southwesterly type of weather, 26, 30-2
Specific heat, 19
Spring drought of 1893, 95
Spring frosts, 37, 72, 237
Spring, a relatively cold season, 37, 40, 152, 169, 171, 216, 248
Sprinkling Tarn, 78
Sprowston School, 110
Spurn Head, 47, 53, 57, 58, 59, 64, 185, 224, 270, 271, 274, 277, 320
Squalls, 34, 35
Squall-line, 34
Stacey, W. F., 230
Staffordshire, 183, 284
Standard Atmosphere, International, 142
Standard deviation, 12 ff
Stanground sluice, 79
Stationery Office, H.M., v
Stations, climatological, 2, 6
— synoptic, 6
Stevenson screen, 3, 8, 232
Stoke-on-Trent, 284, 285
Stoneyhurst College, 107, 146, 150, 152, 153, 174, 237, 239, 247, 253, 329
Storm, 4, 5,
Stornoway, 47, 49, 50, 88, 89, 104, 146, 174, 185, 239, 247, 253, 272, 274, 277, 317
Stourhead Gardens, 108
Stratford-on-Avon (Milcote), 114
Strontian (Argyll), 105, 106, 107, 252, 253
Stye, The, 78
Stye Head Tarn, 78
Suffolk, 79, 92, 187, 192
Sumburgh Head, 146, 239, 247, 252

Summer fogs, 270, 272, 274, 276, 279, 280
— thunderstorms, 40, 248, 252 ff, 295
Summers, exceptional, 99, 122, 135, 136, 174, 175
Sun, 3, 15, 19, 177 ff
Sunderland, 239
Sunny days, 197 ff
Sunrise, 9, 164, 177 ff, 185, 285, 286
Sunset, 9, 164, 177 ff, 185
Sun's apparent movements, 177 ff
Sunshine, 9, 10, 177 ff, 280, 296, 304 ff
Sunshine recorder, 9, 10, 177, 185, 194
Surbiton, Vronvelin, 114
Surface run-off, 129, 130 ff
Suspended impurity in the atmosphere, 258, 281 ff, 306 (see also Atmospheric pollution)
Sussex, 95
Swansea, 108
Symons, G. J., 76
Synoptic meteorology, 1, 32
— stations, 6, 224

Tables, climatic, 313-34
— hygrometric, 8, 14, 230
Talla Water, Peebles, 121, 122, 128
Tank, evaporation, 9, 55, 121 ff
Tarbetness, 79
Tavy Cleave, Dartmoor, 241
Taylor, G. I., 280, 286
Teddington weir, 131, 132
Temperature of the air, 3, 6, 7, 140 ff, 278 ff, 287 ff
— measurement of, 3, 6, 7, 140, 141
— sea-surface, 3, 19, 20, 23, 24, 31, 69, 70, 148, 149, 278, 279, 292 ff
— soil, 3, 237, 238
Temple Combe Rectory, 114
Tenterden, 94
Terrestrial radiation, 19, 20, 141, 149, 165, 232, 236, 278 ff, 302, 303, 309
Thames, River, 78, 79, 131 ff, 294
— basin, rainfall and run-off, 131 ff
— Valley, 89, 132, 224
Thanet, Isle of, 98, 99
Thermographs, 6, 8, 164, 165, 205
Thermometers, 3, 6, 7, 8, 141, 166, 168, 205, 231 ff
Three driest years, 85, 86
Thunder, 34
Thunderstorms, 34, 35, 40, 99, 103, 248 ff, 250 ff, 295, 296
— rainfall in, 40, 99 ff, 118, 119, 254

Time, British Summer, 6, 180, 283
— Greenwich Mean, 6
— Local Apparent, 181
— standard, 6
Tipperary, 18
Tiree, 47, 57, 58, 59, 62, 63, 64, 183, 185, 189
Tonbridge, 174
— (Ferndale), 114
Tongue, 108
Topography, 15, 49, 72, 169, 280, 298, 301 ff
Torquay, 189, 192
Tottenham (London), 183, 305
Town climates, 41, 183, 186, 303 ff
— fog, 41, 282
Trecastle (Blaenau-hydfer), 108, 110
Trostan, 18
Trowbridge (Sunnyside), 114
Turbulence, 53, 204, 285
Tynemouth, 46, 47, 146, 174, 274, 319
Types of climate, special, 287 ff
— of weather, 26 ff
Tyrone, 18

Ultra-violet light, 304
Underground water, 129, 130
Upwell, 79
Usk, 175

Valentia Observatory, 46, 47, 51, 52, 55 ff, 62, 63, 65, 104, 112, 113, 117, 121, 146, 147, 148, 150, 152, 162 ff, 168, 172, 173, 174, 185, 187, 188, 197 ff, 212 ff, 239, 241, 247, 248, 252, 253, 272, 274, 276, 332
Valley climates, 72, 169, 296 ff
— fog, 303
Vapour pressure, 8, 206 ff, 211, 214 ff, 220, 225 ff
— — extremes, 228 ff
— — geographical distribution, 223, 225, 226
Variability of rainfall, 80 ff, 93 ff
Variations, casual, of temperature, 140, 142
Vector (wind), 42 ff
Velocity of the wind, 3, 5, 42, 52 ff, 296
Velocity-equivalents of the Beaufort scale, 3, 5, 54
Very dry months, 95
— — years, 81, 82
Very good visibility, 11, 35, 259, 262, 264 ff
Very rare rainfalls, 114, 119
Very wet months, 96
— — years, 81, 82
Visibility, 10, 11, 35, 257 ff

Wadhurst (Lower Cousley Wood), 114
Wakefield (Stanley Vicarage), 114
Wales, geography of, 18
Walters, R. C. S., 139
Warm-front, 32, 249, 254, 280, 281
Warm-front fog, 280, 281
Warm periods, Buchan's, 154
Warm sector, 32, 33, 99
Wash, The, 79, 110
Water, physical properties of, 19
Water fog, 258, 278, 280
Water supply, 2, 75, 80, 96, 129, 130, 135
Water vapour, 119, 205 ff, 278, 282
Weather, characteristic types of, 26 ff
— maps, 30, 33, 36, 38, 39, 244
— study of, 1
Weather of the British Coasts, 42, 43, 45, 67
Weather-house, 207
Wedge of high pressure, 35
Wellington, 175
Wenceslas, King, 238
Western Highlands of Scotland, 17, 144
West Linton, 175
Westminster (London), 183, 284, 300, 305, 307, 308
Westmorland, 18
Weston Favell, 249
Weston-Super-Mare, 189
Wet-bulb thermometer, 3, 6, 8, 205, 206, 228, 229, 278
Wet days, 8, 104
Wettest places, 78, 89, 93
Wexford, 110

Whipple, F. J. W., 116, 120
Wick, 36, 224, 239, 274
Wicklow Mountains, 18
Wiltshire, 95
Wind, 3, 15, 20 ff, 26 ff, 42 ff
—direction, 3, 42 ff, 48 ff, 62, 66 ff, 294
— force, 3, 42 ff, 52
— velocity, 3, 42, 52 ff, 296, 310
Wind-rose, 46, 48, 49, 50
Winter thunderstorms, 35, 253 ff
Winters, exceptional, 162, 175
Wisley, 183, 307, 308
Worcester (Diglis Lock), 114
Wolverhampton, 88, 89
Worksop, 168
Worthing, 184
Worthy Down, 274
Wrexham (W. W. Office), 114
Wythburn, 110

Yarmouth (Gorleston), 46, 47, 51, 52, 57, 59, 64, 72, 146, 174, 185, 239, 274, 277, 288, 320
Y ffoes ddyfn, 243
Yes Tor, 18
York, 13, 14, 147, 148, 150, 158, 239, 253, 288, 326
Yorkshire, 17, 18, 85, 110, 183, 273
— Moors, 18, 77, 92
— Wolds, 18, 77

Zero, temperatures below, 175
Zones, rainfall, 79, 80

PRINTED IN GREAT BRITAIN BY ROBERT MACLEHOSE AND CO. LTD.
THE UNIVERSITY PRESS, GLASGOW